THE THREE TILES

A remarkable account of what was,
what is and what just might be

By Julian Evan-Hart

Published in 2012 by Julian Evan-Hart

ISBN 978-1-897738-44-3

Printed and bound in Great Britain by 4edge Ltd. Hockley, Essex.

FOREWORD

Julian Evan-Hart, like myself, has been writing articles for Treasure Hunting magazine for some years now. It was through this shared interest in metal detecting and the rewards via the ancient finds it can bring to the individual that we first started chatting via e-mails on a regular basis. He recently asked me to read this, his latest work, The Three Tiles and write a short foreword. This was a departure from his recently published works and I must say I found this story utterly absorbing and is in fact one of those 'you can't put down' type books. Anyone, not necessarily those with an interest in metal detecting will find, like me, that it represents a thumping good read; and as Jules says on the back cover if this does not make you want to go out and buy a metal detector then nothing will.

(Roman) Ron Morley

INTRODUCTION

The following is an account of the many and rather convoluted events that can now be seen to have surrounded one of the greatest archaeological discoveries made in twenty-first century Britain. This discovery was eventually brought to light with the use of metal detectors in a normal every day agricultural field just outside the small village of Melton Briarsville. In addition to this incident, the site of a long lost battle ground was also pin-pointed, finally explaining and revealing how it had remained un-located for so long. This ancient battle ground site is now the subject of a long and extensive period of ongoing field work and archaeological excavation under the direction of the eminent archaeologist Neil Fisher and so far has yielded some incredible results. This "greatest archaeological discovery" arguably perhaps does not quite rival the wealth and ostentation surrounding the discovery of Tutankhamen and other similar Pharaohs tombs in Egypt's Valley of the Kings. But in the rankings of archaeological importance and learning in Britain is something that will almost certainly remain unequalled or will it? As some of us ever hopefuls will always say upon the discovery of something astounding.

Nevertheless this was an issue that caused one of the archaeologists involved to state: "I think it fair to say that we have the UK's greatest archaeological discovery to date here, a major and magnificent discovery, and it is directly linked to one of our most important periods of history. Oh, and yes I should, and must add, that it was made by metal detectorists! I simply can't at this stage say any more."

The find itself, incidentally, was only made possible by the sheer dogged determination of people who were determined to uncover and preserve our past heritage. In this case a group of aviation archaeologists and a single metal detectorist combined, of course, with those required elements of sheer luck and fate as always. The efforts of all the archaeologists involved in the final excavation, recovery and conservation of everything that was found are of course also a vital element often overlooked in such astounding situations.

Of course the discovery would create a media frenzy the like of which has never before been witnessed in relation to a UK metal detecting-based discovery. The finding of the Roman hoard at Hoxne and other significant discoveries such as the Staffordshire Saxon treasure decades before would of course still be regarded as extremely important. Back in 2012 there had also been the fantastic discovery on Jersey of thousands of Armorican-issue Celtic silver coins, which certainly gave a hint of the flavour of things to come. But in comparison to this latest new discovery these previous finds would seem in every respect very minor discoveries indeed.

Some of the factors and details leading up to this discovery now seem with hindsight to be almost too coincidental; some may even say far-fetched. However, as it unravelled the situation would clearly show that sometimes what we consider to be too unlikely when combined with fate and luck can become very likely indeed, and in some rare cases like this will actually occur as a factual event. It is perhaps our attitudes and inability to consider improbable events or link small clues and facts that had denied the making of this and similar discoveries for so long. Each year metal detectorists make many thousands of finds ranging from ancient brooches, coins from all ages, jewellery such as rings and bracelets and occasionally even fragments from long ago crashed aeroplanes. In some cases detectorists are highly privileged being able to research and actually return some finds to their original owners, or show a relative where something happened. This can vary from a wedding ring lost a few weeks ago in a public park to a dog tag recovered from a battlefield or aircraft crash site. Sometimes historical research and the actual item itself can lead us to identify long dead owners but to achieve this is something quite unusual. As objects become hundreds, and indeed thousands, of years old sometimes it's the surrounding clues as well that may also help to confirm ownership of a specific person or more often just a likelihood of ownership or identity. In many cases identifying an owner or likely person is more often than not simply down to those two often-quoted, but vitally essential, ingredients which are of course luck and fate.

Well what of this village charmingly called Melton Briarsville? It wasn't always referred to by that name for in Norman times one can find that it was recorded and known as Molton de Braville. There is possibly some connection with the de Bravielle family? Who, according to early deeds and other documents, had at around the year 1095 resided at a moated manorial site known today as The Clumps, which is situated just to the north of the present day village.

That people have indeed been settling around this area for the past four thousand years is evidenced by the remains of a henge in Pickards Wood and a handful of stone axe-heads from fields to the north. The village itself is rather a quaint little settlement in reality, just like many others that can be found in rural England. In fact is has even been said that it is "quintessentially stereotypical of what one would expect of an English village"; others simply say it is "Chocolate Box featured".

There are a sprinkling of mediaeval thatched cottages, a somewhat more recently-developed housing estate, a single shop, one public house and even a museum. The small village green with its rather decrepit wind-damaged Chestnut tree serves as a stark reminder of the "Great Storm" of 1987. This tree suffers a further, almost ritual, damage starting every September as bands of children, and sometimes their parents hurl sticks at it to retrieve handfuls of its notably generous sized conkers. There is a deep and dark-watered village pond surrounded by ancient willow trees, complete with white ducks and some unusually-sized mallard cross-breeds. Children play in the small copse and smaller spinneys that fringe the recreation ground, which is adjacent to an established cricket pitch, with its whitewashed pavilion dating to 1898. Elderly people walk small dogs along the pavements edging the narrow roads that even these days are surprisingly not too car-congested.

Situated in the tall clattering branches of the ash trees just behind the flinty towered late Norman church there is a large rookery. Whose residents begin their raucous cawing from dawn until dusk in the spring and summer months and who have, it must be said attracted several .22 airgun pellets on the odd occasion for that very reason. On sunny mornings it can seem that the village is shrouded in sounds that remind the listener of the chinking of thousands of falling coins. Not arising from a wealthy resident miser counting his spoils, but the "Chillup Chillip" chirping from the hundreds of sparrows that seem to be everywhere here. Their messy dry grass and feather nests are stuffed and crammed into about every square inch of the ivy that encroaches up and over many of the houses, old walls and trees. Like the rooks too over the years these small birds have attracted their fair share of airgun pellets from youthful would-be marksmen. In summer months swifts dive and scream around the church tower and shuffle to their nests under the tight eaves of high street houses. So all in all a typical rural scene, perhaps rather delightful, but certainly nothing to indicate then that this village was any more special than the neighbouring one, but one day it most certainly would be.

As someone once said "It's a sure thing that everywhere is regarded as quite normal until something is discovered or remarkable takes place there" How true for when something does indeed happen the media descend and perhaps sightseers too and a small rural village or urban district is catapulted into the limelight. Often though these days it seems it is for sad, serious or horrific reasons, that we all become familiar with a place name. Such a name that undoubtedly many of us will never have heard of before, and from then on it remains in our memories forever more. Fortunately for the inhabitants of Melton Briarsville on the whole their place of abode would become known for a fascinating discovery that was made here. For many years local folklore in this village which incidentally is in Oxfordshire persisted in the form of tales of an ancient battle nearby and of death and slaughter. Some variations also included the theme of a British chieftain or someone of importance anyway buried in the locality possibly with a great silver treasure. Whether the chieftain, treasure and the battle were all connected was unknown. As is very typical of these local types of legend it was also suggested that this long dead chieftain would rise up again in defiant spirit if Britain was ever in peril.

Similar rumours can of course be found all over Britain concerning golden chariots buried on hill tops and kings or chieftains buried in suits of golden armour etc. Strangely, in some case like the Mold Cape found in Flintshire they have been proven to be true and accurate. But so far of course no deceased ancient king or chieftain has been known to physically rise up from the dead to defend this "Sceptred Isle" in its times of need. But then again I suppose that could be defined by just what it is that one considers being the meaning of rising up. For it is a sure thing that on occasion long-dead persons can maintain or suddenly create influence or actions even in modern times. Quite how it was that the rumours relating to this small village had originated is as in most examples lost in the mists of time, and to be fair no-one over the last few centuries past had really paid that much attention to them anyway.

In the mid eighteenth and early part of the nineteenth centuries a few passing antiquarians came to stay in the village whilst on their travels, and some of them even made a few brief notes concerning the rumours. Which, when these are consulted it must be said, are of a highly suspect nature in their content. It would seem likely that not a few local persons quickly discovered the advantages to embellishing some dubious rumours in return for a few worn and darkened pennies or even a tankard of ale or two in The Waggoner's Inn. One antiquarian actually stayed for a few weeks up at the Manor house and made it well known he would pay handsomely for any ancient finds. This of course encouraged a few locals to make an extra effort; however this only brought to light some pottery fragments, a broken stone axe-head and six or seven small much worn bronze Celtic coins, which were clearly not what the gentleman in question had hoped for. A few better condition Roman coins were finally offered which were purchased for the rather forlorn sum of two shillings, and were seemingly all that could be extracted from the village. Since these times further Roman coins and other items have been occasionally ploughed up or have been found whilst digging drainage ditches and the clearing out of hedge rows.

Back in the 1690's a rather small nondescript barrow was dug into and then levelled. Not for research reasons of course, but because local children had then adopted it for maypole dances and as a general meeting place. This infuriated the local Curate, a rather portly man by the name of Samuel Mortimer Frendyshe, who considered such activities to be "The pagan responses of a work-shy community" therefore in his opinion "this rural pimple" required removal.

The ancient mound was hacked into, levelled and the resultant soil dispersed quite roughly across the field. In the centre of the mound were discovered a few sharp flints and "an urn of rustic and rude fabric" that contained a gritty mass of partly burned and crushed bone fragments. To ensure the task was done properly and according to his instructions Curate Frendyshe oversaw the entire proceedings.

He only permitted a few minutes rest that day, and that was to enable all those present to witness the burned bone contents also being poured and scattered out onto the field. Once emptied the small urn itself was hurled over the hedge, with some pompous ceremony. The urn wobbled in the air as it flew towards the hedge top, momentarily getting caught in some large thorny overhanging fronds of dog rose. These deflected its trajectory somewhat and created a strange hollow rasping noise as the urn ripped through them. The sombre event wasn't without some humour, though, as after the satisfying smashing sound on the drove way over the hedgerow a startled cry was suddenly heard from the same area. This was immediately followed by an unmistakeable series of cursing and threats of violence from an all too familiar source.

Looking terrified, Curate Frendyshe suddenly hitched up his long overcoat and high-tailed it across the meadow, with both his large liver-spotted hands to his head, and holding onto his large flat black hat into the bargain. It wasn't so much the locals having a laugh and a good old smirk at this portly man with his atrocious Madeira-soaked breath as he now stumbled away. As it was the fact that the local mill owner had only just missed being crowned with the small earthenware urn as it flew over the hedge. Very colourful and foul-mouthed exclamations continued to come from that area, much to everyone's delight. At twenty three stones and just over six feet tall, Symon Collman, the miller in question, was not a man to make a habit of throwing anything at!

It was with some excitement that the hard working "Barrow breakers" now looked forward to future developments with some relish. They hoped for sure that this was not the last they would see or hear about this incident. Unfortunately for them, such hopes were to be dashed by the culinary skills of a rather rotund middle-aged lady. Returning home one afternoon the sturdy Symon found two large pear tarts and a jug of egg custard carefully set down on his doorstep. He later told everyone about this and was satisfied in the common knowledge that the Curate's sister, Eliza, was renowned in the area for being an accomplished cook and linking the gifts to recent events he considered that the matter was now settled.

At that time very little had so far been found, or perhaps it is better to say officially reported or even appreciated in Melton Briarsville that gave any real credence to the rumours of ancient goings on here. Unofficially there would be several discoveries in years to come that pointed at something unusual, but these would be made in times when such findings could easily be interpreted as challenging the authority of the Church, or were simply not convenient for the land owner. But in such cases someone usually makes a record of such events, even if it's only one of an oral nature. It's just luck and fate once again that also usually determine as to whether such records themselves are finally written down and survive or if they in turn are perhaps on occasion discreetly avoided, or even ignored. It was around March in the year of 1767 that something very unusual was discovered here but the then landowner and local clergy finally united to "lose and forget" the discovery, albeit for different reasons.

What of the rumours? Well they still persisted, handed down from each generation to those who would listen and in turn remember, eventually passing on the details yet again. However, with the ever evolving use of the land agriculturally things would change, but within the well-developed rural code of secrecy it would take many years for events to be clarified, confirmed, and put into some sort of context. As village life continued to experience change these rumours persisted until quite recently. But as the older generations took their turn to fill the ancient churchyard eventually the continuity of these marvellous oral records was hampered by lack of interest, and perhaps even imagination.

Today the local children are mostly far more interested in their scooters and computer games than to have an interest in any rumours of ancient battles and long-dead chieftains. There was a time in the late nineteenth century when teachers at the local school did briefly introduce the "ancient battle" and its rumours into the occasional classroom lesson, but even then it was just a mention, a mere passing reference.

This situation was reversed and remedied for a period with the arrival in the village of Miles Henderson in 1910. Mr Henderson was the Headmaster at Melton Briarsville school from 1910 to 1914. A tall, sombre-looking, upright gentleman; although certainly not as old as he would have liked to make out he was. He had a clearly defined passion for all things historical and nature-orientated and an infectious ability to create interest on a wide variety of such subjects. Fond memories were retained by many ex -pupils remembering the early spring afternoon when Mr Henderson keenly announced that a skeleton had been found up at the "Big House", to which he always referred to the Manor. They were briefly all marched through the village to the "Big House" and regimented in a very disorderly line to view the excavations that were taking place for an extension to the Library. Near the bottom of which lay rather disappointingly a totally crushed Human skull and an assorted jumble of very broken and splintered bones.

Mr Henderson's sheer animated enthusiasm went some way to alleviate the disappointment of some pupils, who had somehow expected rather more than this. As far as I have been told it was fact that several pupils had rather excitedly been nurturing the expectations that the so called local chieftain or king had at last been found, with of course a heap of treasure thrown in for good measure. Like many of his generation Miles Henderson later volunteered for active service in 1914, and thus his passion and enthusiasm were to be clad in a khaki uniform and sent to France as part of the British Expeditionary Force. Sadly also like so many others there too his life was cut short. In his case this took place during the first day of the Somme offensive on the 1st July 1916 near Gommecourt in France, when a German heavy artillery shell fell directly into his trench, killing him and fifteen others in a brilliant orange coloured flash and a huge arch of fractured clay that was blasted skywards. In a split second a brilliant, caring and astute mind had been blown to the heavens and Miles Henderson entered the official lists of those who were classed as missing in action.

Over the last two decades or so the author has been privileged to meet and get to know the oldest inhabitant of Melton Briarsville, who, as a seven year-old child in 1912, was actually very much inspired by his then head teacher, one Mr Miles Henderson. He had actually been one of the original pupils taken up to the manor house on that day when the so-called skeleton had been discovered. "Mr Henderson", as he recalled, "was always passionately interested in local issues of some sort or another". Whether it was observing and recording the rare Honey Buzzards that had finally returned to the area and nested in the spring of 1910, it had been Mr Henderson who spent hours looking at the circling birds and had finally located their nest high up in one of the tall beech trees above the valley, or searching the area for any evidence of a rumoured temporary encampment for some late Georgian period militia men.

It was Mr Henderson everyone went to see if they found something curious or unusual. Consequently he had, amongst other things, built up an admirable collection of Stone-Age flint tools given to him by the local farm workers. Henderson was a man born out of his time, a kindly compassionate man who was always fair but strict in his dealings. He was remembered fondly by all the people who had come into contact with him, both pupils and colleagues. In fact schoolchildren used to compete to find and bring in something which "would get Old Hendy side-tracked" and hopefully avoid a mathematics or grammar tuition class. Henderson knew this of course but drew the line one day when a normally quiet pupil brought in a green glass marble from a recently smashed lemonade bottle. A futile attempt was made involving this pale green glass sphere to avoid algebraic appreciation "Could it be from an old slingshot sir?", a claim to which most of the pupils in the class tried to strengthen, but to no avail, with a wry smile "Old Hendy" then plunged them into one of the most complicated and lengthy algebra sessions ever. After this no more green glass marbles or similar things of base interest were ever to appear in class again.

During the year of 1914 Miles Henderson would meet Frederick Pearson, who then had only just freshly graduated from Cambridge University. Frederick was staying as a guest of the Melanby family up at the Manor. It wasn't long after the two had met that they discovered a mutual interest in archaeology and, to some extent, natural history. They spent many an hour field-walking, collecting pottery fragments and the occasional varied coin from the freshly ploughed fields. There had been that time when Miles Henderson had even insisted on stuffing the decomposing remains of a sparrow hawk into his tatty old tweed blazer side pocket. Typically, this dead raptor now intruded upon an already bulging pocket content of pine cones, fossils and small animal skulls. Much of this content which now had to be taken out was then dispersed into the not-too-readily offered hands of Frederick.

It was Frederick who would finally show Miles the strange earthenware tile that he had recently discovered in the Melanby's store room. This was part of a sizeable collection consisting not just of foreign travel-acquired souvenirs, but also of many local finds given to the Melanby's by various villagers and farm workers over the years. Some of these finds were labelled such as the "Stone axe found winter of 1841 Melton Briarsville" or just "1836 from Farrows Mead field"; not brilliant in detail but at least something to go on. There was also a near complete Roman coolus-style helmet in the store room too, but sadly this was totally unprovenanced. There was some hearsay that it had been found by some old poachers many years back, but there was nothing tangible to confirm this at all. With the amount of foreign travel the Melanby's had been involved with it could have originated from just about anywhere?

This oldest inhabitant, whose name, sadly, I cannot reveal, as he wished to remain anonymous back then and also in any future records that were made, so naturally I must still respect those wishes. Enthrallingly, he did tell me that on one hot summer's day Mr Henderson had begun to discuss the topic of the local chieftain rumour in some depth. It was recalled that he had also mentioned "I have found something of great curiosity in my garden", and had caused an irritating anti-climax by refusing at the time to say exactly what this discovery had been?

Sadly this oldest inhabitant passed away some years ago back in 1997, but over many cups of tea and afternoons spent talking in his overgrown primrose-infested garden he slowly began to share and reveal his experiences. It always seemed to me that he felt more secure for some reason talking in the early evenings. As the sun set and the blackbirds started to select a local Tawny Owl-containing conifer to mob, it was usually then that he would present me with new documentation and yet more of his valued opinions. He subtly suggested that he either knew, or strongly believed, something historically magnificent was present in this area; I could never quite determine which? He never failed to leave me on an excitement-enhancing cliff hanger until the next visit took place. I'm fairly sure that he trusted me, but one can never be sure on such matters, and one also wonders what other details he may well have either forgotten or indeed perhaps chose not to inform me of? Finally, after some months he revealed that all those years back, Mr Henderson had finally shown him what had been found in the garden. It was something spotted in a thin slice of turf and picked up whilst Mr Henderson had been edging a rose bed.

Tantalisingly, the "oldest resident" said that he now possessed that very find and then held out his hand, on the palm of which was a small folded envelope. He then placed the small package into my hand. "Have a look for yourself lad", he said, with the faint suggestion of a satisfied smile. Tilting the crisp white embossed envelope upwards a thick gold coin then slid heavily into my hand. It had that lovely yellow tone, tinged with burnished orange; the colour of very ancient gold.

Handling the coin, which I knew to be a Celtic full stater, (Authors

Note:- a "stater" is a general term applied to any coin from this period, most often used in relation to gold and silver examples) I appreciated the little target-eyed prancing horse, surrounded by what appeared to be wheels and stars. Whilst on the other side, an ear of wheat, or some other cereal, was clearly depicted.

Upon signing up for the Army back in 1914 Mr Henderson had given the coin to him as a young lad, requesting that he look after it until he came back, as it was indeed in those days a "very special coin". Mr Henderson, sadly, was never to come back and this fact lends an additional emotional factor to this coin, which of course is still regarded as very special today, almost a century later.

Note: - the author is now in possession of this very same coin. In 1998 the Probate of this "oldest resident" was finally read and I discovered to my amazement that this gentleman had very kindly willed the "special coin" to me. In 2006 I visited Melton Briarsville again and stood looking at the name of Lance Corporal Miles Henderson on the local war memorial. In my shirt pocket I could feel the weight of the "special coin". I went there that day for no other reason than to take the coin to the memorial, funny how we do such nostalgic-type actions? In fact I have done this several times, mostly when possible, on the anniversary of Miles Henderson's death. Sometime afterwards, when I was recounting these events to a fellow metal detectorist he said something curious: "Why do you think a Head Master with society contacts was only the rank of a Lance Corporal?"

I hadn't considered that issue at all, but the more I discovered about Miles Henderson the more it seemed to fit his personality. So hoping I'm not being too presumptuous here when I say, I believe he wasn't bothered about rank and all that, he quite simply wanted to do his bit, and just went off and did it. So with the help of research completed largely in the 20th Century by Melton Briarsville's 'oldest inhabitant', and since then many other parties, it is now possible to have a privileged glimpse at some of the discoveries made in and around the village in the past centuries.

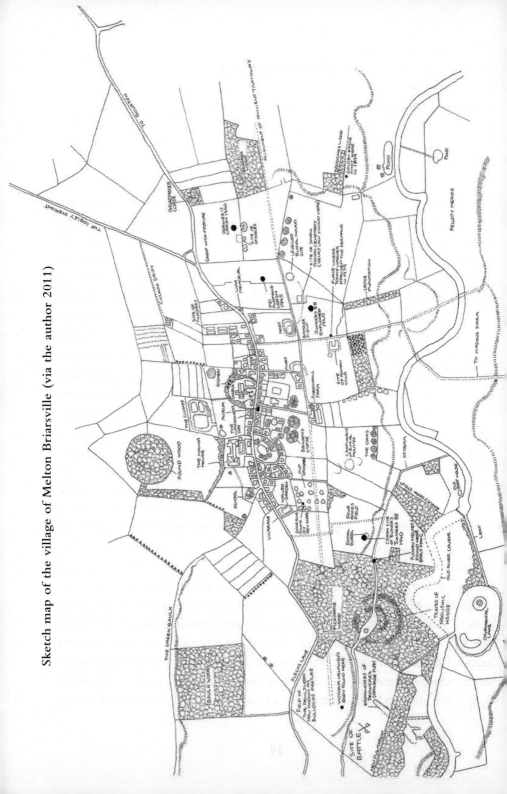

Sketch map of the village of Melton Briarsville (via the author 2011)

CHAPTER ONE

DIGGING DITCHES AND SHATTERED BONES

The area of land to the west of the village mainly consisted, and still does to this day, of dense woodland areas. These flank a large but fairly shallow low lying valley which is prone to varying degrees of flooding when the nearby river occasionally bursts its banks. Throughout the winter period large areas of this land were always waterlogged, and the meadows still occasionally flood in modern times. Records show that in the 1780's parties of gentlemen shooters had achieved bags of up to a hundred varied ducks and snipe from the area. This terrain had been subjected to various drainage attempts from the laying of fired clay tubes, to form mole drains, to wholesale trenches and ditches, but moisture has always remained a problem. Attempting to tackle the issue once again saw another new land owner, a certain James Marlborough Fenwicke, considering what to do here. This was much to the delight of many villagers for whom the additional income would be most welcome. So in March 1767 those men and women not engaged agriculturally, and even the elderly, found a new source of employment, even younger children were hired at a penny a day for carrying the rather large heavy wicker baskets of soil chalk and clay uphill to be deposited near the wood.

The main planned task here was to dig a trench almost of canal-like proportions and to have many sideways leats of smaller ditches all leading into it. The plan was that this main ditch then would drain away into the river. Whether this would actually work in practicality was a matter of some debate amongst the men, many of whom had worked before on similar drainage projects in nearby areas. As always they contemplated such issues only amongst themselves but always did what they were asked without question, as was quite normal in those times.

By August, to be fair to all involved, quite an extensive earth-moving operation had been completed but there was still much to do, a huge section of the main ditch still had to be prepared. This remaining section would continue to run across some low-lying pasture and when completed would stretch over a total of nearly four hundred metres of land. It was when they had reached about six feet down that some very curious objects were to be encountered.

Numerous oval lead lumps were found along with bits of preserved leather, and there were one or two long lengths of corroded iron which, to all extents and purposes, looked like spears. The first brown coloured bone was encountered and dismissed as being that from a long-dead cow or oxen. But as their spades bit deeper and ever wider into the fertile soil, the first skulls and associated teeth were uncovered and these were unmistakeably of human origin. The skulls were quickly followed by hundreds more associated bones. This was not good at all. Mr Fenwicke was called for; as it was evidently clear some of the work force was getting a little nervous of this unusual situation. If they had accidentally disturbed an old churchyard or plague burial pit this would not go down well at all. It was one thing breaking into an ancient barrow, or similar, after all those were pagan burials, but the disturbance of more recent possibly Christian inhumations would be something that was definitely unacceptable. The situation and the unnerving of most individuals concerned was somewhat remedied by the offer from Mr Fenwicke of another shilling a day for the men and a generous increase of two pence for the women and children.

That was James Fenwicke's answer to all of life's problems, throw money at them, and see what happened next. There was every possibility that some of the villagers had taken advantage of this well known factor, and why not? More bones and skulls were eventually located and upon examination several had what can only be described as cut and hack marks on them. The skulls in particular had several oval shaped long holes in them. One of the older men, called Jeb, had remarked "That aint bin done with God's blessing whatever anyone says, I don't like what we be a finding ere, and I reckons it's now gonna take

15

ye Mr Fenwicke sir much more than a shilling extra eh, lads?" But the rebellion as such was short lived and Jeb was left just muttering away to himself as the sounds and sights of digging, hauling and spade blades once more cut into the soil.

Over the next few days more skulls were unearthed. But these, due to their size, were obviously from small children, and some also bore the same cut marks. After two weeks literally thousands of bones and over one hundred skulls had been unearthed. Included in the mass of mixed up bones, as if to justify the very first assumption there were indeed found to be some bones from oxen and quite a few horses too. Now once again under Jeb's influence it was widely felt amongst the work force that the time for pursuing what could be yet another extra shilling was definitely due. Having none of it, James Fenwicke rather angrily came down and looked again, whilst he knew how to solve issues with money, he was no fool, and knew when things were definitely being taken advantage of. He stumbled into a part of the ditch and picked up a snapped femur bone and a section of Human skull and announced "I've paid additional for the experience of finding the first twelve or so of these skulls and that's the lot, now those who want to carry on may do so, and those who wish to no longer be paid will leave right now".

Now normally in such situations the feudal system would have kicked in; they were lucky James Fenwicke was a fairly mild-natured man and had given them a choice in the matter at all. Mild-natured he may have been but he still carried the views of class and order prevalent in those times. However Fenwicke had underestimated their religious beliefs and had totally lost control of the situation when it began to be whispered amongst the crowd something about "The Devils work has been done here". When pitched against the Devil and his reputation Fenwicke stood little chance.

James Fenwicke now briefly considered whether purchasing this additional land had been a good idea? Of course it was, he convinced himself. Who was it but him, James Fenwicke, who both managed and owned several tea and sugar plantations in the New World using vast slave communities? He would be damned if those Negro slaves would ever give him so much aggravation as he had experienced here in this village. Of course they wouldn't, and neither was this motley workforce of rural land workers going to be allowed to do so either. Admittedly he considered there was a slight difference between a plantation slave and these people before him. That they would also do as they were told, well he felt certain of that, on this account he was once again to be proven wrong. As soon as the Devil had been mentioned that was it, out of nearly seventy people only two remained at work, and even they were being called many derogatory names by the slowly departing crowd.

It was just at this stage the Reverend Joseph Bartrapp, from Burford, came in on the scene. The departing crowd suddenly parted to allow the single horse and carriage containing the Reverend into the field, which truly gave him rather a dramatic entrance. Bartrapp continued through the crowd whilst having thoughts of Moses and the Red Sea, brought his carriage to a halt, nimbly alighted and then headed over briskly to Fenwicke. Being another enthusiastic antiquarian in the district he immediately offered his services to Fenwicke. Having heard about the skulls, Bartrapp had been meaning to go over and have a look for some time now, "If some quality ancient things can be found, sometimes a princely sum can be obtained", he had said to Fenwicke. Money usually stimulated Fenwicke, but he now seemed truly deflated. "Fine Bartrapp. do as you wish. However you must personally guarantee the payments for the costs of any further diggings not directly related to my proposed drainage specifications". "Of course of course" replied one very excited Reverend Bartrapp almost rubbing his thin claw-like hands with joy.

Bartrapp did indeed do just as he wished, and also paid a team of six men who he knew from a neighbouring town the very princely sum of a half crown a day. This certainly ensured some dedicated degree of continuation, albeit incurring perhaps not the best relationship prospects with some of the more local men who had recently left the site. It was not drainage that Bartrapp had any intention of achieving; he didn't care whether Fenwicke dried this land out or not. But when it came to ancient objects the Reverend Joseph Bartrapp was passionate. However, after finally having parted with a sum of money that amounted to the region of one hundred pounds his passion was somewhat curtailed. For all this expense had only procured the finding of yet more skulls, bones and one tiny green corroded coin that defied any attempts at identification. Therefore he decided this was not the "investment" that he had both predicted and hoped for, and so closed down the venture.

It would seem that any monies for whatever reason invested in this water-sodden land would come to little or nothing. For some weeks Fenwicke hung onto the possibility of his drainage scheme. Originally he had made plans; plans not only to drain this land but to also have it landscaped by a well known and very much desired architect. Once again he tried to engage workers, and once again he failed. So now it was his turn to call upon the services of Reverend Bartrapp, who he, and everyone else locally for that matter, knew to be of a stern and mighty character when delivering his sermons. Such a sermon was just what might remedy this annoying situation, thought Fenwicke. The entire village would be required to attend and he would put this so-called Devils work to rest for good.

On this matter Joseph Bartrapp extended even his dedication and gave a very fiery sermon indeed, loaded with many aspects of grate-fulness to employers, somewhat loosely linked to the New Testament. However, halfway through even he could tell that just like Fenwicke had misjudged his listeners in relation to money, he too had misjudged them in relation to the element of fear. In those times the unknown and the Devil were sources of true fear that were considered by almost all to be of a very real and forceful nature. Bartrapp then side-tracked, looked upwards as if to the heavens for some help and then announced it would be for the good of all concerned then if no more was ever said of what had been found.

Seeing reason, most of those who attended saw the logic of this and after a time perhaps the fear would ease and the whole event be forgotten. Finally, Fenwicke did manage to re-employ those few who would still work there to infill the previous diggings. This action was greatly assisted and reinforced by Bartrapp, who had said: "In God's view this would be like giving these poor souls a Christian reburial". However, in principle it was thus wasting yet more money, with the consequence that the land never did get drained, or indeed landscaped.

Fenwicke was to eventually sell the estate shortly afterwards to the Melanby family and is reputed to have disappeared overseas, most likely to oversee his profitable overseas investments that had so far caused him far less trouble. Something must have gone rather wrong, though. For just fifteen years later a filthy drunk character was seen for a short period wandering the streets of Holborn, in London, staggering and always muttering something about "The Devils work". Passers-by would often be accosted by this man, who never asked or demanded for money, but just seemed to want to inform people of his problem. His stale sweaty odour and slurred speech meant that on not one occasion did anyone give him their ear. More often than not he was pushed away, people pulling disgusted faces that they had actually been forced to touch this filthy specimen. His actions on occasion were accompanied by the clatter and chink of a few coppers landing on the cobbles behind him. No one could ever know how embarrassed and hurt his pride was at this seemingly charitable action. Not once had he ever been seen to retrieve such pitying donations. Of course not being missed by anyone at all, his eventual disappearance went unnoticed. It was sometime later that this same drunk was found dead on the cold filth-covered mud banks of the River Thames. The body was later identified only by the examination of some stained and folded papers found in his grime encrusted silk embroidered waistcoat, as that being of one James Fenwicke.

CHAPTER TWO

THE GREAT STORM OF
1810

I t is probably fair to say that one can normally expect a series of blustery gales to occur around the month of November in most years. But what ageing Vicar, the Reverend Berwick Cholmondeley Snape, had endured along with all the other residents of Melton Briarsville on the night of November 24th 1810 was quite something else. The winds had howled down the valley and streams of autumn fallen leaves hurtled across the fields like brown blizzards. The rain was driven in torrential sheets that shimmied along the wet surface of the muddy high street looking like water-based Northern Lights. Things clattered against, and slid down the slated roof tops. The fierce wind whistled and moaned around poorly sealed window panes causing tallow candle flames to flicker. Occasionally one could hear a crack as one of the mature but brittle beech trees close by shed yet another bough. Fortunately Snape had a particularly large tree close to his Vicarage cut down just this July gone and now that seemed to have been a very wise decision.

Next morning with a clear blue sky, and just a hint of a breeze remaining, Melton Briarsville awoke, and its residents began to examine the damage. Several of the smaller less-well thatched cottages had been totally stripped of their roof coverings leaving uncovered beam structures and great dense clumps of varying coloured decaying damp thatch lying all over the high street. One of the lanes reaching out to neighbouring Bourton was inconveniently blocked by a huge fallen tree, which eventually took four whole days to saw up and remove.

The gilded weather vane, in the form of a cockerel that sat atop the church spire, had been spun around so violently it had worn through its mount. Thus detached, it literally flew off and embedded itself in the thatched roof of a neighbouring cottage. Fortunately no one had been hurt by any wind assisted projectiles. Although there were certainly some curious sights to behold; a series of slate tiles from the church roof had been blown off and lay stuck in the grass below, looking like miniature grey grave stones. A woodpigeon had been blown against, and actually impaled, on a nail sticking out of the lumpy pitch-coated wooden slats on Farmer Wilsons main barn; and was still alive into the bargain.

Snape saw all these sights, and more, whilst he did his rounds, checking that all his parishioners were safe. Returning home he decided there was just enough time for the imbibing of a small glass of fortifying Port, before checking on his precious fruit orchard. Thus strengthened, he went around the back of the Vicarage and headed out across the lawn. Things did not bode well: several courses of crumbling red bricks had come down from along the orangery wall and the row of ancient pear trees alongside had been crushed, "The Devil himself is damned for they are ruined", Snape cried out! The apple trees, which were slightly more sheltered, had fared somewhat better. But the largest, and his most favourite mature Bramley, was totally over. The round-shaped root pan sticking up sideways next to a freshly torn patch of grassy turf. Upon closer examination one of the finger-like roots had actually grown through something, a certain something that looked very much as if it might be gold.

The condition of fruit trees now briefly forgotten, Snape then, somewhat excitedly, broke off the fresh thick sappy root with a sharp crack, and he now grasped the object, rotating it in his hands to clean it. It certainly was gold. He acknowledged the reassuring weightiness of his find, and looked down at what was most definitely the largest finger ring he had ever seen. The hole in the middle was too small for any of his fingers. "The surrounding metal must be over four ounces in weight", he considered, it was huge. On the top of the bezel he spotted some type of inscription, but it needed cleaning. The dark orchard soil was also trapped in what looked like some damage to the top of the ring.

Snape held the object up and appreciated the glorious contrast of gleaming gold against the streaks of dark soil smeared over his discovery. Perhaps he wondered who ever had planted the apple tree years

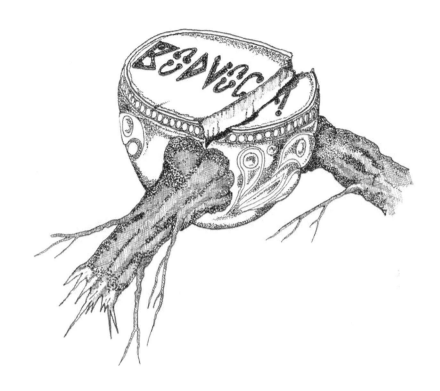

Drawing of the ring as found in 1810 (Courtesy of the Snape family via the
original diaries of the Reverend Berwick Snape)

ago had accidentally struck the object sharply with a spade? Grasping
the huge ring in his hands, as if praying, he ambled back up through the
garden to a stone sink and washed his treasure. Looking around to ensure no-one was in the vicinity he once again admired the rich yellow
of the metal, and then considered what on earth he should do with it?

Reverend Snape lived on land, and also in a house, supported on an
income from the Melanby family. By rights the ring was their property.
He considered the matter with some thought and decided, after some
time it must be said, to finally take the ring up to Sir James at the Manor.
Upon his meeting with Sir James the two men began by discussing the
previous night's storm and the damage to the village. Snape reassuringly
felt the ring in his waist coat pocket, he felt certain its weight was mak-

ing the garment hang slightly unevenly. "So, Snape, what brings you up here anyway?" asked Sir James. "Well it's an interesting matter indeed", said Reverend Snape, removing the ring from the pocket. "I discovered this object below the roots of a tree blown down last night", placing the huge gold ring on top of the large walnut dining table. Whatever the two men discussed, decided, or agreed on at that stage was not the matter of further records, or of facts supplied from an eaves-dropping servant. However just a week later the engraved letters of 'BODVOC' began to distort, as the gold ring slowly melted into the crucible of the village Blacksmith, a local man known by the name of "Spitter" Hargreaves.

From the molten mass, which had once been the ring, two ingots were cast, one large and one a fair bit smaller, exactly to Sir James's instructions. The smaller one, also according to instructions, was given back to Reverend Snape and Sir James took the other considerably larger ingot. Nothing was said, each man understood his position in the matter of such things.

The one given to Snape was unfortunately lost to history, on several occasions. But the one that came into the Melanby family had a rather curious history attached to it. Four years later, Sir James' daughter, Victoria, was the recipient, on her birthday, of a large gold ring from her father. He'd had it fashioned and made by a jeweller in London during a recent visit. Victoria was not what one might say, by any standards, a normal young lady in the high society that travelled between country seats and London. There were rumours about her, to which several acquaintances were only too keen to make her aware of, which did nothing to enhance her manner or feelings of security. She hated London, its people, and dreaded the time when her Father took the family for the "City Period". She was awkward in company and would rather remain upstairs or out of sight reading he beloved classics. A pale complexion and hair of such reddish colour made her stand out even more in the surrounding society she so wished to shun.

Victoria was different, even she was aware of that. She couldn't be bothered with all the tittle tattle trifling and sniggering behind her back, or those of others. She quite simply didn't want to be in such places or with such company anyway. As soon as Sir James presented her with the ring she had looked grateful but at the same time somewhat pained as she slid the large ring on her finger. She did have the social poise, though, to ensure that her father was unaware of her discomfort. Although her father was kind and generous the ring was obviously too large a design and weight for her delicate fingers.

One day Victoria simply went missing. She wasn't noticed for some while, as she was always alone somewhere about the house or gardens. After six hours, and the weather turning to rain, Sir James firstly became concerned, and then rather worried. Soon he became desperate and requested urgently that a search party from the village should be gathered and scour the surrounding estate. Fortunately it would at first seem just two hours later Victoria was found. Quite some distance from the village, someone had spotted something pale billowing and flapping in the breeze in the grassy field known to some as "The field of the Devils work". Upon investigation several villagers were frantically called over and there lying on the ground before them was the rainsoaked body of Victoria. Unfortunately it was quickly apparent that she was quite clearly dead.

"How is Sir James to deal with this?" said an elderly villager, looking down at the body. Just then a teenage boy rushed forward, took off his hat and knelt down beside the body. When he picked up one of the porcelain-white hands he actually began to cry and make a wailing moaning noise. A man with an untidy shock of black hair, probably the boy's father, looked very embarrassed, glancing from side to side to see who had noticed, then quickly and quietly reprimanded the lad."Boy now come on, don't you go doing that now. She's not for the likes of us to mourn so obviously."The other villagers then decently pretended they hadn't seen anything at all and walked away, stopping some yards back from the dead girl. After all, it wouldn't do to be too close when the gentry arrived at the scene. How indeed would Sir James deal with this? For his daughter had dressed herself in a white sheet, draped and fastened over her like a character from one of the Greek classics that she had so often read. Her red hair had been twisted crudely into two large plaits, one of which she had cut off and was lying on her chest along with a gold ring. Later when Sir James came to the scene he awkwardly knelt down and quietly said "No worry my angel. Father is here and he's taking you back home". As he was assisted to raise the body a small sheet of crumpled damp paper was seen under her arm, it stuck to her chest and floated away on the breeze, getting caught in a dead thistle just a few feet away.

Reverend Snape delicately retrieved the damp paper from its prickly surroundings and passed it to Sir James, who seemed oblivious, just crumpling it further and then forcing it deep into his coat pocket. Later in his study Sir James had unfolded and smoothed flat the still-damp paper and saw there was a note written upon it. Although the ink had run slightly, it was unmistakeably his daughter's beautifully neat style. It read: – "Dear Father, I am so sorry for the actions I have taken, but the ring that was given to me confirmed even further in my mind that I am too misplaced in today's world. I came here to this field, a place of which I feel there is a great sadness. To bring the ring back to where I feel it surely belongs and to go myself also to that place and hopefully that time where it may be considered I belong too".

At least that is what the Reverend Snape later recalled Sir James had, sometime afterwards, stated the note read. Snape never actually saw the note, and in fact didn't want to. The fact that he had originally found that large ring, and that another ring made from it had been quoted in a fearsome and Godless suicide note did not rest easy with his conscience. That evening the golden metal of the second gold ingot would once again find itself in the hand of Reverend Berwick Siddeley Snape, but for the very last time. For some reason he felt like he could not bear to possess it any longer and so the little yellow ingot began to rotate and spin as it hurtled through the damp evening air. It smacked against the thin brittle bark of a damaged pear tree and was deflected straight into a patch of nettles, where globular droplets of evening dew now rested upon its bright surface. That was the last anyone saw of it for over four decades, until it was re-discovered sometime later by a certain Lemuel Klake.

CHAPTER THREE

FROM OLD GOLD INTO NEW BEER

E ver since 1817, the year that old Sir James had died, some said from a broken heart, they had begun their crafty and stealthy trade. The two local poachers, one a certain Joshua Klake and his associate, Ezekiel Foukes, had been taking pretty much whatever they could steal in the way of game, eggs and anything else that took their notice from the Melanby estate. In almost all their doings they were ably assisted by their black and white Cocker Spaniel, that had the rather odd name of Proot. The two men usually preferred dark and windy nights to creep around the woodlands. The wind covered up the sounds of their, even then, rather ancient muzzle loading flintlock guns that they used when taking the odd pheasant or two. It also covered up the excited barking of Proot who, when retrieving a flapping pheasant from the undergrowth, seemed to be possessed. This was a habit Joshua had tried to control with a whip-like section of willow on many occasion, but had always failed.

The two guns were pitted with rust and both their stocks had split badly. With such poor maintenance it was remarkable that a serious accident had not occurred. But then again on occasion the two men shall it be said were rather conservative with the amounts of black powder they used. Once, Joshua had taken aim at a roosting pigeon and fired, resulting in a hissing fizzle of smoke and smouldering powder leaving the end of the barrel, and the ball just dropping into the oak leaves at his feet. Recently Joshua had tried a different angle with some fair level of success, and that involved holding a small sheet iron handled container on the end of a long ash pole just beneath a roosting pheasant. For this method they preferred moonlit nights when they could easily pick out a roosting bird silhouetted against the bright moon.

This wasn't as simple as it might seem, for inside the rusted container held aloft was a burning mixture of pitch, sulphur and wax, and a few of Joshua's own secret ingredients. Which, if snagged or caught up in an overhead branch, these contents could, and occasionally did, end up deposited on the head and shoulders of the pole holder below. The smoke given off was most pungent to say the least, but incredibly it worked, and many a pheasant "fell asleep for the pot" whilst roosting and ended its life crashing downwards through the bushes towards the two pairs of grubby, but very grateful hands. When they were after rabbits, and other small game, they would set wire trace snares, which could be disguised and then discreetly checked and emptied during the day time, providing one took care.

The estate at this time had no gamekeepers, owing to the fact Sir Giles Melanby, unlike his father, simply wasn't partial to the pastime of shooting nevertheless great care still had to be taken by the poachers. It wasn't that Sir Giles found hunting or shooting cruel, he just thought it was all rather dull and boring, and had once said "Oh bye and bye we just leave the wretched pheasants and woodcock for the locals". Whether Sir Giles was just being dismissively magnanimous, or genuinely knew that some locals were actively helping themselves is open to question? Therefore the abundance of game, etc, went unchecked officially, but was of course unofficially rather efficiently controlled to some degree by Ezekiel and Joshua's nefarious activities.

Despite the lack of official control over the estate, there were still plenty of persons in the village who would take any opportunity to impress "those up at the Manor", so Joshua and Ezekiel had to be as devious as possible. Also firmly fixed in their minds were the three men who, when caught poaching near Kidlington recently, had nearly beaten the gamekeeper to death. All three had later been hanged. So for Joshua and Ezekiel avoiding confrontations with anyone was their main aim.

The cunning pair would deposit the odd haunch of venison or a brace of pheasants in the gardens of those they thought posed some threat, and no questions seem ever to have been asked about these welcome, if rather mysterious, gifts. It wasn't just the risks of being seen, or someone reporting them either; they faced many concerns of which most were totally unpredictable. But often the crafty pair could turn misfortune to their own advantage. For example, one time they had been considering what else to use as wadding in their guns. Their decision needed to be a good one, due to the sparing amounts of powder both men used. It was Joshua who finally had come up with the idea to use sheep's wool, it didn't cost a thing and there was plenty of it stuck on the hawthorn bushes up by the Church. Without further experimentation they set off early one September evening.

Joshua and Ezekiel "Dishonesty in January 1819"

It was a cloudy but fairly light night, but their families needed feeding, so there was little choice in the matter. Coming to the edge of Pickards Wood they spotted a small covey of partridges running down the side. Two loud bangs and two puffs of thick creamy white smoke and six of the partridges were bowled over. However, this was not all that occurred. As each man had fired they noticed a great clump of black powder-dusted wool fly out of their barrels, fizzling and flaming, looking more like some type of exotic firework. The explosive-infused woollen lumps fell to the ground amongst the tinder-dry oats and that was it. Firstly, they ran to get their dead birds and then back again, dancing around like wild things, sending up showers of sparks as they tried in vain to stamp out the increasing crop fire. It was to no avail. Within a minute the dry cereal crop had caught ablaze to a serious degree. Joshua and Ezekiel immediately decided to run off from the scene, but they were not neglecting the situation at all. Joshua gave Ezekiel his partridges and gun and told him to lay them all down, along with his possessions, in the hedge and then get back to the fire straight away. Running into the village, Joshua raised the alarm, telling everyone gathering that "They had seen the fire from Ezekiel's cottage and that he was in fact down their right now trying to put it out".

It turned out to be a long night indeed, but eventually the combined effort saved most of the crop from being burned. The two poachers were hailed as heroes within the village community, something of which they both revelled in and had no intent whatsoever of altering by ever admitting the truth. Had they, or indeed someone else, perhaps told of the real version of events that night, then for certain neither man would have received the old half-guinea that Sir Giles presented to each of them after the following Sunday Church service. Ironically, that very service had been about honesty in life. When Sir Giles was out of earshot, Ezekiel, with a sly grin, had asked Joshua what he had thought about the service? To which Joshua had replied "Twas a load of rubbish friend. Aye, it may be said honesty is the best policy alright, but for the likes of us, it'll keep you beggar-poor"

One day in late March 1823, around midday, both men were near the beech wood and the valley, a few miles from the village. They were just walking along aimlessly, having just checked three snares and found nothing in them. Coming out of the side of the wood, they forced themselves through a damp glistening barrier of Hazel bushes. As usual Ezekiel was too close and only just avoided a whip- like cluster of thin branches coming back at his face. Fending off the branches, a few cold drops of water departed from them right down between his soiled neck scarf and somewhat grubbier neck, causing him to shiver. Then something caught his eye. Joshua had also stopped. He had obviously seen it too - something very unusual indeed.

They had great poachers' eyes, knowing all the hues and colours of plants and animals at various times of the year. It was a skill that often revealed a hidden rabbit, or any other thing worthy for the taking. Although of the two, it was Joshua whose eyesight was really sharp, as he all too frequently informed Ezekiel. However, on this day, looking in the same direction, both their eyes had focused at the same time upon something green and bulbous that was jammed in the front of one of the large openings of a badger sett.

Both curious, they walked over and found it was actually some type of helmet that had been dragged up, it seems, when the sett's occupants had changed the grass and leaf bedding of their deep-down accommodation. Inside the same hole was yet another round-looking object, jammed some five feet further down. Three feet to one side, another tunnel clearly had yet another of the strange things stuck in it. Although in this case only the green rim was evident, protruding out of one of the chalky sides close to the surface. They are strange things indeed? Some type of rimmed bowl made of thin brass, they reckoned, with a sliding chin strap thing. Ezekiel grabbed the first one they had seen and, whilst laughing, jammed it on top of his head. "Reckon you is right with that one Ez, they are helmets aren't they? Look a bit like the ones worn by those horse riders we see up at the Manor" said Joshua. "And by the looks of that green colour these are pretty old too", he added.

After about half an hour of curiosity-based effort they had now got the second one out. And, by using a large stick, had managed to prod the third specimen out from the crumbling chalk side of the badger's tunnel. Knowing Sir Giles had a partiality to such curious things, they decided to take them all up to the Manor. They considered this would be a good opportunity to show once again an honest angle to their characters, and hopefully offset any future suspicions, or accusations, that they were plundering the estate. A useful tactic for certain, as it had been Joshua who had persuaded Ezekiel to shin fifty feet up a massive elm tree some years back and relieve a pair of Honey Buzzards of their three large cream and brown mottled eggs. On that occasion Sir Giles had been very pleased indeed when they had taken these to him; he had one of the largest and finest egg collections in England.

Sadly, though, that was the lot for the Honey Buzzards. These magnificent, and rare, birds would not nest again in this area for nearly a century. However, in relation to their new 'gift' Sir Giles frustratingly didn't did not seem to be too interested in these finds from the two 'honest' villagers. He said that they were "almost certainly relics from the Civil War about a hundred and eighty years ago". If the truth be known it was the classic style of these helmets that for some reason reminded Sir Giles of his dead sister Victoria. However true to the Melanby family's passion for collecting all things curious Sir Giles placed one of the helmets in the great hallway. Later on, after his death, this would, like many objects of curiosity, end up in the storeroom. The other two 'valueless' helmets found themselves placed outside the front door, in one of the two huge stone flower troughs that stood there.

Decades of exposure to rain and frost would eventually turn them into crumbling flakes, and bits of sheet bronze that eventually sank into the acidic soil. When the troughs were totally cleaned out, over thirty two years later, the fragments of bronze were not even noticed, as they were thrown out onto the composting pile.

Sir Giles might have been more interested, however, in the five small, but thick, gold coins 'with running horses on them', that Ezekiel and Joshua found just two years later in virtually the same place. However, this time their discovery was not going to be used to safeguard the characters of the two finders. Far from it, in fact. Sir Giles was destined never to see these coins, that Joshua had luckily spotted in the gravelly base of a tiny stream. They were just opposite to where a small section of the bank had collapsed, and had slid down into the water. Neither Joshua nor Ezekiel had any idea what these coins were? Neither did John Harmer, the publican at the Waggoner's Inn? But all three of them were certain of one thing; and that was that they were made of gold.

It wasn't too difficult for John Harmer to persuade the finders that in return for the coins he would guarantee them a good and steady supply of fine ale from his hostelry, for an agreed period. So it was that the gold coins were 'spent', and thus converted into two year's-worth of evening revelry, and many a morning of rather intense hangovers. Like some type of ancient alchemists experiment in reverse, Joshua and Ezekiel had rather successfully found a method of quickly turning gold into ale. But there were no complaints from any of the parties involved.

CHAPTER FOUR

SAMUEL AND THE FIRST TILE

By 1851 the village had seen quite a few changes, many influenced by the new machinery then becoming available to the landowners for cultivating crops. Some of the smaller fields, once having been tithe plots, have now had their hedgerows removed. Also, large areas of once accessible land have now had their accessibility reduced, due to the ongoing effects of the unpopular Enclosure Acts: The Melanby family had also had a section of their westward estate landscaped, although in a style not considered by the former landowner, James Fenwicke. He had been more concerned with drainage, whilst the Melanby's had quite simply been concerned with improving the appearance of the estate.

A considerable part of the river had been re-routed in the valley, and this now acted as a supply for a medium-sized ornamental lake. This lake had a leat dug from it that acted as an over flow, which in turn rejoined the original course of the river several hundred yards away. This improvement did, somewhat temporarily, assist in draining the western section of the estate to some small degree. However, the lie of the land meant that when the winter rains came the lake itself often burst its banks on the southern side, flooding the fields of a neighbouring landowner. Fortunately for the Melanby's, litigation was easily avoided, as this other landowner, a certain Captain William Relyan, who, being a very enthusiastic wild fowl shooter, was absolutely delighted with his newly-acquired water meadows. In wintertime vast flocks of Widgeon, Mallard, and healthy flocks of Snipe, appeared on these flooded fields. The Captain and his shooting parties, on some days, could be heard reducing their numbers from dawn until dusk.

Lemuel Klake, the son of the old poacher, Joshua, was now,

ironically, one of the junior gamekeepers on the Melanby estate. And apart from keeping a sure eye on game stocks, he was also responsible for controlling vermin. The reason for the estate now returning to game-shooting sports was due to Henry, one of Sir Giles' two sons, who had developed a taste for the London life. And, after having been invited on several shoots himself, had decided to return the compliment and to organise his own shoots on his ageing father's estate. The now extremely good relationship with the neighbouring Relyan's also resulted in numerous invitations to shoot the meadows adjacent to the newly created lake.

Whilst regarding his vermin-controlling responsibilities, Lemuel Klake went to deal with a pair of Magpies, which had foolishly constructed a large twiggy nest in a hawthorn bush just opposite the Waggoner's Inn. In those days, as much as today, Magpies were considered little more than vermin. Lemuel's first shot killed the male bird outright, spattering the surrounding thorny twigs with bright red blood and a few white feathers. However, his second shot just winged the female, who fluttered back into the bush ,and somehow managed to get back inside the nest. From there the chattering alarm call from the wounded bird could be heard for some distance.

Damn that bird! thought Lemuel, who then cut off a stout hazel pole, reached upwards and began to poke at the nest until it fell apart. A mass of dry twigs and muddy dust started to fall inside the bush, and also into Lemuel's face. But not distracted, he managed a third shot, that finally put paid to the flapping, squawking, bird.

Reaching inside the thorny bush to retrieve the two dead birds, as evidence of his 'job well done', Lemuel then spotted a silver sixpence amongst the mud and stick debris. This is good luck indeed, he thought to himself. These birds are known to love such shiny things. And in this case, so do I, considered Lemuel. Next to another piece of dry mud was something else that also drew his attention. Something that appeared to be a small yellow lump of gold? Placing it deep inside his pocket for safety, he would look at it later on.

What happened to it from here is unknown, as are of course many small snippets of such local history. Perhaps his family history had repeated itself in more ways than one, though, as Lemuel was shortly afterwards seen to have a smart new pair of boots and a coat of some considerable quality. Furthermore, it was noticed that he became a much more frequent visitor than usual to the Waggoner's Inn for the remainder of that entire year.

The middle of the year 1862 would see Samuel Callum having been a farm labourer in and around the village for some thirty odd years. He had, on occasion, taken up work on several farms, according to the seasons and the availability of work. In the past three decades Samuel has had quite a wide variety of responsibilities. But none as important, in his opinion, as looking after Clara and Sentry, who were 'two of the three ladies in my life', he would often say.

'Clara' and 'Sentry' weighed in at a fraction less than two tons each, and were a truly fine pair of bay -coloured Shire horses, which had been purchased by the Melanby estate back in the 1840's. Samuel loved these two horses, admiring the sheer strength derived from their unmistakeable Clydesdale -influenced physiques. The highly polished tack and gleaming brasses worn by each horse were exceptional in the area and were purely down to Samuel's dedication and pride. Samuel had even been allowed to help choose the design of the decorative brass work himself. And it had finally been decided to purchase some large disc-shaped decorations, each having a central floral-shaped star cut-out design.

Years later, with all the rubbing and movement, the waxed supporting thread securing one of these treasured brasses had finally frayed through, and the highly-polished artefact had swung sideways and fallen down onto the ground. It lay there only a few seconds before it was deeply ploughed into the soil. Frustrated at its loss, Samuel had spent ages retreading the area ploughed that day, but to no avail.

Despite the requirements of being a ploughman meaning that Samuel was often out in all weathers, there were some distinct advantages to this. Whilst mainly checking the furrows for depth, he spent much of the time looking downwards, and had often picked up curiosities from the freshly-sliced soil. There was the occasion when he spotted a delicate silver ring with a blue stone mounted on it. The ring was there one second and the next it had slid down a deep crack in the furrow. Samuel stopped the horses and levered back a huge slab of earth. Locating the ring, he was pleased to note that it was quite silvery in colour, albeit a bit greyish, and had a lovely blue cut stone mounted on its top. He had also managed to form quite a collection of coins. Some were modern and spendable, which would supplement his wages, but others looked to be of great age.

Many of his finds adorned the shelf above the fireplace, delicately balanced between the few pieces of china ware his wife, Mary, had brought to the estate-tithed cottage they shared. Mary didn't quite share his passion for collecting oddities; 'My husband collects them, and all they do in turn is collect dust!' she would say.

One November morning in 1862 Samuel had been requested to clear quite a considerable patch of rough land, and its bordering hedgerows, on the estate. Then, when prepared, to put it to the plough. This task took Samuel, and five other farm workers, nearly three weeks to complete. Then, in late November, the ploughshares took their first advances into the unkempt grassy soil. This won't be good for cropping until several seasons and ploughings break up the soil, thought Samuel, as he watched the two huge horses take turns to pull the single-shared plough, the steam rising from the muscular bodies and jetting from their nostrils.

After about three hours, Samuel took a break. During the earlier ploughing he had noticed some cobble-like stones, broken pieces of tile and a mass of pottery fragments in the turfs, and was now keen to go back and have a closer look. Pottery of all colours was visible everywhere. And from amongst this Samuel managed to retrieve seven very small greenish-coloured, coins. Plus another thick silver coin with a bearded man on the front, and also a bent bronze finger ring.

In the afternoon Sir Henry came down with his two Spaniels to inspect the progress. Samuel showed him the finds. With little of consequence happening in Sir Henry's life at the current time, and to amuse himself, he decided to investigate the area further and requested that Samuel could perhaps organise a team of locally sourced workmen, who could then be directed to excavate the site. Sir Henry, in reality, had no real idea of how to undertake such an excavation at all? But back then there were no real set rules on procedure. Most enlightened antiquarians of the day were still stuck fast in the general attitude of 'dig into it and get the artefacts'.

In fact, Sir Henry only thought of this as it was now most fashionable amongst several of his peers to have someone examine something ancient on one's estate. If you didn't have something ancient then, so as not to lose face, one could always pay to have a ruinous folly, such as an old castle, or church, erected anywhere on ones property. This all seemed rather exciting to Sir Henry Melanby who, in just over a month and a half, had taken over all organisation of the excavation, which had now revealed the extensive remains of a large Roman building.

Amongst the building rubble, several intriguing finds were made. Sir Henry took some of these to a friend of his, a certain Mr William Brightwell who, being a member of the Society of Antiquaries, Sir Henry considered well disposed to be able to identify some of them. Brightwell would later confirm, much to Sir Henry's amusement and great pleasure, that the majority of finds were all of a Roman date. Of particular interest to Brightwell was a small bronze figurine of the god Mercury, which, after much appraisal and comment, was eventually presented to him by Sir Henry. Although tolerated, it was well known in polite circles that this man, Brightwell, was not the type of person embarrassed by continually repeating himself. Indeed such repetition had its virtues. Brightwell had often found that in doing so he would eventually be presented with the object of his attentions.

Late one afternoon, the tiled flooring of a recently-uncovered room with a small central polychrome geometric mosaic was being swept with coarse hazel brooms and doused with pails of water. Sir Henry wanted to have both the large central mosaic, discovered the previous week, and this latest example cleaned, as he had recently commissioned a local watercolour artist to make accurate coloured representations of them. These, much to the artist's delight and honour, were going to be framed, and would eventually hang in Sir Henry's study.

The main section of the large mosaic was made from thousands of tiny coloured tesserae and had fortunately remained quite level and flat. With its central design depicting a winged Cupid riding a Dolphin, surrounded by various exotic animals, it was certainly impressive. Around the mosaic could be seen thousands of larger plain red tile tesserae set into the floor which, over the centuries, had ridden up in lumps and waves, which Sir Henry likened to looking rather like a huge draped carpet.

The smaller polychrome mosaic was surrounded by large reddish orange-coloured floor tiles, many of which had been broken. However, in one area they could be seen to be mostly intact, and lay almost as flat as the day when they had been placed in position. As the coarse bristles swept over one of the tiles in this unbroken area there was a sudden shout. Amongst the moist soil sweepings and frothy water what was clearly a gold coin had just been found. As the water drained away, closer examination of the area revealed yet another similar-looking coin that was still jammed down the side of one of the floor tiles. The tile was carefully raised up to obtain the coin, and also out of curiosity, to see if any others lay beneath it? With the tile taken out, a hole was then dug to a depth of around a foot. but no further coins were found. Several other tiles were also pulled up, but to no obvious benefit. It seemed likely that there were only two such coins present?

Later on, Sir Henry came down for his usual daily examination, and was duly presented with the two gold coins. He asked to be shown where they were found, and was escorted to the area. Looking at the upturned tiles, he saw that one of them appeared to have had some sort of an inscription made upon it and he asked for a broom. That was a event of no little amusement; Sir Henry actually labouring physically in front of all his workers.

Clearly there was not only some type of writing on the tile, but what appeared very much like a map, or something? Sir Henry knelt down to closely examine the strange markings; it was obvious to him that this was only part of something, as the inscription and diagram both appeared to be incomplete? Sir Henry then requested that many of the other tiles should be torn up immediately to see if any more of the inscription could then be located. This proved to be as fruitless as the search for more gold coins. It was only the polite, but firm, reservations from two Society of Antiquaries members, who were in attendance that day, which prevented the entire mosaic itself from being torn up and taken apart. Sir Henry, with his enthusiasm slightly dampened by officialdom, then departed with the two gold coins, and afterwards had the tile carried up to the Manor house by Samuel.

Sketch of Tile 1

The two gold coins were of the Roman type known as 'Aureii', and both were struck in the reign of the Roman Emperor, Claudius, who Sir Henry knew full well had been responsible for the invasion of Britain in 43AD. The coins were later wrapped in a cloth and placed in a small decorated hardwood box, that had originated from Sir Henry's earlier travels to India; both accompanied with a short note explaining where, what year, and how they were discovered.

Examining the tile further, Sir Henry had been truly intrigued. And since the part-inscription, or so he believed, appeared to be in Latin, he eventually had the tile translated by a Classic Latin scholar at Oxford University. As a result it was revealed to him that the text scratched onto its surface appeared to refer to a certain Queen named 'Bodvocca'. But only being part of the complete inscription, its references remained wholly obscure to all who looked upon them. What exactly did she do half a mile from this tile? Sir Henry pondered, thoughtfully.

Some days later he was still pondering this mystery when the inscription he was staring at so intently seemed to go a bit out of focus. Then it was only visible from one eye, and quite quickly Sir Henry began to feel rather unwell. A brandy didn't help resolve the matter, so he retired early to bed. Three days after this, Doctor Pelham turned around to the gathered family, with Sir Henry's wrist in his hand, and stated: 'I am so very sorry to announce that Sir Henry has gone!'

Sir Henry's untimely passing certainly stopped the tile being assessed any further. Eventually it would be placed into storage, along with all the other worldwide-gathered curiosities that privilege and fortune had permitted the Melanby's to acquire over decades of travel. Interest in the excavation soon waned without the driving force of its benefactor. And Samuel was soon involved in replacing all the excavated soil back into the remains of the ancient rooms and corridors of the Villa. It wasn't long until the site looked very much like it did when Samuel first found it a few months back. It was now early 1863, and it would be another fifty-two years, or so, before anyone would wipe away the accumulated greyish dust from the tile and once again show any interest in it at all.

I of original name Velas am

I took part in- My age is advanced

Day the great wrongs done to our

Understood and those who will know of

So that our Queen will then be hon-

truly deserved-when our Queen is

up to be of importance to the people

honoured for my long life and to that

battle and our Queen BODVOCCA who

half a mile from where this rec-

BODVOCCA REGINA

Tile 1 Inscription found in 1862

41

CHAPTER FIVE

HAZARDOUS TIMES AHEAD

In 1879 the Melanby family had leased their entire estate and manor house and moved to India where they remained for twenty years, before returning in the autumn of 1899. The villagers were delighted to have their 'local royalty' return to them, having felt that the estate had rather been left to its own uncontrolled devices for the past two decades. As if to seal, rather symbolically, the return of the Melanby's with their 'local Royal' status, a juvenile golden eagle was seen, and finally shot, alongside Brooches Wood just one week after they'd returned.

Such a rare bird had never been seen, or heard of, in the locality before. On New Year's Eve, the villagers, who had managed previously to organise a collection enabling the dead bird to be sent to a taxidermist in Oxford, proudly presented the mounted bird to Sir Edward Melanby as a gift. If you visit the Manor today and look to the left as you walk into the dining room you will see a glass display case containing a large brownish bird. This is that very same eagle. These days, though, it doesn't look quite as magnificent as it once did. A few of its feathers now lay crumbling on the bottom of the case, and the bird has only got one eye. The missing eye can also be seen on the bottom of the case, it was dislodged in November 1944 by the blast, when a German V2 rocket had exploded over the village and, for some reason, was never put back in place.

The year of 1914 would turn out to be a momentous year, plunging Europe, and many parts of the World, into a terrible war; the experience of which, many would never forget, nor indeed, survive. For one young particular History and Classics graduate from Cambridge University, by the name of Frederick Pearson, it would, for a short period, also remain a memorable one for quite another reason: it was the year when he took a room at the Melanby's Manor house in Melton Briarsville.

His parents, or so he had gathered, had met Sir Edward and Lady Cecilia Melanby whilst on a business trip to London some years before, and had since become firm friends. The Pearson family owned, amongst other business ventures, a large bakery, and chain of some fourteen associated, and very successful, shops in Cambridgeshire. The entire concern was registered as Pearson's Bakeries of Cambridge Ltd. With expansion into cakes, sweets, and then biscuits, the company had been responsible for injecting quite some considerable new wealth, and therefore status, into the family. As time went on, the Melanby's suggested that perhaps after he had graduated, their son, Frederick, could come and stay with them for a while? The invite was finalised with 'There is plenty of history and age about the place. We are sure he would enjoy it?'

So it was that one day the housemaids in the Manor spotted a tall, somewhat awkward-looking, young man walk rather rigidly up the gravel drive. As he approached the front door it became obvious he was neither a new servant, nor any other member of the household staff; unless he was a particularly inexperienced one? Soon it became common knowledge in the household that the young man was indeed a guest, being the son of some family friends, and that he was possibly here to stay for some time?

One afternoon the guest popped his head around the side door and informally introduced himself as 'Freddie' to the household staff. This caused quite a stir downstairs. Soon, all the staff were used to seeing Freddie pottering around with his notebook, making sketches of the Tudor-style chimney stacks, and measuring decaying bricks in the crumbling garden walls. One day he was found on his knees in the Herb Garden by old 'Willet', the gardener. Frederick shot up, energetically, looked at 'Willet' and simply said: 'Possibly Iron Age?' Saying this straight after he had, rather over-enthusiastically, thrust a fragment of pottery under the elderly gardener's nose, and then strode off. Willet watched him with a squinted eye. More likely one of my old herb pots? The damned harmless young fool! he thought.

Frederick was later informed by Lady Cecilia, over several lengthy dinner conversations, that there had been some sort of rather disorganised attempt at the excavation of a local Roman Villa some fifty years back by Sir Henry Melanby. 'He collected God only knows what from up there? But I believe Edward has heard there were two gold coins, or something, isn't that right Edward?'

'Yes, yes, my dear. Somewhere about? Haven't seen them since I was a boy' replied Sir Edward. 'Anyway, most certainly such things are somewhere down in the store room now?' he reckoned. 'Perhaps, Frederick, you may care to have a look and sort through it all?' asked Lady Cecilia.

Frederick certainly did care to. And the very next morning he found himself amongst all the dusty clutter of the family store room. Clutter that included, amongst other things, a veritable stack of wood -wormed Zulu spears, and many oval shaped buck skin-covered shields that had a very curious odour to them? Frederick suspected that there were going to be some very interesting items to look at here? He started to think it worthwhile perhaps publishing a pamphlet, or similar, on the Melanby family history? Or perhaps even one combined with a potted history of the village of Melton Briarsville itself? He eventually decided to concentrate mainly on the village, and considered the Roman period a very worthwhile period from which to begin his research.

Sir Edward had given his very enthusiastic support right from the start for such a literary venture. Discreetly suggesting that the possibility of such a pamphlet, or even small book, being published would be very much enhanced, and almost certainly guaranteed , with the suggestion: 'If it could be possible to outline the generosity of our family towards the village whilst having been here at the Manor, you know the sort of thing, Freddy?' Of course, Freddy did.

There were heaps and stacks of things to examine, and hopefully record, in some type of catalogued order, as the Melanby's themselves had absolutely no idea of what was present in here? Removing a load of faded old carpets, even older and dustier rolled-up sketches and paintings, Frederick then found what was clearly a single Roman floor tile. It had been propped up against a cracked bell-shaped glass dome, that Frederick noted to contain the rather decayed, and mildewed, remains of what had once been a finely mounted male Cuckoo. The bird, according to a cream and brown mottled, rather brittle -looking label, had been shot on the estate in 1849.

His attention focussed back to the tile. He wondered why anyone would keep an example of a common Roman floor tile? It must have been a souvenir from the villa excavation that they told me about? he thought to himself.

Turning it over, his fingers began to brush away the dust and cobwebs, which fell away to the floor in neat little grey spindles. He blew away the residue and saw that some crude-looking text was now visible with part of what might possibly be a stylised map, or plan, of some sort? He had seen Roman tiles before that had animal paw prints on them, even a sandal sole impression, but never a tile that had actually been written upon. Below this text was an image of what appeared to be some sort of fanciful animal? Adjacent to this was a square surmounted by a capital letter 'B'. Above the square was a small figure with a shield and spear. As a student of classics, the Latin language was second nature to Frederick, who quickly translated the text scratched onto the tile. References to a 'Queen', and the name 'Bodvocca' were all rather confusing? He had never encountered such a name before, in any of his previous studies. However, something about the tile was very curious indeed? Frederick started to complete some detailed diagrams of it so that he had a ready reference. Much more practical than lugging the tile everywhere! he thought.

Frederick considered the evidence before him. 'I have something that appears to record an event? A place? Possibly a woman? Seemingly, no ordinary woman either, but a Queen named 'Bodvocca'? What does it all mean?' He puzzled.

During his research, Frederick re-established contact with an old associate from Cambridge, who was then working part time in the numismatics department of the British Museum. This proved to be a good decision, as it was later confirmed that in the British Museum coin collection there were nine thick heavily-struck ancient British gold coins. Two of these had been recently found in Kent, the remainder in Norfolk, and they had the name Bodvoc included on their design. After contacting all other relevant persons and departments, Frederick's associate could verify that there was nothing in the numismatic, nor indeed historical records, for the name of Bodvocca. Frederick was however quite delighted with this news. 'Bodvoc' or 'Bodvocca', that's pretty close, he thought.

Two days later Frederick found and opened a small hardwood box, which he'd found, that was much the worse for wear, due to yet more invasive investigations from several woodworm larvae. Inside were the two Claudian gold coins still wrapped in cloth. Frederick read the note outlining the details of their most interesting discovery. These must be the coins Lady Cecilia and Sir Edward mentioned? thought Frederick, and assumed that this reference to a tile must be for the curious tile I have recently located?

Examining the coins in some detail, Frederick considered it unlikely that if they were just dropped they would never have both slid down the side of a tile? They must have been placed there deliberately after the tile was laid in position? To confirm this he had noticed that each coin, when viewed under a magnifying glass, was quite deeply scratched on the bust side, and also there were minute traces of a reddish dust, the same colour as the tile present in these scratches. The coins had definitely been forced down between the tiles, he guessed. Why would someone do that? To hide the coins possibly? which couldn't be ruled out, of course. Or perhaps they were placed there to draw attention to something? To draw attention to the actual tile itself, maybe? Of course, that was it! Someone had wanted this tile to be found, due to the information that was incised upon it, Frederick concluded. Assuming that it was only half of the information, then, logically thinking, there must at least be one further tile somewhere else? Several things stuck firmly in Fredericks mind. Namely, that someone had gone to a lot of trouble to prepare this information, and consequently, whatever it all meant it must relate to something of considerable importance?

Frederick was then introduced to Miles Henderson, who had arrived in the village some four years before to take over the role as Headmaster for the local school. Henderson, he discovered, shared many of the same interests as he did and, after some weeks, Frederick decided it would be a good idea to involve this new friend in the intriguing research that he had been undertaking. The two of them now spent much time comparing ideas and notes. Between them they both finally came to the same conclusion: that the woman referred to on the tile may, and only may, just be Queen Boadicea?

History may not record any 'Bodvocca', but the likeness of the two names, it was noted, could not be overlooked. The tile also gave reference to a Queen. As far as they both were aware, history had only recorded one Queen of any note in this period, and that again was Boadicea. One evening Frederick had asked Miles a question of some gravity, given the amount of time they had so far spent discussing the issue. 'Miles, you don't think that someone is having a decades-old joke at our expense do you?

Miles looked over the edge of his fine bone china teacup and saucer. "No Freddy. That tile is as genuine as can be! So I don't think this is a hoax at all?', he replied. 'I am, however, uncertain whether either of us will ever live long enough to crack this complex mystery - which indeed may never be solved? But I will tell you something. I feel that it's connected to something well worthy of our research. Who knows where it will all end up, eh?"

Both men knew that to make such a claim at this stage, without the sound proof of either some artefacts, or substantial physical evidence, it would render them a laughing stock. And so it all remained, only a theory. Both men were now convinced to a very high degree that there was indeed something well worthy of further investigation here. Frederick scrupulously began to note down every conversation and idea that they shared into a small many-paged notebook.

As the months went by, Frederick began to wonder how long he could appropriately, or politely, stay at the Melanby's before they tired of him? On that account, though, he needn't have worried. The Melanby's delighted in his presence. But they had recently suggested that perhaps every four weeks he should return to visit, and stay, with his parents. However, Frederick would shortly have another totally different, and much more pressing, concern than his current accommodation, one shared by many young men in those times, and it was born here of partial guilt. To enhance this guilt the research time that the two men shared would shortly prove to be of quite a short duration. Despite his being older than normally acceptable, it was soon surprisingly confirmed by Miles Henderson that 'he was off to war.'

Further explaining to a rather shocked Freddy that he had used some old contacts, and that 'whilst education was paramount, he couldn't just sit back'. His final words to Frederick had been, 'Remember Freddy, if this all does relate to Boadicea, then the translation relating to half a mile is the most significant factor so far!' he said. 'There has to be at least one other tile to complete the tablet of information. You could do worse than ask Sir Edward if you could potter about up at the site of the villa? After all, it was where his ancestor originally found this tile, and it's quite possible there are more of them still up there? Whatever happens Freddy, for the time being, the tile, and what it means, if anything, and what more can be found out, will all be up to you, my good friend'. Then he was gone.

The last thing Miles did before leaving the village was to go around to the parents of one of his pupils, who were at first rather puzzled as to the nature of this unusual visit. 'I would like young ******* to look after something for me whilst I am away.' he asked. 'Your son has such a passion for history, I know he will cherish and look after it, as well as keep it safe.' He added. With that he produced a heavily embossed white envelope; opening it to reveal a small chunky gold coin. Looking at them, he placed a finger over his lips, then stood up and saw himself out. Still rather puzzled, the two parents later gave their son the envelope and its contents. Upon seeing the coin the boy ran out and down the road towards his headmasters house, but it was too late, Miles Henderson had gone.

Spurred on by Miles' decision, Frederick now began to ask himself, once again, some very grave, and somewhat serious, questions. Whilst undoubtedly he could not deny that he enjoyed his current life style, which was after all settled, secure, and most rewarding, he was unsure exactly where it was all heading? Combined with this, his conscience, fuelled by World events, began to truly concern him. Just a few hundred miles away, young men of his age, as well as younger and older, were fighting and dying in the trenches, defending Britain, or so he believed, directly against the threat from the Kaiser and his huge armies. Perhaps it was as a direct result of their conversations but eight weeks after Miles Henderson had signed up Frederick, too, announced his intention to do just the same, and go to join the fight.

Arriving in France, the sights and experiences of combat were literally hell on earth. Like the thousands of others, Frederick wondered just what was going on? He began to lose focus, if indeed there ever really had been any? Young men who now suddenly found that the powerful finger-pointing posters of Lord Kitchener, as well as the reassurance that 'It'll all be over by Christmas anyway!', the bravado, the honour, the comradeship, as well as the guilt, had all fatefully combined to deliver them to these terrifying foreign fields. Frederick wasn't easily fooled either. He questioned: 'Just why were men slaughtering each other without question, whilst their senior officers, it was often noted, relaxed many miles behind the front lines?'

Of the few comforts Frederick now had, it was the eagerly awaited, and fortunately quite regular, food and clothing parcels sent by his own family, and also the Melanby's, that became the most prized. In true spirit, Frederick would share these among the rest of his fellow comrades. Other consolations came in the form of letters from his parents, and of course the reassuring lump in his breast pocket, his old notebook. In between the shelling, the bullets, the shouting, and sudden death, he would occasionally open the pages and reflect on how different things must be back in the village, and at the Manor.

Frederick had by then witnessed the first tanks ever used in warfare, and amongst the rifle fire he noticed more and more frequently the staccato noise from the ever-present German machine guns. One morning a series of profound heavy shelling was experienced. Amongst this, several gas canisters crashed and thudded down into the waterlogged soil and began to release their toxic contents downwind. Quite soon afterwards a smell like freshly cut grass was faintly evident. The effects were not widely experienced until almost twenty-four hours later, when many men were beginning to have acute breathing problems.

Lieutenant Frederick Pearson had been feeling absolutely fine only an hour before, but was now decidedly unwell and having serious breathing-related problems. He stumbled about and stood up, others grabbed him to force him down, but in a desperate attempt to reach, or achieve something only known to him, he broke free. Slowly scrabbling up the side of the trench, supported by a rusty section of corrugated iron, he made it to the top, and finally collapsed. Just over fifty metres away some of the mud-plastered crew of a bulky looking German MGO8/15 machine gun were just having a cigarette when they spotted this opportunistic target, and clumsily swung the heavy gun round to bear. Mud had got into the mechanism and the machine gun jammed.

Frederick stumbled yet again, with his trouser leg now caught in a strand of barbed wire he fell, supporting himself on one hand whilst the other was wrestling with his silk neck scarf. Frenziedly cleaned with an oily rag, the machine gun's mechanism was finally cleared. As if in slow motion, the sodden mud around him seemed to spit up in sprays of fine soil. Frederick was in too much pain to notice, and then he was struck by five loosely-aimed bullets. One hit him just below the breast pocket that contained his notebook. Another two then entered and passed cleanly through his stomach. A fourth grazed his groin. The fifth, and final, bullet created a small opening just below his right eye and exited in a thick streak of blood from the back of his head.

Falling into the puddle-pocked clay, with his life quickly ebbing away, Frederick once again thought how peaceful it must be up at the

Manor. His one functioning eye dimly observed a frightened courier pigeon as it flicked terrified through the dirty looking smudges of aerial shell bursts, and then everything rapidly faded into the darkness of eternity.

Not long afterwards, as the afternoon light was receding, the Germans finally took advantage of their recent successes to have a look around and see what could be salvaged from the British lines. Slipping and sliding in the mud, a young German infantry soldier came across the body of Frederick Pearson lying to the side of a large water-filled shell crater. The body of this British soldier, he observed, had fallen, or been deposited, by a blast at a very strange angle indeed. The Infantyman noticed something that was sticking out of this British soldier's bloodstained uniform pocket. Edging down on the chunky torn clay surface of the crater with great care, he managed to grab what he then realised was a small black, board-covered, notebook from the corpse.

Vize Feldwebel Willi Hempel wasn't sure why he took the notebook? It was just there - a small annotated source of someone's life, and he was just curious. Perhaps one day he might be able to find out from the diary just who this soldier was, and maybe return this very note book back to his family? He didn't really know. A week later with the fluidity, and fluctuation, of certain parts of this war the British Army once again regained control of this shell-cratered battlefield, and quite a bit more land to the west. Frederick's body was located and later identified. He was one of the fortunate ones, not destined to be interred in one of the numerous battleground cemeteries. His body would be repatriated at the request of his devastated family. As a result of this request, his remains now rest in peace in the church yard of Orwell village parish church in Cambridgeshire, marked by a slender white upright slab of pale Portland limestone.

Back in Melton Briarsville the news that Frederick had been killed was met with great sadness, as were all the associated Great War death's that would come home to this village. That their school headmaster, Miles Henderson, would also not be returning home was also confirmed some time afterwards, which created a double blow that hit the village community hard. A small commemorative service in the village church was accorded to both Frederick and then Miles, and many villagers attended. At both services, the front pews were occupied by Sir Edward and Lady Cecilia Melanby, as they had been for many of the prominent local funeral services held in the village over the last five decades.

Up in the Manor house, Frederick's well-organised groupings of artefacts slowly began to be lost once again amongst further acquisitions and objects collected by the Melanby's. Frederick had always kept them informed of his discoveries, and opinions, and while interested in passing, it was all really above their heads; 'long-lost British Queens, and all that stuff!', they thought. The First World War was, apart from the Norman invasion, the only conflict so far where the enemy had come anywhere near to their village.

One evening, in May 1917, Sir Edward and Lady Cecilia were having drinks high up on the balcony of the Manor's east wing. As they admired the light evening skies a distant hum was heard. Looking over in the direction it was coming from, they both saw the most stunning sight. Far over to one side of the estate they observed two huge cigar-shaped objects, some distance apart seemingly, suspended in the sky. 'Damned Hun Zeppelins!' cursed Sir Edward. Moments later, as if in response to his curse, they both heard a distant small explosion.

By next morning the village 'grapevine' had conveyed the astounding news that a small bomb had been dropped on Bourton village. The device, it was said, had glanced off the vicarage wall and fallen into the churchyard, whereupon it had exploded harmlessly. Even today, nearly a century after, if you know where to look, just pull back the ivy from the churchyard wall and you can clearly see the different courses of brickwork showing where the bomb had struck.

It was late 1920, and the "War to end all wars" had now been over for some two years. But it was still difficult to resume a normal village life. Melton Briarsville, like many rural communities all over Britain, had been hit very hard. The pride of its men folk had been decimated, leaving a shortfall in agricultural workers, and indeed the birth rate, for many years to come. However, younger men stepped in where they could and began to fill their absent fathers', or elder brothers', places. Gradually things began to improve. In 1923 a few sections of land around the village, including 'The Field of the Devils Work', were finally put under the plough, or at least partially, in the case of that particular field. As down its slopes, it was still very sodden, and it was considered that crops may indeed be lost there.

However the top of the field was subjected to several years of deep ploughing just to assess the quality of the soil, according to the landowners. But more likely, though, thought eighteen year old Cecil Callum, it was to 'show off their newly-acquired John Fowler & Co. K7 12 Horse Power steam tractor they had recently purchased'.

'With the horses,' Cecil complained, 'I have faced their wind and dung, both of which I can reasonably well avoid. But the smoke, and spats of oil, all over my face from this mechanical monster is something else!'.

Ploughing finally commenced, with the steam tractor being driven by the disgruntled Cecil Callum, who was, in fact, a relative of the same Samuel Callum, who had discovered the local Roman Villa way back in 1862. Despite his young age, Cecil was a far more secretive man than Henry, or indeed his father, had ever been. What was his business was his business. And what he saw, or found, in his fields was also his business.

Although the top section of Bullocks Pasture was only ploughed for three years in that time Cecil had found a 'right old rum collection of bits and oddments', as he occasionally put it to one or two of his close confidantes. He had heard the odd rumour about some great 'chieftain' or other, and a battle that happened in ancient times around these parts. Perhaps some of his finds 'are all to do with this?' he occasionally thought. These finds so far, had varied from a giant horseshoe, strangely twisted and bent almost double, some almost perfectly spherical flints, to a huge selection of fossil ammonites. But these formed just part of his collection of curiosities. The most interesting discoveries are in two old shoe boxes that he kept under his bed, both safely secured with a length of old parcel twine. Not even his mother, with whom he lived, was aware of their existence. Cecil had no real idea at all of what he had found and placed in these boxes? And as far as it went, no one else will either? These things were for his eyes only. Occasionally he would open each box to examine, and in some cases admire the sheer beauty, of some of their contents. In one box were a considerable number of iron arrow, or spear heads, some in quite good condition, but others had started to crack and flake apart, weeping a brownish viscous fluid that stuck to the boxes like treacle.

There were also a few tiny little silver coins, each one depicting a little prancing horse on one side. And there was another, slightly larger, coin with the same type of horse, but which Cecil knew was made of gold. The second shoe box, however, contained his favourite find. Inside, wrapped in old newspaper, was a large metal eagle. True, it had one wing totally missing. But Cecil admired its powerful glare, and grasping talons. He reckoned it was 'well old', appreciating its rich blue and green colour, and its smooth feel. He felt a certain amount of guilt, though, as he looked at the large gold- tinted gash down the eagles back. He was pretty certain his plough had done this?

In the June of 1922 the thatch on Cecil's mother's small cottage caught alight. At first, a slight crackle, and wisp of thick creamy and grey-coloured smoke spiralling up, and then down, around the garden. Then the fire really took hold. Within in quarter of an hour flames were gushing from all the blackened and heat-shattered window panes. The glossy green paint began blistering on the outside of their front door.

Why the thatch had caught alight remained a mystery? There had been no bonfires in the vicinity. Actually, it was caused by something shiny that had been dropped onto the roof by a magpie. Its reflective surface had magnified the sun light, causing the adjacent straw thatch to ignite. Next day Cecil and his Mother rummaged through the ashes. Hardly anything that had survived the heat was worth rescuing. Neither of them noticed the blackened George 1st silver shilling that lay in the ashes. Had Cecil done so, he may have wondered at it? He had never found such a coin before, and certainly would never have guessed that it had been the cause of the house catching fire? Amongst his lifelong possessions, most of his collection of curiosities had been consumed, also. Strangely enough, one thing that hadn't was the eagle. Cecil looked at it and, as always, it returned its cold, fixed glare at him. But not for long, though. Fifty six seconds later it was sinking down through thirty feet of cold, dark, decaying leaf-laden water. He had, for some reason, dropped it into the garden well. And there it would stay. It's time for a total change now, thought Cecil.

CHAPTER SIX

CHANGING TIMES

Five months after finding Frederick's notebook, Willi Hempel, now a Feld Webel, and also fluent in English, had looked through and read most of them, on several occasions in fact. It was clear that the young British soldier had a very keen interest in history, and finding ancient objects. But, in his opinion, the notes relating to the tile all seemed to be rather the fanciful account of a dreamer. In the attrition stakes of this slow, vacuous, style of warfare, that was slaughtering men in their thousands, Willi himself was not destined to live all that much longer. Unlike the original owner of the notebook, that he now possessed, Willi's death would be swift.

It occurred one day, just after Willi was taking a second sip of the foul-tasting coffee from his tin mug. For a fraction of a second, Willi heard a 'Tack' sound, as something seemed to have impacted his steel helmet. Then he felt a sensation of something warm running down the side of his nose. He touched his top lip, then looked down at his blood-stained fingers, smeared the blood with his thumb across their tips and, a second later, was dead. Two hundred metres away a sniper by the name of Lance Corporal Miles Henderson reported: 'I can't be sure sir, but I think I got that Hun bugger fair and square?'

Willi's body, and possessions, were eventually returned to his family, in Stuttgart, for burial. It was another young life cut short. Among Willi's personal effects was Frederick Pearson's note book, which was the cause of some puzzlement to Willi's family? What on earth was Willi doing with this amongst his possessions, they wondered?

Years later, around the early 1930's, Gustav Hempel was showing some of the treasured mementoes of his dead son, Willi, to a visiting distant family cousin. Cousin Hans was very keenly constructing some type of detailed ancestral family tree. Gustav was amazed at the detail so far collected but had been more than a little uncomfortable when

Hans had suggested: 'It is a good thing to know one's heritage, as it will undoubtedly be of value in all our futures – to see that our family can be proven to be Jew free.' Whilst considering this unusual statement, Gustav saw Hans pick up and examine the small black notebook, and begin turning its pages.

'No, that's not Willi's!' Gustav quickly stated, the family aren't quite sure why that came back with his belongings? He must have found it on the front somewhere?'

'Looks quite interesting?' Hans commented, as he began to slowly, and considerately, thumb through the stained and tattered pages.

'You may as well have it then, if it's of any interest to you? It's hardly related to our family, or Willi's, for that matter." Gustav said thoughtfully. 'And anyway, it will surely only get lost at some stage,' he added.

'That's very kind of you, very kind indeed, Gustav.' said Hans, gratefully. 'My brother Walter has developed quite an interest in archaeology, and all that sort of thing. I'm certain he will be curious to see this?"

So it was that Hans Wust, the distant cousin, departed from the Hempel household, bearing the small black-covered notebook that had once belonged to Frederick Pearson. His brother Walter was, as Hans had suggested, very interested in the contents of the note book, and began showing certain pages of it to a select group of his associates in the SS.

Having had the diagram text translated (strangely, the one thing Frederick Pearson never actually added to his notebook was the total translation. He had kept that completely separate.) they then occasionally discussed its contents in detail for over three months, amongst other pressing concerns. Just like Frederick Pearson and Miles Henderson nearly two decades before, the same conclusions were rapidly drawn as to the identity of the person mentioned on the tile.

From that point, Wust decided it was time to inform his superiors to the fact that there just may be something, not only of great interest, but also of great potential here? If this went to plan, he would continue to take the credit for it. If not, well, he could probably involve so many influential people that, hopefully, the matter would be discreetly finished without too much unrest.

By 1937, the German Wander Vogel attitude had continued to develop itself even further, and was particularly evident amongst youth groups. These were of mainly politically-motivated teenagers, and also some slightly older members, many of whom were also in Der Bund Deutsches Madel for girls, and the Hitler Jugend for the boys. It was also popular to join link-groups, such as the Anglo-German Friendship Society, and similar groups that had started to spring up in neighbouring countries. Many of these young people also found themselves in neighbouring "Nordic" countries, like Norway and Sweden. Some visited France, and many others were sent over to Britain. They acted as a truly rich source of potential information gathering; a source that was most certainly not going to be overlooked by several very high-ranking Nazi Party leaders of the period.

To further facilitate the ease of travel, and exchange of foreign students, German educational organisations began to form links with educational establishments in Britain, such as the prime Universities and Colleges. There was at this time a very keen interest in cultural heritage developing in Germany, along with a wider desire to learn where the German race had originated from? A desire which was being stimulated by several very influential figures. Outwardly this appeared to be of a quite innocently-based curiosity, but later would go on to form the basis of the entire attitude to racial issues by those in control.

In August 1938 just one such small party of travelling German students found themselves newly arrived at Croydon airport. They were part of the continually-promoted cultural exchange. In return, this group would, in a few months time, act as hosts for a similar party of British students, who would then take part in a German archaeological excavation near Koblenz. Unfortunately, the excavations in England would, in all events, take somewhat longer than anyone at this stage anticipated. By the time things were satisfactorily under way, World affairs would eventually determine that the Germans could not keep to their part of the plan, and consequently the British students would never get to see the excavations at Koblenz. But for the time being, as was planned, these new German arrivals were then to travel from Croydon onto Oxford University, who would then make all the arrangements for accommodation, travel and activities.

The eldest member of this group was Waldemar Euker. A tall, fair-haired, nineteen year-old, who it had been decided would be responsible for overall supervision of the German excavation team for the entire duration of their visit. Unknown to Waldemar at this stage, he had already, been processed and assessed for quite some considerable time. He had been closely scrutinised from the various academic classes he had attended to exactly where he sat in the park. Who he regularly spoke to, his family's political beliefs, contacts and any other details that were deemed relevant had also been examined. Not only this, but his personality and physical appearance were just typical of what the new order considered to be 'Aryan', further enhancing the positive outcome of all this scrutiny. The final results of which meant he had been selected to carry out what could be a particularly important operation for Nazi Germany itself.

Deemed trustworthy, Waldemar had finally been briefed in almost every detail of the situation in relation to the existence of a notebook, once belonging to a British soldier who had been killed over twenty years previously. The briefing had been given to Waldemar by a gentleman named Walter Wust, who made it flawlessly clear just how this notebook could be of major interest and benefit to Germany. Amongst other responsibilities outlined to Euker, he had also been requested to verify if there was still a Roman tile in existence in the museum of a certain Oxfordshire village? Apparently, as Euker understood it, this tile, if it still existed, was the very same one mentioned in the notebook.

This village, and its museum, were situated conveniently near to where some of the planned principal British excavations would be undertaken. In fact one of these proposed sites was actually the very same villa from which this tile had been originally discovered. However, as it was pointed out, there was no guarantee that the British would start, or even include, this specific site in the agenda. Initially this entire briefing had all been slightly puzzling to Waldemar? But as he listened, and it had been explained to him fully, he then took pride - a great pride - in that he, Waldemar Euker, had been selected to serve Germany in such a pivotal manner. To serve, what his Father kept annoyingly referring to as: the 'Fatherland'. To Waldemar, however, this phrase seemed out-dated, he much preferred to serve, what he referred to, as: 'The Reich'.

The original Pearson notebook had, for a long time, been kept very securely at the office of Walter Wust, in Munich. But there was also an additional copy, produced and provided strictly for field reference only. This copy was now safely secured in the zipper section of Waldemar Euker's rucksack. Euker had been asked to discreetly stimulate as much interest as possible in re-opening the Roman Villa site near the village of Melton Briarsville, in Oxfordshire. By coincidence Oxford University had also been considering for sometime re-excavating, and excavating for the first time, a number of known Roman sites for evalu-ation. One of those sites would be that same villa at Melton Briarsville.

Unknown to Euker, or even his superiors at the time, a small sur-vey, and preliminary excavation group, had already been present at the Oxfordshire village for about three weeks by the time the Germans landed at Croydon airport. Oxford University, previously having veri-fied that the villa site was very extensive indeed, had proposed to com-mence excavating here, utilising their additional foreign student labour. It seemed the ideal site not only for the University's own students but would provide certainly enough experience and activity for their for-eign guests. This, when revealed to Waldemar Euker, caused a feeling of great relief and satisfaction.

Trying to divert attention from other suggested sites to the villa at Melton Briarsville and then getting this site approved, Euker had believed could be a particularly difficult element to achieve success in. Confirmation that this element of organisation on the desired specific Roman site had already been completed for him was marvellous news. 'The British have already helped me, without even being aware of do-ing so. Excellent!' he muttered quietly to himself. Prior to this he had had doubts, and previously wondered: what if the British have their own ideas? I can't just go off and excavate where I wish?

The German students were actually offered the choice of several sites to assist with. But Euker had said they would take the nearest one to the University, reducing travel costs and inconvenience for their hosts. He was only too well-aware this just so happened, fortunately for him, to be the site located at Melton Briarsville.

Back in the summer of 1935 the community of Melton Briarsville had quite a surprise. It was announced that they were to have their own official village museum. There had also been a few changes up at the Manor. Several rooms had been cleared of their contents, and these auctioned off. A new summerhouse had been constructed, but had become almost instantly cluttered with the contents of the storage rooms, which the Melanby's had now wanted cleared. Hundreds of years of, not just Melanby, family history but also that of the village lay scattered around the summerhouse floor. Something had to be done?

And so, with the cooperation of the parish council, the Melanby's had agreed to finance the building of a quite sizeable museum building. The site of which had been chosen as the vacant plot of rough land, almost opposite the Waggoner's public house. This met with great fervour and dedication, as many villagers wished to include their own contributions, as well as help with the building work. Beatrice Phelps bought in the case containing the record 4lb Brown Trout her husband, Colonel Phelps, had caught in the river back in 1901. It didn't weight 4lb now, though; in fact it looked decidedly shrivelled. However it was treated with due reverence and positioned, appropriately, next to a rather better looking male Otter.

As a result of all this involvement, just eight months later the Museum building programme was completed. There followed an inaugural opening with many festivities, centred mainly around the Waggoner's Inn. By unanimous decision, Millicent Klake had been elected to be the part time curator of all the collections. Born in 1886, she was frequently to be seen riding around the village on her old black Raleigh bicycle, with its clattering chain guard and shrieking brakes. Clad head to toe in tweeds, and with her hair tied back in a tight bunch, she looked rather severe. But behind those rounded spectacle lenses shone a pair of kindly, albeit very inquisitive, eyes.

Millicent had the interior of the museum organised into a series of rooms, each dedicated to a certain age or period. The corridors and walls were to be the place where displays reflecting the natural history and wild life of the village were to be featured. One of the first donations made by the Melanby's took the form of a huge wooden and glass case full of stuffed birds, which need no small amount of cleaning. Once completed it could be seen to contain over two hundred birds that had been 'obtained,' or 'shot', if one had to be more specific, on the estate. Millicent noted the Hoopoe, shot in 1870. Once such a beautiful bird, though now rather faded. Whilst looking at the pair of Bee Eaters, she had thought it was wrong to shoot such birds. Although, she conceded, if they hadn't back then, I suppose we would never have known such exotic foreign visitors had ever been to the village?

It was Millicent who'd said, delightedly: 'One can visit this charming establishment, and leisurely walk back through the ages, and then pop right back out into the present day. It's so exciting! Rather like having H.G Well's Time Machine right here on your very doorstep' So please everyone, do take time to come and have a look.'

In the Roman section of the museum there were plenty of coins, broken urns and a large quern stone. Positioned centrally in the display was the floor tile, found locally some eighty or so years ago on the site of the Roman villa nearby. Beneath this was a large label, beautifully hand-written by Millicent, explaining all about it, and stating that it was a 'typical, but uncommon, example of Roman graffiti'.

During the mid to late 1930's period it was not unusual for the Mayors, senior civic dignitaries and major business owners, from Britain's large industrial towns and cities to be invited to Germany, to witness the new order of things. Germany had wanted to impress, and on the whole she had done so remarkably well. Many people returned with infectious enthusiasm on how to apply similar policies of the so-called 'new order' to Britain. This created a great process of cultural unison, and many smaller -scale exchanges between various youth movements also began to take place between the two countries.

World War One now seemed a long time ago, and resentment of all things German was now seen by many sections of society as to being a barrier to progress. Therefore, during this period of new order, and increased so-called 'cultural awareness', it came as little surprise to Millicent, one day in September 1938, when a representative of Oxford Municipal City Council visited the museum. Millicent was informed that they were hoping to organise an exchange of artefacts between a museum here, and a similar-sized museum in Germany, and that Melton Briarsville's museum had been selected to participate. 'It seems these Germans are cropping up everywhere these days. Up at the villa excavation, and just about anywhere!' she somewhat guiltily concluded.

Just a few weeks earlier, one of them, an abrupt but very polite young man, had walked into the museum and introduced himself curtly as Waldemar Euker, or something similar. After aimlessly regarding the displays, he had eventually asked specific questions about the whereabouts of a certain Roman tile in the collection he had heard about?

Millicent escorted him to the Roman display section, where the light bulb had blown some hours before. The area was now quite dim and she apologised accordingly. The young man then produced some official-looking notes, looked at the tile, and kept comparing it with his notes. He then departed saying: 'Madam, thank you for a most rewarding visit. I will return sometime shortly and bring some things that we have found up at the Villa for you to see.'

Four days later, a sealed, typed memo appeared on the desktop of Walter Wust back in Germany. Upon opening it was confirmed that the original Roman tile was indeed still included amongst the museum displays and bore the exact detail as evidenced in the Pearson note book. Regarding the museum artefact exchange, Millicent was to discover that the initial German approach concerning this had been made according to the council representative by a certain Herr Wust. Who had, by the way, actually heard of her museum here at Melton Briarsville. This must be taken by her as credit for all her hard work, he had suggested.

The council official further informed Millicent that this Herr Wust was not only the curator of a similar museum but was also a well known, and quite eminent archaeologist in Europe. Not that the council gentlemen actually had any knowledge of these facts at all? He had simply quoted third hand from Herr Wust's telephone conversations, and a few official-looking letters. The council official continued reading from a document: 'This German gentleman, Herr Wust, has a great interest in Romano-British buildings and ceramics and is also, apparently, a specialist of, erm ....oh yes Roman period graffiti. He has asked if we can particularly concentrate on these aspects for the exchange?'

So it was some months later many of the village museum's Roman cabinets now looked quite empty. But no matter, thought Millicent, they would shortly be crammed full of Roman coins and other objects found in Germany. How very interesting that would be?

The tile was considered by Millicent as 'perfect subject matter for this Herr Wust', and was packed up along with many of the other exhibits. This exchange exhibition, so she was informed, had been planned to last for three months, and then all the loaned items would be packed up and returned to each respective museum. Having at last packaged the huge amount of parcels and containers, they were finally sent from the museum to Germany, courtesy of the Melanby's, who kindly paid for all the postage costs.

Millicent was delighted when, a few weeks later, a considerable number of parcels arrived back at Melton Briarsville Museum from Germany. They were all addressed for her attention. Their German origin was pretty obvious, due to every square inch of postal label seemingly covered in small teutonic -looking eagles grasping over-sized swastika's. This seemed rather over-zealous, and Millicent wondered if the German post master had deliberately over egged the franking, knowing the parcels were outward bound for England.

Soon she was meticulously unwrapping the packages, but was not quite so delighted to find after finally opening the last package, the sum total of her new exhibits for display amounted to little more than a broken vase, of indeterminable date. This was accompanied by a load of building bricks carefully packed in wood shavings. 'Well this is not exactly what I had considered as a cultural exchange!' she said out loud to herself. Wondering what all this was about she had then telephoned the Melanby's to inform them that all was definitely not right with her delivery, and to ask politely what she, or they, could now do about it? Millicent also decided that Lionel Thripe, that rather oily, horrid little man from the council, who had visited her some months back, would also receive a call.

Herr Wust, meanwhile, was experiencing totally the opposite feelings; he had been thoroughly delighted with the receipt of his delivery from Britain. He had arranged for all the recently arrived parcels to be unpacked immediately, and when the tile had been located it was examined with great enthusiasm.

Herr Wust was very interested to see for himself whether Frederick Pearson's many sketches contained in the notebook were accurate, and also how reliable Waldemar Eukers observations had been as well. Wust later appeared quite contented to have personally observed himself that indeed all factors were just as they should be. It had been some huge relief to see the tile at first hand; firstly to see that it did actually exist, and secondly that it was genuine.

Touching its gritty surface had seemed to animate Wust, as he allowed himself the privilege of fantasising just how far his influence might now develop. Back in England, a few weeks after the unsatisfactory delivery to the museum, the Melanby's had even gone so far as to approach the German Embassy, but apparently no one had ever heard of this Herr Wust? As for the institution, that it was claimed Herr Wust worked for, well once again a total blank was drawn. Apparently that was unknown as well.

The Embassy official promised Sir Edward that he would personally investigate the matter, he was sure that there had been a mistake? Perhaps it was suggested all the objects concerned were stuck in transit somewhere? Again, the Embassy official promised to investigate the matter in depth. Once the caller had put the phone down the Embassy official considered it would most definitely not be a good career move to investigate what was going on, and consequently made no effort at all to do so.

Walter Wust now commissioned some fine detailed scale drawings to be made of his newly acquired tile. The months passed and, to be fair, it can be said that the rumoured "German theft" from the village of its artefacts did little to enhance the opinion of some villagers towards the young men of the same nationality working up at the villa excavation. In fact Millicent herself added to the increasing concern when cycling past the excavation one day.

She had stopped quickly to observe what she thought was a humming bird hawk moth. But it had disappeared before she could really make a confirmed sighting in her records. However, what she did see, with her small field glasses, through a gap in the hedge were two German students clearly wearing Nazi swastika armbands. 'Well that really isn't on!' she whispered to herself, and of course later delighted in sharing this observation with as many villagers as would listen.   She now wished in earnest that she had questioned the council official slightly more. For example, she now questioned: 'How is it that this Herr Wust, such an eminent archaeologist, is just the curator of a small town museum?'

Millicent now suspected something was seriously not right with the artefact exchange, and on that account it looked like she would be correct. A feeling further reinforced by the fact that whenever she telephoned the City Hall the oily little man from Oxford City Council was always seemingly in a meeting, or at lunch. Sadly it looked like Melton Briarsville Museum's Roman history display would be seriously depleted forever.

Amongst Millicent's many other passions was her aim to try and lend credence to the local legend of the battle, and chieftains burial, amongst the villagers. To many a small child she would enrich this story and end it with: 'When this country needs help, and is in times of peril, the great chieftain will arise from his earthen slumber and come to our aid.' This was all well and of goodly intent, and gave Millicent a certain air of importance amongst the younger generation. That was until one day a cheeky young pupil at the school announced that the 'Chieftain must be a bit of a coward then?'

When questioned how the boy had arrived at this assumption, Millicent was then informed by him 'Well he conveniently didn't seem to wake up when the Vikings came, and he seems to have still been snoozing when the Normans came by here. Perhaps old Herr Hitler can wake him up?'

Millicent looked awkward, what the boy had stated was quite true, and she could offer no satisfactory explanation. 'What a bright young man indeed!' she said afterwards. From that day on, Millicent Klake would always have a sort of 'respect' for that young Tommy Warner, as she delicately put it.

A day or so after Tommy's rather astute, and historically accurate observation, an important meeting was held in Germany. At number thirty six Linkmann Allee stood the police headquarters in the city of Chemnitz, within which an arranged meeting between the SS Reichsfuhrer Heinrich Himmler and several other Nazi Party leaders was taking place. Most of those present were, to some extent, associated in some way or another with a most unusual, and somewhat clandestine, organisation. This was an organisation known in official circles as the Ahnenerbe, and at this stage consisted of a collection of mostly academic individuals dedicated to the study of intellectual ancient history and German cultural heritage. Naturally in this capacity the organisation was also of great interest to the SS Reichsfuhrer himself.

For the meeting, Himmler had taken his time and walked in last, as usual, a fact that some considered was done to deliberately enhance and dramatise his entrance to such meetings. He returned the salute smartly to all present saying: 'Gentleman, once again, as is my privilege, I ask you to please tell me in every detail just what it is about this small, and to all intents and purposes, seemingly insignificant British village called Melton Briarsville that so engages us? The details I have so far are of great interest and possible potential, but are they based on a satisfactory degree of fact for us to act upon?'

It was SS Gruppenfuhrer Darre who went on to outline the entire story from the discovery of Frederick Pearson's notes, back in World War One, right up until the current state of affairs at the time of the present meeting. Summarising, Darre had stated that: 'In this matter, Germany has only got a small battered notebook and a Roman tile. These are all we possess in effect, and in honesty all that we have in total gentlemen. But our experts have evaluated both and believe that there is something worthwhile following up here. True, it is only just a hint of that something, I agree. However, should something, or a burial of major historical significance be able to be located by German efforts it is felt that its political implications could be far reaching - very far reaching indeed!' Darre explained further and then the summary finished rather abruptly, somewhat sooner than many attending had anticipated, as Darre had eloquently but very speedily given his detailed account. Now a heavy silence descended on the room.

The Reichsfuhrer allowed this to mature into a sweating, bottom shuffling, and paper gathering awkwardness and then, as was also his manner, appeared to relieve the stifling atmosphere. 'Gentlemen, Gruppenfuhrer Darre, my thanks to you all. Just one thing, I take it you are all still in agreement then with the selection of this Waldemar Euker, and for him to continue leading the project in England?' No one said anything out loud, but all just nodded their heads in unison. 'Fine! Fine! That's excellent!' said the Reichsfuhrer. 'Right gentlemen, and let us now go get something to eat".

Over the next few months Euker would be requested to return to Germany on several occasions to inform his project superiors on how the whole thing was developing. On one such occasion he was interviewed at some length by the now familiar Herr Walter Wust, who he had since discovered was the president of something quietly referred to as the Ahnenerbe. Also in attendance had been SS Gruppenfuhrer Walter Darre, of whom it quite quickly seemed to Euker, had an absolute obsession with the potential for exploiting the facts concerning anyone, or anything, linked to Germany that may, or could definitely demonstrate, having had humble peasant origins. Especially admired by him were people who had come from just such earthy humble beginnings, and who had risen to influence the masses.

Without saying a word, the comparisons to the British Queen

Boadicea were clear to Euker, who wondered on this occasion why no one mentioned her name directly? He was then presented with the facts showing that the Ahnenerbe had researched quite thoroughly into this unusual situation, which he was told by Darre had just expanded importantly.

Ahnenerbe research, Euker was informed further, had only recently discovered possible evidence indicating that many ancient British tribal rulers had originated from Nordic settlements in what was now Western Germany. Wust interjected: 'that anything that can establish such a claim is of course instrumental to German heritage.'

Darre turned to Euker and said: 'So young man, it's now up to you to make this British heroine into a good German national at last.' This preposterous piece of fabricated waffle was totally accepted at the time by Euker without a moment's hesitation. Later, though, he would briefly wonder at just what this research had been, and how had it been so conveniently possible? If his superiors accepted it then it was undoubtedly a new archaeological discovery which supported their statements. However, during the meeting the ever-eloquent Darre clearly had more immediate concerns and had gone on to explain that: "If we Germans could locate the burial site and unearth the remains of this most British of Queens it would prove an interesting bargaining point amongst others. It could well help to hold Britain back from, shall we say, making any anti-German decisions in the future?'

Euker considered whether such an event could possibly steer the course of history? An event in which he was very much involved with, what an incredible honour had been bestowed upon him! Could archaeology, or more to the point, a single notebook relating to a solitary Roman floor tile play so large a part in the politics of Europe, if not indeed the entire World? Looking around the room his logical thinking was instantly relegated in the face of such seniority and experience.

Some of those present that day, including Herr Wust and Gruppenfuhrer Darre, had previously introduced themselves to him. But of the others, all of whom were senior SS and other military ranks, remained anonymous. No introductions were made and Euker had not recognised any of them. Any further pondering or questioning was then interrupted by a huge creaking oak-panelled door, that took an age to open, as whoever was behind it was involved in some much muffled conversation. Briskly, in stepped a small man in the uniform of the SS. Not a striking man at all. Euker noted the rather piggy weak chin and small round-lensed glasses. Almost involuntarily, everyone in the room shot up stiffly and gave the Nazi salute. For with his weak chin and all, into the room came the unmistakeable figure of no less than the SS Reichsfuhrer, Heinrich Himmler, himself. Euker was noticeably the last to stand and salute, not out of disrespect but more from simply being awe struck.

Signalling with a brief flutter of his hand for everyone to be seated, the Reichsfuhrer removed his field-grey overcoat and then sat down. Looking around the table, and after some brief acknowledgments, he then fixed Euker with a long hard, rather sweat stimulating, stare. He then apologised, saying: 'I just wanted to look at the face of the young man who may hold the key to such a very important objective. That, of course, being the security, and potentially the strengthening and preservation, of our glorious Reich.'

After a brief discussion and presentation of facts, Euker was asked to leave for a short while. In his absence, the potential for diplomatically taking Britain out of a war-declaring position in the future was discussed in some depth. Himmler sat back in the large hand-built wooden chair, the product of some Black Forest dwelling peasant's carpentry skills over two hundred years before. After looking around again, the Reichsfuhrer said: 'Gentlemen, thank you. Our Fuhrer, Adolf Hitler, will eventually, I assure you, cleverly oversee the destruction of this so-called 'Mother Russia', and all other regions of concern too. But this will take time and we Germans must at all costs avoid a war situation on two fronts at so early a stage. I have heard enough, and seen evidence, that lends me to present the background to this possibility to our Fuhrer himself. And I intend to do this very shortly.'

Walter Wust looked rather smug and pleased and then self-importantly suggested that Euker should be asked to return to them. Himmler confirmed his agreement. 'Herr Euker, we have decided to continue to fully support your investigations in England, where you shall of course be returning to immediately. And Herr Euker, you, and perhaps all of us here, need I'm sure not, be reminded that you are charged with laying a most important section of the foundations for our glorious thousand-year Reich....Gentleman......Heil Hitler!'

Nobody's return salute was as smart, or as enthusiastic, as that given with the dead-straight arm and hand of Waldemar Euker. Out of general earshot, one of the meeting attendees whispered to an adjacent colleague: 'Nothing worse than a young fanatic out to impress. We may have to keep our eye on that one, what say you Ernst?' The SS Gruppenfuhrer politely agreed. But as the person who made the comment should have known Ernst Kaltenbrunner kept his eye on everybody these days.

CHAPTER SEVEN

THE FINDING OF THE
SECOND TILE

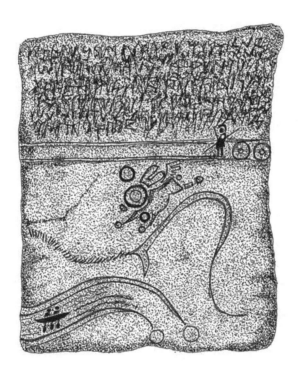

Sketch of Tile 2

I n the field close to the village of Melton Briarsville the student
excavation of the villa was now well under way, and good progress
had been made. In late October 1938 Euker and his team were to
be very honoured, as they had an important visitor turn up.

It was on a Friday morning that their distinguished visitor arrived, totally unannounced, at the excavation site and was immediately recognised by the German students, resulting in a flurry of feverish activity. It can hardly be said that Euker, or any of his party, would ever have expected to see none other than the German Foreign Minister, and Ambassador to Britain, Joachim Von Ribbentrop; accompanied by several other men trudging down the hedge-side towards them.

Euker tried his best to gather everyone together in some form of orderly line-up. As they had all just given the Nazi salute, Von Ribbentrop had returned the same, albeit rather weakly, by just lifting his arm to his chest and flicking his hand up. He then waved his hand aside, so as to appear dismissive of the formalities, but had clearly quite obviously enjoyed the impact his visit was creating. The Oxford University students were almost as surprised at his arrival as their German counterparts. But although respectful, they stood around in whispering and watching groups, with their hands stuffed deep in their trouser pockets.

They were rather enjoying the situation and smirked as the German students tried to look organised amidst the total surprise. After being given a tour of the excavation, and even allowing his photograph to be taken, Von Ribbentrop took Euker to one side, placing his arm over the teenager's shoulder. He went on to say: 'If you succeed in your objective here, young man, the Reich will forever be indebted to you. Many people are watching you, Waldemar, people with the highest expectations.' With that he smiled, walked back up the field, got back into the large black car and was gone.

Joachim Von Ribbentrop had been staying at Brocket Hall, in the village of Ayot St Lawrence, in Hertfordshire, as a guest of the estate owner Ronald Nall-Cain, the second Baron Brocket. Nall-Cain was a prominent member of the Anglo-German Friendship organisation and in the high society of that time was well known for his very pro-German opinions. In Germany, senior Nazi officials had for some time been listing and assessing prominent individuals living in Britain who would be sympathetic to their cause, and Nall-Cain had a very high position on that list. Nall-Cain had ensured that his important guest experienced the very best of Hertfordshire's shooting and fishing locations. It was during one such pheasant shoot that Von Ribbentrop had quietly said to his attaché: 'You know that very shortly we need to go to Oxfordshire. To that village, whatever its name is? Find an excuse, any excuse, for us to make the trip. I want to leave within the hour.'

Nall- Cain would later recollect, on that same day, that Von Ribbentrop had politely made his excuses and had disappeared for about six hours, using the excuse: 'Official business, Ronald. Always official business.'

About an hour or so later, Nall-Cain had received a telephone call from a man who shared the same political views as himself. Having met two years before, Nall Cain and this other individual had kept in fairly regular contact ever since. The caller, a man Nall Cain simply referred to as 'Brillo', lived in a village called Bourton.

'I thought the Foreign Minister was with you for this trip, sir? Are you aware he has just turned up at Melton Briarsville, on some sort of an archaeological dig?' asked Brillo. 'Rather strange itinerary for a Foreign Minister, don't you think?'

Nall Cain pondered its significance, and knew how fascinated some Germans were with heritage, ancestry and archaeology, but hardly thought it constituted, what had been termed as 'official business''. He felt a little peeved that Von Ribbentrop had not included him in sharing the precise reason for this unusual detour. After all, had he, Ronald Nall-Cain, not already done enough to convince his friends, the Germans, that he was a worthy supporter? However, it also felt very satisfying to know that he could monitor the movements of many people if he so wished with an established group of politically-sympathetic observers living in many rural and urban parts of Britain.

A week later the SS ReichsFuhrer, true to his word, had indeed requested a few minutes brief to address his Fuhrer, Adolf Hitler, on several important state matters; he also intended to raise the Melton Briarsville excavation issue.

As he was escorted into the room the ever-present Martin Bormann hovered around, until finally dismissed by the Fuhrer. Bormann had successfully wheedled his way into the Fuhrer's close entourage and it had been said that some Nazi Party officials were unable to approach him directly without going through Bormann first. Well, that does not apply to the SS Reichsfuhrer, thought Himmler. Certainly not yet anyway. Without doubt, Bormann, that odious little toad, will get his just desserts one day!

The Fuhrer was leaning over a large dark-wood table pondering over maps, military orders and what appeared to be a stack of several hundred typed sheets of official looking papers. 'Heinrich. As always, good to see you.' said Adolf Hitler, walking over and putting his hand on Himmler's forearm. 'As you are no doubt aware, this is a pressing time for Germany. The foundations of great plans must be laid right now. And I am, without doubt, the only person able to orchestrate all of this!'

The Reichsfuhrer looked a little uneasy. He knew what was coming, especially when he raised the Melton Briarsville issue, the opinions, the can't-be-bothered attitude. But he felt he must make his point concerning the potential of this small English village, and how it may bridge in-depth relations between Britain and Germany for quite some foreseeable time. If a European war was definitely coming, Himmler was one of those who considered it was now inevitable. If they could just only stall a potential enemy into delaying aggressive intent until Germany was more prepared with her European quest of Lebensraum, etc., then that surely would only be a good thing?

Himmler began his outline of state matters, and when finished he then looked decidedly awkward. The Fuhrer glanced upwards. 'So, Heinrich, are we all done?' The Fuhrer, briefly returning his attention to another huge creased map, had started to sort through yet more documents. Reichsfuhrer Himmler seized the opportunity but just managed to blurt out in a rather dry voice, 'My Fuhrer, the matter of Melton Briarsville?'

Hitler began massaging his fleshy nose, and looked directly at the Reichsfuher with squinted eyes, then said: 'Surely Heinrich, not more potsherds and digging around? I sympathise with your Aryan quest , you have always known that. But for now, the Reich has more urgent

75

matters of concern: will this Czechoslovakian issue ever settle? If you feel this is truly worthy of pursuit, and I must say Darre and Wust have already been to see me on this account, then that's fine. But please do not raise the issue again, at least not until it develops positively, and can be seen to be of a proven benefit to Germany. Indeed, Wust brought along that little black notebook, taken in the Great War, to show me. Admittedly, it was intriguing. And to reinforce this, Goebbels has suggested that what you are working on could be a developed into a massive propaganda coup for us? Once again, this is all fine, Heinrich. Thank you for outlining the issue, but long-dead, possibly Aryan monarchs? Well in my opinion that is certainly your realm, not mine.'

'Thank you my Fuhrer.' The Reichsfuhrer responded, 'Of course, should we find this buried matter, there is of course no need to instantly reveal this fact to the British authorities at all. After the invasion of Poland, perhaps, we could reveal it then and use it as a bartering factor that may delay Britain making a declaration of war on us? The potential, if we are successful, is limitless.'

For a second or two the Fuhrer looked just a little more interested. But his eyes squinted again. 'You really are convinced that if this issue was successful, and was able to be brought to the political table, that, in turn, the mighty British Empire would stall, aren't you? Well let us see, Heinrich, indeed let us see.' replied the Fuhrer.

Himmler took the hint, saluted smartly, and then almost appearing as an afterthought, he respectfully reminded the Fuhrer that he had been invited to the birthday of the SS Reichsfuhrers daughter, next week, and she would be honoured, as would all of his family be, if he could possibly attend? As the large doors were swung shut behind him, and as he walked along the marble floored corridor, two things were then being considered by the SS ReichsFuhrer. The Fuhrer had not cancelled the research that he was doing; and that in itself was a good thing. Irritatingly, the other thing was that he would most certainly put Darre and Wust in line. No one consulted the Fuhrer on an Ahnenerbe or SS issue before he, the Reichsfuhrer, did.

Back in the huge room Adolf Hitler, the Fuhrer of the Germany's

Third Reich, allowed himself just a moment's thought. No doubt now, Heinrich is well on his way to see Darre and Wust? Well it never does any harm to play one off against the other. I believe it keeps such people on their toes, as the British have a habit of saying.

January 25th 1939 was one day in a bitterly cold, windy and drizzle-ridden period of weather that had gripped most of Britain. Like almost everyone else, many of those in Melton Briarsville didn't even venture outside, it was so unpleasant. Some, of course, had no choice in the matter; there was war work to be done. Charlie Mayes, the village Postman, could be seen holding his bicycle and bag one-handed, whilst clutching his Post Office cap with the other - battling the wind and rain, determined that his post would be delivered.

Charlie had often wondered why, after so many months, he had never delivered any mail for the German students? Nothing, apparently, from family, or even anything official had ever passed his way. This was because, unknown to Charlie, the German students had their own efficient postal system, through which came all their mail from both family, and also other more official sources. Their postal system took the form of a small rodent-like little man who stopped every Wednesday by a gap in the hedge, put his old bicycle down and then whistled. Normally Euker strolled over took receipt of, and delivered, the mail.

Only one person was aware of whom this little man was, and how he fitted into the order of things, and that was Euker. He had been previously informed that this would be the normal procedure for communication both to and from the Reich. Euker had also been told the man's name. It was Oliver Brillo. Why he had been told this very precise detail he wasn't sure?

Shivering in the cold damp, wind were the twenty or so German students. Those students from Oxford had all been allowed to return to the University, defeated by the inclement weather. Little concern regarding this foul weather had been shown to the German students, for whom it was rather inconsiderately stated: 'Well, no real worries about that lot eh? After all they have their tents, don't they?" However, for the supervisor of the German students this neglect was considered to be perfectly suited to his cause; he had refused to stop operations. Waldemar Euker had an objective and was as determined as Charlie Mayes that nothing would stop him, bad weather or good.

In the afternoon a solitary Hawker Hurricane fighter was visible below the grey gloomy cloud layer. It had circled the village, and then completed a series of complex aerobatics, which included a victory role right above the excavation. This, despite its potential irony, must have been a totally independent action, as it was unlikely the pilot was actually aware that German nationals were below him? However, it tickled several of the villagers, one of who was heard to retort: 'Good show! Well done that fellow! Nothing like letting Jerry know exactly whose bleedin' country they are in, eh?

A critic might have noted the irony of that comment later on. Unknown to anyone at the time, fate would go on to dictate that, all too soon, the German army would need no informing of which country they were in and would also be aware of the next one that was in line for invasion and occupation!

At the villa site, the earliest piles of excavated top, and sub-soils, had been placed down the far end, and had already become covered in thistles, coltsfoot and other wild plants. Nature was reclaiming the disturbance. With the return of the Oxford students, the excavation was now actually ahead of its planned schedule and almost all the flooring areas of the main villa had now been revealed, and of course, discreetly checked. Previously there had been a bit of confusion and concern at why the German students had always lifted the floor tiles and looked at the undersides? Indeed some of them, when questioned, were not at all sure of the reasons why they had been required to do this, and kept looking over towards their supervisor. Euker managed to say ,and imply, not very convincingly: 'This is the way such things are done currently in Germany. And my fellow students find it hard to avoid doing this here. We regard it as an efficient, acceptable, search method. For example, if you turn the tiles over sometimes it is possible to find dog or cat foot imprints, which are of interest. I do apologise for this, I have mentioned it several times, that this is not acceptable as a research method for archaeology in Britain.' he added, rather weakly.

'I don't believe that for one moment!' later commented one of the Oxford students. 'When we asked them earlier, most had no damned idea why they were doing this? So in my opinion it's not standard archaeological practice at all over in Germany, else surely one of them would have just said so?'

Another observant Oxford student took delight in loudly pointing out that he had never heard Euker question any of his students about doing this, even though he had just claimed to have known this was not the way things are done in Britain. Furthermore, he reckoned that they just might be looking for something - and not just animal paw-prints either?

Millicent, up at the museum, said: 'Some time back, their 'supervisor fellow' was up there, and he'd shown a lot of interest in that marked Roman tile in the display case. Apparently it was found on this very site back in the 1860's. Curiously, I might add, this was the very same tile that was packed up and recently sent over to Germany. Am I being a fool here, or could there be more than just coincidence surrounding all this?'

Coincidence or not, the next morning that same observant student had a very black and deeply -bruised eye, as well as a rather bloodied nose. The fellow was noticeably quite withdrawn for the next few days and, for some reason, he wouldn't say exactly what had happened to him? But suspicions already ran high. The relationship between the Oxford University students and their German counterparts was definitely taking a turn for the worse. This already strained and brittle relationship was soon to be further tested by the German students delighting in revealing that amongst their equipment they had brought along something called a 'Mine Detector'.

After a brief seemingly typical, over-inflated, explanation of its metal-locating ability, this quickly became an issue of concern. The Oxford students and their supervisors were not in the least bit happy about the use of such a machine within the planned archaeological remit. 'They simply cannot use this mine detector thing on an organised archaeological dig! Such results it may yield will be all over the place. Artefacts and coins must be excavated and recorded in context, not simply plucked from the ground at random!' was the generally expressed opinion.

Sensing the atmosphere, Euker deliberately requested that the mine detector was therefore unpacked and proudly assembled in front of their counterparts during the lunch break. It looked very technical, and in reality, hardly anyone on site had even ever heard of such a thing, let alone seen one before. And that also included Waldemar Euker. He was going to lose the glory of the moment if it couldn't be assembled, or worse, operated, and the instruction manual was therefore consulted in earnest. This caused a delay, much to the mirth of many who were watching with eager anticipation. Unknown to Euker, who may perhaps not have been that concerned, apart from the obvious honour involved, he was in possession of one of only three such devices to exist.

All three grey spray-painted detectors had been manufactured by the company of Wolfgang Frohmann und Sohne, in Hamburg, and were a real technical advancement. There were three buttons on the control face, which, when depressed, allowed the operator to see an optionally backlit meter that registered the depth of objects located. Another large switch alternated between non-ferrous and ferrous metal discrimination. In other words, it offered the Germans a choice of targets, and when looking for treasure these functions would be very useful.

Once operational, the German students delighted in starting a test run for their British onlookers, who despite being seriously against such methods, could not resist at least watching the proceedings. Of course it was an Oxford student who was invited to place a large Roman coin just below the soil surface, with all the Germans standing looking the other way. Then Euker, and two other students, who were required to manually operate the enormous battery pack, began sweeping the ground with huge oval-shaped search head.

A continuous humming sound could be heard emanating from the detector, and then it made a rather different high-pitched whine. The large coin had been easily located and retrieved, much to the obvious dismay, but fascination, of their audience. Euker himself now knew just how useful this highly advanced piece of equipment was going to be? However, it was destined, by a mix of jealousy, devilment and one-upmanship, to never be able to assist him with his future objectives.

During the daytime, about a week later, one of the Oxford students, Charles Taylor, saw with satisfaction that the case box containing the mine detector was at last neglected, and positioned quite near to the hedge that ran alongside some of the Germans tents. They had been using this as a covered storage area since their arrival, and it was neatly piled with all sorts of boxes and packs. Also, now causing a degree of increased satisfaction, were the ever-present two brown glass bottles of Sulphuric Acid. What the Germans needed these for was anybody's guess?

Charles, however, had just thought of a very good use for the contents himself. A use that would make him at least feel rather good about himself, and act as payback for his colleague's, now yellowing, black eye and recently-discovered broken nose.

As darkness fell most of the Germans had yet again gone off on some type of physical training march and run, and Charles saw his chance. Those that remained had gone for what they thought was a, hopefully unnoticed, cigarette at the edge of the lane. Funny buggers, with so much discipline. They're like robots - no individuality at all.' thought Charles. He too then lit himself a noticeably crumpled Woodbine cigarette and casually strolled about, discreetly getting nearer and nearer to his objective. Using the dark backdrop of the hedge, he crouched down and soon had unfastened the three hinged clasps of the Mine Detector's case.

There lay his target, with its superbly crafted grey-painted engineering, that very soon would be hissing and fizzling. Quickly pouring half a bottle of acid into the delicate wiring did the job. The other half was then poured over the case ,and the bottle quietly broken and strategically placed on its side on top of the case. He nearly gave the game away. After inhaling the sharp acrid fumes from this destruction, he began to choke. He staggered up and quickly ran off some distance.

Finally allowing himself to breathe again. Gasping, he began to cough rather violently. This drew the attention of several of his colleagues, as well as three of the German students who were heading back. Charles took the woodbine stub from his mouth and hurled it to the floor in a shower of sparks. 'Blasted ruddy things! I must give this habit up,' he said just that little bit louder than required.

Back at the scene of his sabotage, to all extents and purposes, it would appear the bottle had fallen over and broken against the case and the acid had inevitably seeped inside, thus totally spoiling the equipment. Even fifty feet away the occasional acrid whiff was quite evident. But the Germans, fortunately, neither spotted, nor smelled anything of concern. By the time they did, the acid-bathed equipment had been totally ruined.

Next morning there were shouts from the German tents, as some poor innocent was being blamed for storing the acid so close to the mine detector. Observing at a distance, Charles thought it was typical that Euker, who had himself put the detector where Charles had later wrecked it in the first place, did not consider for one moment that he had also been foolish placing the equipment so close to the two bottles of acid. This factor undoubtedly passed through the mind of German student, Odilo Plotpfennig, who was the poor innocent currently facing Euker's anger. On occasion, the actions of a single person can change history, even if no one ever finds out about them, or acknowledges the effects they create. However, in this case people would find out, and therefore would be able to congratulate the perpetrator. After a diplomatic period of time had elapsed Charles informed his colleagues about what he had indeed done, and it was met with rapturous applause and cheering. But fate would dictate that neither he nor his Oxford-based colleagues would ever know just how seriously he had disabled German efforts by wrecking that mine detector.

Two days after the sulphuric acid and the mine detector had been introduced to each other the remains of another medium-sized Roman outbuilding were discovered a short distance from the main villa complex. Work had continued during a break in the rain showers. Euker now hoped, after this discovery, for a period when the Oxford students might depart once more from the site. On the 25th January the recent bad weather gave him just that opportunity. They had been allowed to return to the university campus if they wished to consolidate notes and drawings made so far. When the last university vehicle had departed from sight, almost immediately a visibly excited Waldemar Euker wanted the entire floor of this new building totally revealed, then brushed and washed down.

The tiles looked very interesting. It was fortunate the English students from Oxford University were not there at this time, for he was going to have every single one of them ripped up and turned over. If nothing he was looking for was revealed they could easily be put back and no one but his team or outside it would be any the wiser.

For his German student colleagues, many also in the Hitler Jugend, this entire excavation was just part of the Reich's programme of opportunities. Only a few of them suspected, or actually knew anything otherwise. Subtly influenced similar groups went on to mainly innocently take photographs of military installations and aerodromes, and anything else that was of interest. Some of the more knowledgeable amongst them enjoyed the clandestine approach and thrill of doing this. But even these students were still very naive as to why they had been asked to do this by their country.

When they returned to Germany all holiday photographic film had to be handed in. They were fortunate if they ever saw any of their photographs again. At the ongoing excavations of the Roman villa complex it would prove to be a truly remarkable day, well certainly for Waldemar Euker anyway. Washing the outbuilding floor with stiff bristle brooms and cold water had dislodged much of the original tile bonding mortar, which was sloshed to the sides by the broom-wielding team. Suddenly, Euker shouted out. There in the popping foam bubbles was a gold coin; examination revealed it was another of the same issues from the reign of the Emperor Claudius. 'Where did this come from? Did anyone see?' shouted Euker. 'Right. Start lifting up all these tiles. Let's see if there are any more?'

Euker enthusiastically joined in, fuelled by the knowledge that in the notes given to him it clearly referred to gold coins of Claudius having been found when the very first tile had been discovered, back in 1862. The Germans began to lever up, and lift every tile of the medium-sized room. Euker examined each one, and then just slung them down without a care. But then finally, between the last remaining two tiles, a further gold coin was seen, still in position. Carefully, it was dislodged from the plaster with a penknife and seen to be yet another issue of Claudius. 'Well done, Dittmar!' said Euker to the penknife operator. 'These are very very rare coins. How amazing! It is clearly the superb skill of we Germans and our dedication to succeed in all adversities that permits the discovery of such rare and important items, eh?'

Dittmar received further praise, and was just starting to feel that little bit uneasy with the whole situation. But Euker had been clever to create such a fuss and concern about these coins, as it made it very easy for him to be able to pick up the two tiles concerned with hardly anyone taking any attention. They were all too busy reinforcing his earlier praise of Dittmar, who was now enveloped in a sea of back-slapping colleagues, and not looking that comfortable about it at all.

Once inside his own tent Euker wanted to clean the tiles and examine them in private. After stooping down to get inside he noticed cleaning would not be all that necessary. As he had turned one of the tiles around a large slab of worm-ridden, dark-coloured, mud had fallen away revealing text and designs which looked instantly to be very similar to the diagram in his notes.

Immediately, he picked away the remaining adherent moist soil. He quickly began making a small sketch, to match the one he already had, which was originally copied from Frederick Pearson's notes and then copied yet again from another drawing sometime later. Euker could now easily match up the two sections of text and diagram design perfectly. 'So, they do fit!' he exclaimed quietly to himself.

He noted what must be a river at the bottom, for what appeared to be two little figures in a boat could be seen on it. On the original tile a series of deeply-incised lines separated the text from the map design.

Making this record of a great event

Now and this is done hoping that one

Chieftain Queen BODVOCCA will be

These happenings will announce them-

-oured with so greater accolades as are

found again she will once more rise

of our great region-the Gods are to be

end I make record of our great

with her noble offspring rest just

-ord has been found

I make reference lies deeply

DE BRITANNORUM

Tile 2 Inscription found in 1939 by Eukers excavation team

There was also a small helmeted figure that could be seen. The second tile had the same layout, but there was another helmeted figure with a shield and spear that could be seen as if walking along these lines. Perhaps it was too obvious, but Euker considered if these incised lines perhaps represented a road or ancient track-way? Why not? After all, the river was clarified with people in a boat, so why not a walking person, confirming a road?

To support his road theory there was also present two small circular designs, that could be interpreted as being wheels? Then there was a series of three circles, one of which was incorporated into the strange design of a winged animal, that looked a bit like an over-fed rabbit. It appeared that the contours of the map had also been made to represent another type of animal? What it was, he was uncertain, as it had a rather long tail for anything he knew of?

He was aware that only he, and therefore Germany now, had access to this completed tablet of information and he was feeling immensely proud. Having made the sketches, he now simply smeared soil all over the inscribed example. Gathering up the other tile, he proceeded back down to the outbuilding. He was pleased to see his loyal comrades tidying up and re-laying all the disturbed tiles. He simply merged back into their group. Appearing as if helping out, he placed the inscribed tile upside down and commented generally that it was 'such a shame no more coins could be found.'

Now he needed to return back to Germany as soon as possible. Arrangements were made via Mr Brillo, and after a reasonable flight, just three days after finding the tile, Waldemar Euker was finally being driven to Berlin. It wasn't long before he was summoned for a meeting at the University with a man, who he only knew as Herr Sieffert. Waldemar suspected that there was a lot more to the usually civilian-garbed Herr Sieffert than was immediately obvious? But knew also that such things cannot be asked, or enquired about, without risk. He must do as he has been ordered. And not only that, he must do it correctly.

Sitting in a large quiet room, adjacent to the Library in the Berlin Dahlem University, was SS Obersturmbannfuher Professor Harald Seiffert, the Head of the Cultural and Racial Archaeology Section. He ran his fingers over the gritty red surface of what he referred to as the 'The original Melton Tile'. This was of course the very tile that had been included in the elaborately-planned exchange of museum artefacts that had been organised a few months before. He matched it with other drawings, and along with those of the second example, made by Euker in Britain a few days earlier.

Professor Seiffert was very capable of translating the Latin text himself, and did so with ease. As he finished he sat back in the small worn leather chair, tilting it on two legs, the palms of his small hands began to sweat profusely. 'So, all that has been suspected over the years, by several people, now appears to have been correct?' he said out loud to himself, and continued, 'Logically, it would seem then that this Bodvocca must be the true and accurate name of that great warrior Queen the British are so proud of, and who they call Boadicea? Why is it that the British always seem to savour a good defeat and then celebrate its participants as heroes? For example, let us examine this Queen, and her finally, futile efforts against a vastly superior army along with the "Charge of the Light Brigade". All failures. Still, it is surely certain that with the guidance of our Fuhrer, Adolf Hitler, the island of Britain will shortly experience another defeat against a vastly superior army. I wonder how they will celebrate that?" he wondered.

Seiffert savoured this most pleasurable of moments and lit a thin dark cigar. As the swirls of rich blue, aromatic, smoke spiralled upwards he continued to marvel at the wonders of circumstances. Circumstances that had catapulted him, Harald Seiffert, onto the brink of something so culturally significant that he then considered all of his life's achievements so far could, no had, indeed just paled into insignificance. Well, with only one exception, and that being of course the time he decided to serve the Reich, and had joined the SS.

Within twenty four hours a new complete map had been drafted in accordance with the completed sketched maps, as evidenced from comparing the information gathered originally from the two tiles. Euker was then given a copy of this new map, praised highly as always and then promptly despatched back to England.

With typical rigidity and order, no one in Germany considered, or suspected, that Euker would already have shown such blatant independence, and had already produced his own copy of the map layout. That no one at all suspected was further evidenced by the strong implication from his seniors that some type of award, or medal, was being considered by those in the highest authority. 'But for the time being, Waldemar, you will appreciate such things cannot be bestowed upon someone who has simply dug up a few old Roman odds and ends. That would look a little strange, would it not? No indeed, we must wait for true recognition for our deeds, nothing less than total success guarantees such recognition.'

From the moment that the second tile had been discovered immediately the importance to the Germans of the actual villa excavation
naturally went into a very serious decline. What was sought after, and
required, was now fully in their possession. However, it's not as if Euker
could now arrive back at the excavation and immediately divert all the
German effort to landscape interpretation. This situation now called
for far more tact and diplomacy. Euker now considered that he might
not tell any of the other individuals at all about the quest. Surely, he
thought, it's now a one man mission.

He needed to scout and check-out the surrounding countryside,
and of course he could disguise the real reason by simply saying it's an
orienteering programme to familiarise themselves with the local terrain for a few miles around the village. It could be part of their ongoing physical training programme. After all, he knew that the locals, and
almost everyone else, thought along the lines of 'Those bloody Jerries
are always marching around the place on exercises, etc.,' That way at
least he would have additional help in the possible interpretation of any
land marks, or identifications, and perhaps the completion date of his
task would be hopefully all the sooner.

Waldemar Euker, having been dropped off at his suggestion, on the
outskirts of the village, considered several things whilst walking back
up the lane. One of them being that that he would perhaps hand-pick
two of his most trusted fellow comrades and inform the Oxford students that he wished to carry out a survey of the surrounding land, to
see how the villa fitted into the landscape?

Before this could proceed, however, there was a small ceremony to
perform, not of Euker's own creation of course, no this request originated from the very office of the SS Reichsfuhrer himself. Later that day,
in total compliance with the Reichsfuhrer's orders, a large chalk-coated
nodule of black flint came crashing downwards. It impacted with considerable force against the surface of the second tile. Looking around to
ensure he had no unwanted company, Euker had earlier walked down
to the river, and then quietly secreted himself down by the reed beds.
Here he had simply smashed the second tile into six large pieces, and a

small conical pile of dust where the heavy flint had impacted. Quickly gathering up the tile fragments he then lobbed them as far out into the dark green swirling waters as possible. The resulting splashes caused a Moorhen to call in an alarmed manner and take flight from the nearby reed bed noisily scurrying across the water with its dangling legs. Euker watched the startled bird and considered that one way to speed up any results would be if only they could have the entire area photographed from the air? However, this was beyond his immediate realms of ability. Why hadn't he suggested such during one of his visits back home? he thought, then immediately retracted the idea. Germany couldn't fly planes willy-nilly over Britain. That was a foolish idea! Well, for the time being anyway, he remonstrated with himself, and took comfort in that he hadn't made himself appear a fool by suggesting it.

The completion of this task was simply going to be down to his hard work and dedication. It could be sometimes as hard to compare details on an aerial photograph as it could be to assess the terrain by physically walking it and observing features. Anyway, the original inscriber of the map had no access to aerial facilities and would have drawn the map as he saw the lie of the land from ground level. Returning to the villa Euker quickly removed a single floor tile from the main building complex, depositing a pile of soil in its place. This tile was then placed in the void in the newly discovered outbuilding created by the hurried removal of the example he had just destroyed.

For a variety of reasons, from the beginning of May 1939, the relationship between the villagers, the Oxford students and their German counterparts would deteriorate further at a very rapid rate. To begin with, it was just minor comments and irritations expressed by all parties involved towards each other. It seemed the pressure of events taking place in Europe was finally starting to be felt, and was being reflected, albeit on a much smaller scale, in the village and surrounding areas.

Head gamekeeper of the Melanby estate, Ronald Flemmings, had seen three years of action back in World War One, and as a result had always said: 'I've never trusted the Huns, and never will!' And now the same, in his opinion, 'goes for those Jerries up at the dig.'

This issue of lacking trust was further enhanced for Ronald when he heard about Millicent Klake's previous observations. Then one day whilst checking his pheasants, he spotted a small group of German students coming towards him, with spades and picks over their shoulders. As they got nearer, two of them saluted him, pointed to their swastika armbands, and then back at Ronald. Each then drew an extended index finger across their necks. That had given old Ronald the frights for sure. 'Like Millicent said, them bastards are now wearing old Adolf's armbands up there. I've seen them too now. What's it all coming to, eh? Things are hotting up again. We'll be at war with the Hun again, you mark my words.' he had said. Every evening down the Waggoner's Inn quietly muttered conversations were becoming all too evident, something of a heavy nature was in the air, but what, and in what forms it would take, were as yet to be determined. But it would not take too long before they were.

The first real signs of things coming to a head came in the form of young Tommy Warner. He had heard his Father talking about the 'Jerries up at the diggings', and had decided that this was just enough of an excuse he needed to take action. Using the finest-cut slender hazel branch, Tommy fashioned what history could claim to be the first manufactured weapon in the British Empire that was used to attack the representatives of Nazi Germany. His grandfather had once shown him how to make a catapult of such serious velocity-related qualities. And right now, his young chubby hands were making the Mark 2 version. All that remained was to carry out a series of field trials, the same as any good weapons designer. For this, all he required now was a handful of half inch diameter spherical lead fishing weights 'borrowed' from his Fathers fishing tackle box, and the testing was set. Tommy decided there was no need for utmost secrecy; after all, every village kid had a catapult, so he wasn't going to attract any particular attention here.

The test results were very impressive; each half inch ball streaked away and had hit all the Brown Ale bottle targets. Some bottles had just exploded, turning into shards of brown glass, whilst others were left with a neat little hole through both sides. The fishing weights had been manufactured with a hole drilled right through them, and as a result each one gave a satisfying whistling hum as it sped away through the air. His last target was a pair of jackdaws on top of a nearby thatched roof. However, targeting the peaceful, otherwise occupied, birds did bring his research and development some attention. The selected lead round did not leave the catapult correctly and smacked off one of the side arms. From there on it hummed away and went cleanly through one of the leaded-glass lozenges that formed the main church window. Mr Pateman, the Churchwarden, was furious. But with no perpetrator known, and as the days passed none having yet been caught, there was little that could be done.

Tommy bided his time and a few tactful days later could be found looking through the same small gap in the hedge, where Millicent Klake had stood earlier whilst also observing the Germans. Between the wavering stems of cow parsley he could clearly see his objectives, and he thought it was unlikely they would see him from his hidden vantage point. Tommy noted that the Germans and the British students now worked in two separate groups, which was good, making his desired targets easier. The weight of Tommy's ammunition made his coat slightly lop-sided. He had brought extra just to make sure, and they were no longer considered to be fishing weights, for Tommy this was an offensive, and in his mind they were now 'artillery shells'. He knew also by trials that he could roughly loose off between three and five lead balls in a minute, not bad for his short stubby fingers. Then again it was these same short stubby fingers that could delicately remove the four or five eggs from the mossy deep-cupped nest of a Chaffinch, without breaking a single one. For it was that just as every self respecting village lad, apart from having a catapult, also had to have a decent bird's egg collection.

Pulling back on the taut rubber strands his first 'shell' went humming off towards the Germans. It impacted an upright spade handle and was deflected away, fortunately not being noticed. His second 'shell' zipped into a puddle creating a neat plume of violently disturbed water. That too seemingly went unnoticed. However, round number three found its target, which careful selection by Tommy, and of course luck and fate dictated, was to be the rounded and rather plump backside of a student called Odilo Plottpfennig.

Suddenly, Tommy then heard someone shout out just before his positively impacted target did. Odilo, who was to be fair a lot plumper than his colleagues, had already been the recipient of many derogatory comments and actions. This one however was physically painful and totally unjustified. Events, in Odilo's opinion, had as of then just gone too far. Odilo's facial expressions were rather an amusing combination, looking both mortified as well as furious. He was also very puzzled as to who it was that had just propelled the lead ball now lying at his feet at high velocity into his backside. 'Just who did that?' Odilo screamed, accusingly at his colleagues. For a second they all looked blankly at him, and then he had his answer.

Actually, Tommy's second inaccurate round had already been witnessed by one German student quietly sitting down making a sketch, who had then looked over at the hedge and seen Tommy whilst he was preparing for his third attack. The sketcher stood up and shouted pointing to the gap in the hedge, but was too late to save Odilo. A couple of Germans had then chased Tommy up the side of the field. He could hear them running, and cursing him, as they crunched through the dead thistles and grass on the other side of the hedge. But they stood no chance, their quarry had been born and bred here, and knew every ditch, culvert and short cut, and consequently got cleanly away.

It was Euker who had finally stopped the pursuit, all before the situation had proceeded into the village high street; attention like this was something he did not need at all. A group of Germans chasing a village boy down the street would not go down well at all. He could just imagine the reactions, and anyway, no British kid was going to jeopardise his responsibilities.

It was increasingly clear to Euker that both he and his party of students were not as welcome as they initially seemed to be at first; or was he just imagining that? Thinking about it, he couldn't exactly recollect anyone making them feel that welcome in the first place? For several weeks Euker had occasionally wandered off, either on his own or accompanied by just a few chosen colleagues. They walked for miles surveying and assessing. Of particular interest was the river. Those large ox-bow type curves, seemed to be similarly represented on the map made from the tile inscriptions. The presence of those two figures in a boat surely confirmed this as a river, or was the original inscriber of these tiles playing tricks, trying to confuse and creating a riddle? He didn't think so. Back in those times the Romans in Britain were making every effort to provide straight linear road systems. It must be the local river, or at least a river. Otherwise there was little else that could be readily identified. Trouble was the curves of this river didn't seem to match the diagram at all, similar yes, but exactly, no.

Once again he considered, had the original 'cartographer' placed a series of tricks to catch the unwary here? Had he perhaps been clever enough to even create a type of reverse image, a sort of negative map of the area he was trying to portray? Euker thought, surely such a primitive, albeit original thinking representative of an inferior race could not fool Waldemar Euker in such a manner?

This arrogance was to delay Euker for weeks, as he wasted time pondering inefficiencies and, almost frustratingly, expected the clues to be automatically solved for him with minimal effort. He was a representative of the Fuhrer's Reich and as such he believed he deserved success. Surely it was owed to him and his kind?

The main trouble was, Euker had no idea in which direction the referred 'Half-mile' distance mentioned in the tile text actually related to? The only real clue he had was the map, and that was simply not working out for him. The reasons for this went back well over a century before. Estate and park developments back then had made this ancient baked-tile map now very problematic to interpret. There were other features that had also been removed or altered and some even obscured by woodland, making the task all the more complicated.

In late May, for some, there was a distraction. News began filtering through that something astounding had been discovered some hundred or so miles away at Sutton Hoo, in Suffolk. Later rumours abounded, but details slowly emerged that it was some type of ship burial, possibly Viking? someone had suggested.

Some of the Oxford university students were actually invited to go and view proceedings there, an invitation not extended to Euker or his colleagues. Later they returned with stories of great golden buckles, and other tantalising finds. Although it was of some concern that the British had found something significant themselves at this period, it did little to deter Euker from his main objective. To him it was a mere insignificant trifle that had annoyingly captured attention. But that was minimal compared with what he believed he could achieve. The Sutton Hoo find was of course duly reported back to Germany where, once again, the event met with as little attention as Euker was paying to it over in England.

Then, as if his previous opinions and attitude had been honoured, suddenly it did work for him. Very early one June morning in 1939, after a restless night's sleep, Euker awoke with a start. Of course, it makes sense! How could he have been so misled, and wasted so much time? he thought. He had noticed a few days before how the river had appeared to have been channelled away from a lengthy section of its original course. This original course was only just visible as a wide, but shallow, depression where darker green grass grew to a slightly taller level than that surrounding it. Following the assumed new course, he had come across a considerable-sized lake, complete with little islands, and that was the key to the whole affair.

The English, Euker had recently heard, had often landscaped their estates in centuries past. And now it was obvious the river course had been changed totally to feed this lake, and consequently that's why the crude tile map didn't seem to fit the lie of the land today.

Feeling extremely pleased with himself, this elation was however destined to be quite short lived. He had almost certainly decoded the map, which was brilliant, but what of the other markings and features in its design? He recalled seeing nothing like the large and small circles, which were obviously meant to represent some type of feature that could then be seen from the ground. If he could locate these additional features then he should be able to reasonably triangulate to the point of his quest. At least this would be of some assistance, as for some time now he had pondered on the actual scale of the map, as well as just how accurate it really was? Perhaps he had missed some of these features or they had now totally disappeared having been destroyed by agricultural activities, he considered.

Then that urge to see the site from an aerial perspective manifested itself yet again. He knew from experience that in some cases features that had long-since disappeared could still be clearly seen from the air. He would of course re-check the approximate areas with a renewed vigour. Before, he had no idea what he was looking for? But now he did. And who knows, he just might be lucky once again.

He hastily arose and, grabbing the notes, slunk off as quietly as possible, heading in a westwards direction. He stopped several times, looking back and forth, holding up some papers, and occasionally huffing exasperatedly with his hands on his hips. After half an hour he found himself in Four Acres Field, walking back and forth. It was here that Ron Flemming spotted him kicking flat several mole hills, then stopping to pick something up from one and then just standing and gazing around. Euker then knelt down and appeared to be digging a small hole.   Bloody Huns! Never satisfied! Now they are even digging up Four Acres. Whatever next? thought the well-hidden game keeper, whilst watching all the while.

Euker now considered his predicament. Not wanting to attract attention to his newly discovered area, he had very few options. In fact he only had one. He had no doubt that he was going to have to return under cover of darkness and start digging test pits. He looked around. He had that strange neck-hackle rising feeling again. He was certain, or at least felt very strongly, that someone was watching him. Ron moved to ease the ache in his leg. Getting more comfortable had not been a good idea, as he now shifted his foot onto a dead elm stick. The stick then broke with a sharp resounding crack. 'Like a ruddy gunshot! Christ! I was a bit worried the old Jerry would see me.' Ron later recalled.

Euker glanced up. Someone is definitely in the edge of that wood,

95

he thought. And then he decided it would be best to leave the area, hopefully appearing as casual as possible. Returning to the excavation, he stopped several more times, looked around, and even dug a few small holes, just in case whoever had been watching still had their eye on him. On the way back he finally decided this was definitely to be a one-man venture. If he was correct, then he alone wanted the full credit. Such credit that could have huge implications for him and his family in the new order of things in Germany.

How he wished that the mine detector, wrecked by such careless-ness, had still been operational now. In relation to a royal burial, there would surely be a large array of metal grave goods? Had he been able to have it working then he could have been equipped to cover and search a much larger area, and far more efficiently. Damn that fat useless ex-ample, Plotpfennig! And then he also rather grudgingly thought: damn as well, my own carelessness and lack of attention!

For a few nights he limited himself to just three holes to be dug per session. he was not even certain what he may find? 'But surely, digging random holes is the only way to potentially locate something that is buried?' he had told himself. But that logic was continually interfered with by the two reoccurring questions of where, and how deep, was that something buried?

Each time for every excavation made, Euker was careful to dig out a large, precise, three-foot diameter circular plug, extracted in sections that he lay down carefully, and re-assembled next to the hole. This could be put back in order and trodden down easily leaving no mess, so that hopefully no one in the day time might wonder just what was happening in Four Acres? Then at around one o'clock in the morning, during one of his forays, Euker uncovered something rather different, and rather unusual.

Digging downwards into one of his holes his spade was stopped dead in its tracks with a violent jolt that hurt his wrist. With some no small measure of excitement he began to clear the loose soil at the bottom. There it was again, as once more he hit the strange obstruc-tion. Using a small torch, and clearing more soil away from the bottom of the hole, Euker now saw what it was that had suddenly halted the progress of his spade. His spade had in fact impacted what appeared to be a flattish piece of buried lead. It was creamy white in colour, but the fresh silver scars on it from his spade gleamed in the moonlight from a gap in the fleeting clouds.

Euker slowly began to get that strange feeling, as if he was being watched. It seemed to emanate once again from the dark woodland at the top of Four Acres just like the last time. No, just my imagination, he thought, to console himself. But what was that? Euker could just make out a dark shape that had emerged quickly from the edge of the wood into the dullish moon light. It stopped, started again and was now very slowly coming his way.

Nearer and nearer came the shape, until in a racing patch of bright moon-light, Euker saw, with some measurable expression of relief, that it was no more than just a lone fallow deer. The deer then suddenly stopped in its tracks again, it had spotted Euker and swiftly bolted away clearing a six feet high hedge in its quest to escape.

Returning to the task, Euker began clearing away more soil and could see that it was certainly quite a large piece of lead that he had come across. Try as he might, he could not locate any edge, which would have allowed him to lever, or perhaps pull it upwards. Could it be some type of funeral casing or a leaden box? he thought. The metal was white, and he knew it had to be of some age to achieve that level of oxidisation. Still, unable to locate any edge with which to lift the metal, Euker decided that the only option remaining was to use his spade blade to try and hack a hole in it. This may reveal a cavity underneath it, or worse, just more solid soil.

Hacking a crude circular section out he shone his torch down the hole. Just more solid soil. Tapping it with his spade did not reveal the hollow resonant sound that would have excited him. "Wasting my time. I know it's here somewhere, just taunting me,' he muttered, as he sat down with the moonlight reflecting off his sweating forehead.

It wasn't just Euker's sweat the moonlight was reflecting off that night either. Twelve year old Albert Dyce was always roaming about the

Albert Dyce watching trout rippling the moonlit river surface

woods and estate at night, not that either of his parents ever suspected anything about his nocturnal traipsing. Albert loved the tranquillity, the sounds and the peace. To him, the darkness made his familiar village transform and was almost as if he was entering a mythical land of greys and blues. He would often stand transfixed below streetlights, marvelling at the moths and other insects attracted to them. He had seen owls, badgers and foxes, and on several occasions, had climbed up the trunk of an ancient pollarded riverside overhanging willow tree. For it was here he had watched the moonlight reflected from ever increasing circles on the surface of a pool created by the sizeable Brown Trout below.

But now he was watching a large fallow deer, one of his favourite animals. The deer, however, was soon spooked and crashed out through the side of the wood into Four Acres field. As Albert watched, he followed it, lost it and then followed it again due to a break in the clouds, and it was then that he saw something else. Something that was dark and also moving about in the field. The deer had stopped short of the dark thing, and then had made a swift dash sideways, eventually leaping over a tall hedge. Something apart from me spooked that old deer good and proper just then, thought Albert, and carried on watching. Albert slowly got nearer to the edge of the wood hoping that in the darkness he wouldn't tread on a dry twig or stick. Due to another gap in the speeding clouds, Albert finally saw what the dark thing was. It was a man, and he looked like he was digging?

Considering this strange activity one definitely worth staying out for, Albert watched for another half an hour, creeping closer and closer against the hedge row, until finally the digger turned on a small torch, looked into the hole and then sat down in an exasperated manner. Finally the mysterious figure stood up, filled in the hole, put his spade over his shoulder and slowly walked away. He was muttering something, but Albert was not that close enough to be able to hear what?

Euker knew that the next night would involve the same amount of effort applied. He wondered how long he could keep up this extra night work? Often by mid-day he was visibly exhausted. Someone would surely notice sooner or later? Tomorrow night, he decided, he would return and examine this lead feature in far more detail, as there was certainly something very strange about it? Not just that, but it was in the right area. Albert got home, up the drainpipe and in through his small bedroom window. He lay awake, unable to sleep, as he wondered just what it was that so interested the digger about Four Acres field.

Next morning brought about a very serious matter indeed; some very official looking people had turned up at Melton Briarsville. They were acting on matters that only that very morning the Dean of Oxford University had also been made aware of. A series of minor complaints from villagers, combined with the seriousness of matters concerning the continually-aggressive actions of Herr Hitler, had necessitated further responses and actions to be taken in Britain. Whilst, of course, the villa excavation itself could proceed unhindered without any associated official difficulties, the entire archaeological operation on the site will be for some while, what may be considered as, short staffed.

The German students were all to be officially deported at the earliest opportunity. And somewhere it had been decided that was to be on this very day, without delay. As if this wasn't enough of a shock, it worsened for the German students, as this fact seems to somehow have got around the village, and many people were heading down towards the excavation site.

A crowd had gathered and assembled with an air of jubilation at the humility of their foreign guests. It took a few hours for the deportees to pack up their equipment and sort out other matters. Initially there was some shouting and jostling and general bewilderment. The German students looked to Euker for support but, for once, he was quiet. He was well aware nothing he could do, or say, could affect the situation. His disciplined nature meant that the inner feelings of anger and frustration that he was feeling, so intensely, were not put on display. He was also somewhat concerned as to whether this would be regarded as a failure by his superiors back in Germany?

'Thank you, but that's Oxford University field work equipment!' said one student, as he wrestled a tape measure and a theodolite from one of the Germans. A small scuffle broke out that was not quite as immediately stopped as it could have been. The several armed soldiers in attendance were quite prepared to watch, unless of course things got totally out of hand. These soldiers had been brought along on the convoy of three lorries, supplied to take the, now very unwelcome, guests away and were parked up at the top of the field. They could have parked right down next to the excavation, but it was agreed beforehand to make the equipment-laden Jerries walk the upward journey.

By now, the group of villagers had amassed to several hundred people. The situation needed completing as soon as possible, it had the potential to take a nasty turn. So the soldiers then tried to make their presence as obvious as possible, with aimless shouts and pointing, which really only confused the issue further. One villager started shouting too.

His comments directed at Euker, 'Oi! you mate! Prancing around our bloody countryside like some type of toy soldier? Bugger off back to Adolf. Same goes for the lotta yer. Goo orn, gerroff out of it! We had enough of your high jinks quarter of a century back!'

Then, without any warning at all, a large, very rotten, brown and white speckly-skinned cooking apple flew through the air towards the German group. It was part of last year's harvest that had been badly bruised, and was supposed to have been thrown away. But fourteen year old, Tommy Warner, had decided to keep some back, amongst his arsenal of 'things especially for the Germans'. Tommy had his chance, and was now reinforced with a few friends. Even more of the large brown Bramley globes bowled like cricket balls splattered on, or exploded nearby, showering the group of Germans with generous quantities of highly aromatic cider-smelling shrapnel.

Amidst this pelting, Euker made his final valiant stance: "Why this attitude? We are archaeologists only, and have been here to assist you in finding your own culture and history!'

This was met with more shouts and abuse, and even a bigger barrage of apples from the now fully- armed, and very confident, self-named 'Warner Division'. Not having received any restrictive comments from any adults during the first attack, they had interpreted this as being given full permission to proceed, and were now strategically positioned higher up on the grassy bank. Even the normally rather formal village constable PC Dimmock could be seen to have the faintest trace of a smile on his face. The indifference of the authorities in protecting them enraged Euker. 'You ignorant fools!' he shouted. 'We will be back here one day to complete our job, and that day will definitely be much sooner than you think!' Then the Germans were gone at last. And just seventy nine days after their hasty departure, England would find itself once again at war with their country.

The village of Melton Briarsville now prepared itself as best as possible to meet the demands of this war. Firstly, by forming a Home Guard unit, and secondly with white sticky criss crosses of tape that could be seen on many window panes. Some sandbags were placed outside the Post Office by the Home Guard, many of whose members, it must be said, rather obviously felt extremely proud to be wearing uniform once again. This pride wasn't at all dented by the fact that the majority of them rather, than having a rifle, possessed a solitary broom handle.

After the initial hustle and bustle, the villagers waited, but there was nothing. This was truly the 'Phoney War'. Individuals leant over, and families gathered around their radios in the evenings and listened, as the outside World changed forever.

Months went past, as the war progressed very slowly. Still they continued to wait, but this time for the ringing of church bells, signifying that the anticipated German invasion had started. Basically, here in rural Oxfordshire, as with similar localities in Britain, village life continued relatively unaffected by what was going on in Europe, and elsewhere. The local ARP Warden at the time, a Mr Daniel Crabb, certainly had his work cut out, though. Not, at this time, assisting the community from the ravages of the Luftwaffe, but trying to persuade certain villagers to abide by the blackout rules, which seemed to be nearly impossible. Throughout the night during his patrols his gravelly voice could often be heard shouting: 'Get that bloody light out, will you?'

CHAPTER EIGHT

A VERY SERIOUS
BUSINESS INDEED

Having returned to Germany Waldemar Euker was extremely relieved to be informed that the official cessation, and therefore failure, of events at Melton Briarsville was considered to be due to events far beyond his control. Now that Britain had actually declared war on Germany people seemed to be far more occupied with other things; the long anticipated war was finally here. Consequently he was also informed this must not be seen as a personal failure. In fact Herr Wust had only spoken to him a short while before and added the encouraging words: 'If things go to plan Euker we could all find ourselves in London very shortly anyway. And as you know, Melton Briarsville is not that far from there, is it really?'

Euker wished Herr Wust hadn't mentioned the issue being 'not seen as a personal failure', as it made him wonder if some people did exactly view the situation as being just that. Herr Wust went on to explain further that the 'Dynamics of this particular operation have as we know now changed.' as he put it.

Wust was quite frank, finding the royal burial now obviously couldn't help to delay a war that had already started. Therefore the entire situation had to be modified, and was about two issues now. Firstly if it could be proven that Boadicea, or Bodvocca, was indeed of German origin this would of course have some minimal value. The precise limits of this so-called value and its interpretation would have to be determined by Propaganda Minister Josef Goebbels and his department. However, concerning this claim Wust clearly now had his own doubts as to whether or not pursuing it could make Germany a laughing stock. Of course to empower this propaganda it would still be necessary for Germans to make the discovery. Now if the war didn't go well for Germany all that effort would have been wasted.

Secondly, if the war did go according to plan, explained Wust, 'If this woman was not of German origin we can assume she is as British, as history tells us. So let us, Herr Euker, imagine the shame and humiliation of a nation that has its missing Queen not only located by, but excavated by the occupying forces of the Third Reich. Now wouldn't that be something? I think these two factors, as the English say, are all about "hedging your bets". said Wust.

'Indeed it is. Indeed it most definitely is,' thought Waldemar Euker.

Who knows, thought Euker, if he survived this war, and he had every intention of doing so, and no-one else involved did, it might even be possible to return to England and conduct the search again by himself. Such a consideration did not rely on Germany either winning or losing the war, it was a solitary independent factor that Euker was quite prepared to pursue alone when or if the opportunity arose.

The meeting concluded with Euker being requested to hand over all the notes and documents relating to his pre-war activities in Britain. He did indeed wonder if events would turn out that would enable him to see that village again. Despite his thoughts on positive plans for the future he remained somewhat crestfallen by recent events for a considerably lengthy period. Waldemar then considered his options and decided finally to enlist for service within the Luftwaffe.

The Kriegsmarine did not appeal to him, and neither did the potential for being stuck in a mud-ridden trench. His request was successful where, after training, he found himself eventually posted to an aerial reconnaissance unit, known as Aufklarungsgruppe 123. This was luck indeed, as it was quite the perfect posting for such a keen sharp-eyed individual.

There now followed an increasing build up of interest in relation to England's airfields and Waldemar Euker and his crew were sent on several sorties to take photographs of primary airfields in Britain. In these early stages of the conflict it was pretty much guaranteed that they could slip over the Channel do what they have to do, and return home without much incident. More experienced colleagues stated repeatedly that: 'The British fighter planes never seem to be about, and their anti-aircraft fire is just as non-existent and very inaccurate when it is evident.'

As the war progressed things slowly began to change and one day Euker noted that many of his scheduled flights for his new brief would now take him and his crew deep into mainland Britain, and in several cases, relatively near to Melton Briarsville. 'So, village of Melton Briarsville, you don't get away from Waldemar Euker so easily, do you?' he mused.

Despite his rigid training, and sometimes almost programmable mind, he considered that it would not be detected should he deviate on just a few occasions and take some photographs of the area surrounding the village. This was of course not the first time he had taken a slight deviation from what was officially expected from Germany's New Order. Euker may well have had the mannerisms and appearance of a typical product of Nazi Germany. But, unlike many others, he was occasionally very capable of independent thoughts and actions, most usually though when it suited his own personal objectives. Although he was not aware at the time, one wonders how he would have reacted had he known that such personal objective gratification in the Reich went right to the top. It is uncertain whether knowing this fact would have made him feel more secure, or would he have felt insecure and perhaps cheated, or even deceived?

Regarding his flight deviations and their results he could always say he thought he saw something of interest down below to justify the additional exposure of the negatives to his superiors. The scheduled flight plans for this crew meant that normally on Sundays they would fly a route over the Midlands, perhaps to Bristol, and loop around, either following the south coast or heading back home across the Channel.

One Sunday in June 1940 Euker and his crew were sent specifically to take photographs of the airfield at Bourton. The start of the mission was the normal, and the usual non-eventful, outbound flight, with Euker and his crew passing over the north of London at twenty thousand feet into the Midlands. Then about five miles distant he could clearly see landscape and features which were definitely familiar to him. Finally there it was, Melton Briarsville itself. Euker circled around the village three times, to the increasing concern of his crew. On one occasion, whilst over the same area, he began circling again and was observed to be struggling with his tunic zip. He then revealed eight thick bars of chocolate, which he suddenly just threw out of the side of the cockpit. His comrades just put it down as a bout of irrational behaviour, a gesture of some unexplainable generosity perhaps; the war certainly did make people do some very strange things. They then headed off to photograph Bourton airfield.

Far below in the village many people saw the German aeroplane that day, and went on to see a similar one for a few Sundays afterwards. Some of the local children had even nick named it 'Listen hear comes old Jerry Sunday!' they would say. At one time Euker's crew had taken a total of three exposures of Melton Briarsville. Later, one would be seen to be out of focus for some reason and that left just two remaining photographs. No interest at all was shown by the photographic interpreters, and so Euker asked if he might simply keep the two photographs as mementoes, which was duly permitted.

Later on, lying up on his bed he examined the photographs as well as his notes. Who can predict, or know what will happen in the years to come? he thought. Comparing them, he could clearly see that back in England he had indeed been investigating the approximate area of his interest when in Four Acres field. His frustration was intense, he had clearly been so close. Consolation came in the thoughts that whatever this thing, is it had remained undiscovered for some 2000 years. A few more years will not make any difference. And as he well knew, only a limited amount of people had the same information he did. But only Waldemar Euker had the photos to make comparisons with that information.

Euker certainly had no wish to see others get rich, or achieve notable success at the expense of all his hard work and efforts. True, he was dedicated to the cause of National Socialism, but he had those same self-preservation type thoughts again. Just supposing National

Socialism didn't survive? Just suppose Germany loses this war? he thought.

It was to counteract any such 'losses' that may occur in his life that Waldemar Euker had previously made the detailed copies of all his notes, and especially the most important things of all, the two diagrams of the tiles. He had concluded back then that security could be a rare thing in life and his own personal copies might well provide some sort of security for his future. Alternatively, if Germany won and he was sent back to complete the operation around Melton Briarsville then that's was all well and good. However, if things did turn out differently, then surely at some stage after things had settled down he could return to the village himself. And if that happened to be some time in the future then all well and good. There would be less chance of him being recognised again. Waldemar was perhaps at this time a politically misguided individual. But he was, when it came to many other concerns, an individual that could be ably considered to be nobody's fool.

CHAPTER NINE

DEATH AND DESTRUCTION AT MELTON BRIARSVILLE

O n Monday 26th August 1940 twenty one year-old Walde-mar Euker walked out of the mess hall on Toussus-le Buc airfield, just like he had done many times before. Admiring the clear blue skies, he had a good feeling about today, and grabbed the chance for another cigarette. A week before, their Staffel Kapitan had shot down an RAF Spitfire. The celebrations were planned for tonight, which no doubt influenced his positive opinions on the day's outlook.

Looking up at the panelling below the cockpit, he admired his artwork. Just two days before he had borrowed some red paint from one of the ground crew, and climbing up a ladder, he had then carefully painted the name 'Magdalene' onto the aircraft. Looking around at all the activity he then touched the blue floral silk scarf around his neck three times, for ritual good luck. Knowing he was not the only one to conduct such pre-mission ceremonies he clambered up into the confined cockpit of their rather war -weary Junkers 88A-1, coded 4U+EK, along with his three other usual crew members. 4U+EK is very much-liked by Euker and his fellow aircrew. They knew her in depth - all her funny little quirks and sounds. 4U+EK had many worn areas of paint and her blue undersides were heavily streaked with oil and exhaust stains. But looks aside, she had always got them home, and that's what counted.

Their aeroplane had been parked in the early morning sun and by mid day, as always, its interior characteristically has a complex odour of dope, oil and stale leather. Its two Junkers Jumo 211B-1 engines coughed and spluttered into life, and steadily 4U+EK, with her confident crew, began to trundle and bounce along the runway. Then at last they were up.

No matter how many times they had done this the exhilaration of take off, combined with a trace of nervousness, never lessened for this crew. The mission briefing was to observe and photograph Bourton airfield, yet again. As this was one of the many RAF-related targets selected for attention in Britain that day. Afterwards, they would proceed to Bristol. For the past couple of weeks Euker's crew have been photographing this area, their flights for this particular route were normally scheduled to take place on Sundays. However, yesterday, heavy cloud formations had resulted in the mission being cancelled and rescheduled for the next day. Now, once again, they were passing over the cold-looking waters of the English Channel. It wasn't long before a downward glance saw the sun reflecting off the Thames Estuary.

Far below, they could see various boats and barges, and what looked like a group of medium-sized destroyers berthed over to one side of the river. Over to the right, a large formation of Dornier 17's could be seen flying parallel to Euker's aircraft and then they all wheeled over further to the right and headed northwards. In the rear of the Junkers 88 cockpit sat twenty five year-old Unteroffizier Edouard Poschenhalter, from Stettin. Just two days before he had been on leave in his home town when his wife and children had quite formally presented him with a good luck charm in the form of a tiny silver bear. This was now pinned to his tunic. It was against regulations, but he had fastened it after take-off, so who would ever know? Looking all around him constantly, he had seen some RAF fighters already, but they were at a considerable distance. However, he continued scanning the skies eagerly, as distance could be all too rapidly decreased to catch out the unwary. Over the last few weeks he had seen several of his countrymen shot down. And he was determined that in no way was that going to happen to Edouard Poschenhalter.

Pilot Officer Kenneth Lumsden was one of a several No 85 Squadron Hurricane pilots that had taken off from Croydon airfield that afternoon. Gaining altitude, it seemed no time at all before he suddenly spotted a large formation of inbound German bombers. Glancing round. he also noticed that all of his colleagues had seemingly disappeared. That was nothing unusual in the action-packed fast combat skies of wartime Britain. Then, as he was considering his lone individuality, he saw what was almost certainly a solitary Junkers 88 some distance off and banked hard to port, swiftly coming in behind to investigate his target.

One last brief check to ensure it was not a Bristol Blenheim? Those RAF light bombers looked very similar to the German Junkers 88, and in some cases had actually been shot down by friendly fire due to this very factor. The swastika on the tail fin, and visible black crosses on the dark-coloured aeroplane out in front, allayed any of Lumsden's previous concerns. The enemy rear-facing gunner had obviously spotted Lumsden too, as the Junkers 88's dorsal gun began to flash and sparkle. Mesmerizingly slowly, the deceptively slow-glowing tracers stacked up in a wavering line, and then shot past his Hurricane. Not all of the enemy aircrafts 7.96mm bullets went past, though. The tell tale 'click – clack', like pebbles thrown onto a corrugated iron roof, told Lumsden his own aircraft was also taking hits.

Jinking sideways, Lumsden hoped to confuse the issue, but that damned Junkers 88 rear-gunner's fire followed him. Slipping sideways again, Lumsden throttled forward and slightly downwards, closing the gap. Lining up the Junkers, he gave it a three second burst. He watched as eight thin white smoke trails of spiralling tracer fizzled and streaked away from his wing mounted guns. The little Browning 0.303 machine gun was not much more than a pea-shooter as a single weapon. But when eight of them were combined, they could be very effective.

Lumsden continued to watch as the white threads wove their way towards his target and then started to hit it. Depending on the angle of their impact, some of the Hurricane's bullets created elongated tears in the enemy bomber's thin airframe, surrounded by paint-fractured dents, whilst other rounds went straight in making neatly-rounded holes.

Immediately the enemy aircraft's starboard engine began to smoke, and small parts of distorted airframe started to break away from the wing root area. Some of these could be seen fluttering and hurtling back past the pursuing Hurricane. Closing even further, another two lengthy three and four and a half second bursts covered the cockpit in explosive flashing strikes and small bursts of white smoke. It certainly stopped that blasted rear gunner firing. In a fraction over ten seconds so far, a total of one hundred and twenty seven 0.303 bullets had actually hit the enemy bomber.

After the first attack the enemy aircraft had begun some mild evasive manoeuvres, but its fate seemed sealed. The final attacks had sent streams of impacting bullets spattering along the length of the cockpit, smashing instruments, splintering glass and bone, puncturing skin and muscle, and then filling the aircraft with the sharp odour of burning electrics. Two thousand feet above, Kenneth Lumsden watched as his fire-bathed victim streaked earthwards. It began to disintegrate, and the last thing he saw was the complete tail section breaking off before it all went out of sight through a thin layer of cloud.

As their solitary Junkers 88 proceeded westwards over the British mainland all the crew were now keeping an eye out for attacking RAF fighters. They had already seen two smoking Heinkel He 111's drop out of the sky, and a single Junkers 88 that had had broken apart. Parachutes had emerged from both the Heinkels, but the Junkers 88 had been heart-rending.

It was attacked, as far as they could see, by a single RAF fighter. It then caught fire, stalled and had gone into a steep dive. As they watched it streak down, the wingtips and tail section had all disintegrated, and not one parachute was seen. How things had changed from the relative safety of their earlier war missions. Back then, effective defending and attacking British aircraft had been quite rare. Today there seemed to be RAF fighters everywhere. As a reconnaissance mission they were very much concerned with not becoming embroiled in combat, they wanted to get in fast do their job and get back home.

Euker spent much time listening to reports and sightings from his fellow crew members and, where possible, headed away from the sighted RAF fighters. This was a game relying on luck, as much as other potential targets being available to distract the RAF pilots away from them. It was a game that could only be played for so long, before someone chose them as a target.

Then it happened. Adding to the excitement, but also their fear, a single fighter appeared, closing the gap between them. The little fighter, which Poschenhalter correctly identified as a Hurricane, was slightly weaving from side to side. Whether this movement was influenced by his over-enthusiastic bursts of machine gun fire at too great a distance was undetermined? The gap between the two aeroplanes was now decreasing at a considerable rate. When would the RAF fighter attack them? It just looked like the pilot was checking them out at the moment. Poschenhalter waited, waiting for that tell tale twinkling, and then the tracers to come heading their way. As he did so, he loosed of several more short bursts. There it was, the leading wing edges of the RAF fighter flashed, and then the thread-like tracers were coming right at the Junkers and its crew.

Unteroffizier Poschenhalter was now literally doing his nut with the rear-facing MG 15 machine gun, slamming on saddle drum after drum of bullets, and actually shouting curses at their attacker. This continued until the British fighter delivered its second attack. One distorted Browning 0.303 bullet glanced off some of the Junkers 88's internal armour plate and creased across the front of Poschenhalter's chest, snapping off the tiny metal bear. The little charm fell onto the cockpit floor and rattled as it slid around from side to side as the pilot made evasive manoeuvres. Another hail of 0.303 bullets from the Hurricane once again smashed in to the cockpit, and the little bear finally stopped moving. Its travels were now restricted by a large, thickening pool of blood.

With many of the Plexiglas panels frosted and fractured from bullet strikes, wind shrieked into the cockpit at over two hundred miles an hour. Waldemar Euker turned around and saw Poschenhalter slumped sideways covered in blood. The second burst of machine gun fire from the Hurricane had killed the remaining crew apart from Waldemar Euker, who despite being hit over four times, still remained conscious.

Then the third burst of bullets had ripped into their aircraft, totally sealing its fate.

That was the thing with the design of this particular aeroplane. For comradeship, all the crew were grouped together, which was fine and worked well in theory. But when trouble arrived, on occasion, this same factor could mean that they could, and often did, all die together too. Unwounded crew members found it very hard to escape the cramped confines of the Junkers 88's cockpit. When the aircraft was disabled, those who were badly wounded stood no chance at all. A loose flight map violently thrashed around the cockpit interior, propelled by the intense shrieking slipstreams of wind, until finally it caught fire and danced around like a Phoenix.

Euker had lost a lot of blood, and being too injured to maintain a grip on the control column, he slumped backwards and let it go. Images of his entire life experiences seem to dance before him. His new wife, and all his family, his Father. Mother and wife again appeared in his mind. How would they all cope with the news of his death? Then, with his mind re-focusing, he knew he simply had to get out.

Desperately, he tried to get to the escape hatch, but his flying boot was stuck fast in some jagged torn metal. And the blood-soaked bodies of his dead comrades seemed to be jamming every escape route. The aircraft seeming to sense no one was controlling it almost immediately stalled and flipped upside down, before entering into a near vertical dive. Inside the Junkers 88, Euker frantically struggled and then started screaming. The smell of burning oil, paper, leather and finally flesh was unbearable. Suddenly there was a violent crack and a tearing sound, as riveted panels were shredding apart. This was immediately followed by a rush of air inside the cockpit; Euker knew the burning mainframe was most likely breaking up. That was his last serious concerned thought. Afterwards, it all seemed to flow into a hazy sort of peacefulness. The burning fabric from his lower tunic fell away in shreds revealing the bloody blackened sizzling flesh of his legs. But there was no pain now, as if mercifully hypnotised, through shattered Plexiglas panels, Euker watched a spinning, crazy, swirling mass of field boundaries hurtling around like a kaleidoscope. Round and round, larger and larger detail evident in the blur, it seemed to take an eternity. For a fragment of a millisecond the last thing Euker ever saw were blades of grass pressed up against the armoured glass cockpit split screen panels. Then, as the breech mechanism of one of the forward mounted MG15 machine guns was smashed into his abdomen, his life was extinguished in a mass of flame and buckling metal.

Upon impact, the engines had been under full power, the propeller blades contorted and twisted violently as they were rammed into the flinty soil. The layered radiators were compressed flat, the engine casings fractured and broke apart, as rotating gears and moving valves were crunched to an immediate halt. The weight of the engines and mainframe dragged this mass of compacted wreckage, and fragmentary remains of some of the crew down to a depth of eighteen feet into the ground.

On 26th August 1940, at around three o'clock in the afternoon, Archie Klake had been slowly walking down to the post office, when he noticed that all the pheasants in the surrounding woods and copses were calling excitedly. His family had been in these parts for the best part of three hundred years now, and Archie understood the ways of the countryside. This familiarity was one of the reasons why, for the last hundred years or so, his family had provided many of the estate's game keepers. Normally such calls herald the presence of a fox in the locality, or even a distant thunderstorm, but the skies were pretty much clear, just a few wisps of cloud here and these loud calls had to mean more than just a fox.

Archie stopped for a moment, surely that was a very distant series of explosions he thought, having heard similar himself twenty three years before. Gradually, something else could then be heard above the pheasant's cacophony, the distant sounds of aero engines and then machine gun fire. The noise was getting louder, filling the sky and Archie thought he spotted an aeroplane diving down behind the tall trees over near Masons Farm. 'Crikey! Summit serious is goin' on!' he said to himself.

114

Suddenly a group of Wood Pigeons burst out from the upper branches of an elm tree just in front of him. It was then he saw it, a German Messerschmitt 110, flying at great speed and appearing to weave from side to side as it hurtled towards the village. As it shot over his head the black crosses were clearly visible on its blue-painted undersides. Moments before, Archie saw that it had a red and white painted shark's mouth on its nose, and that had sent a shudder down his back. It looked ferocious, angry and very aggressive. The enemy machine tore over the rooftops, then a sudden burst of machine gun fire made Archie hurl himself to the ground, and he wasn't exactly a young sprightly man either.

Wrapping his hands over his head, he glimpsed upwards and saw a Hurricane in hot pursuit of the raider. Brass shell casings clattered down over the road surface and rooftops as the Hurricane gave the

The author visited Melton Briarsville in 1986 where Archie Klake still lived and who drew the above sketch from memory of this incident
(Courtesy of A. Klake via the author)

fleeting enemy another good long burst of gun fire. Then they had both gone, the sound of aero engines diminishing into the background. For a while only the sounds of the disturbed pheasants could be heard again. The Second World War had arrived at Melton Briarsville, and had actually caused its first recorded damage. One of the pursuing RAF Hurricane's 0.303 bullets had struck the gilded cockerel on top of the church tower, the very same cockerel that had taken a storm related skydive back in 1810. Even today if you use a pair of binoculars and look at the lower part of the cockerel's neck you can quite clearly see the neat round bullet hole that still exists.

However, before the lumbering badgers had emerged from Bennett's Copse that evening, war time- related events and damage would have visited this small village in a much greater capacity. Most of the villagers had of course been politically aware of what was going on in the World in the late 1930's, but in April 1938 they had still launched a petition when the lorries of the construction firm Sanders and Gray Ltd had first been seen. These heavy vehicles trundled through the village commencing work some four miles away on a new aerodrome adjacent to the neighbouring village of Bourton.

When asked individually, not many even knew why they had signed the anti development petition? Perhaps it was just that it seemed to be an indicator that the World was once again preparing itself for conflict, and they were frightened. If the airfield was built somewhere else they could carry on convincing themselves that the politicians would sort it all out and there would be peace, instead of dreaded war again. When the seemingly inevitable war finally came, much pub gossip that had originally fuelled the petition was now concerned about the possibility of a nearby airfield attracting unwanted enemy attention to the whole area? The villagers clearly thought this would be the case, and they would soon be seen to have been very accurate as regarded that opinion.

It would be just forty five minutes after Archie had flung himself to the floor that once again distant explosions began to be heard, but these ones were getting louder and louder. Thick black swirling clouds of smoke were visible from Water End, a few miles away, and then they were seen. A large straggling formation of enemy bombers. 'They're going for the airfield.' said Mrs. Flemmings, staring open mouthed. Some cheers went up, though, when it was seen several determined RAF Hurricanes were heading straight into them, looking like those annoying wasps around a pint of cider. Moments later, the Camdown Anti Aircraft gun battery opened up, and the sky around the raiders went all spotty, with black and brown bursts of flak. 'I thought those guns were supposed to give our fighters clearance? Or is it the other way round?' someone queried.

Many villagers came out and watched from the 'security' of their gardens, whilst some ushered children indoors with a flick of a dishcloth, and hurriedly slammed the front door. Being so close to the airfield, now under attack, it was surely inevitable that the odd bomb would be dropped around the village? This was soon confirmed when the first German SC50 bomb fell, and exploded, at the far corner of Simpsons Meadow. And then more strung along, blasting apart a stone cow trough, the last one stopping just short of the Vicarage.

Amidst all the smoke, noise and confusion a German Dornier 17z bomber could be seen, obviously in trouble with three Hurricanes and a single Spitfire behind it. 'Bloody hell! Look at that. It looks like they are almost queuing up to have a squirt at the old Hun plane?' someone shouted out.

The Dornier's starboard engine was already a mass of flame and it was flying at a very odd angle, leaving a long smoke trail. Just then, a parachute canopy blossomed out, but it got snagged on the twin tail fins and burst into flames. The man attached was frantically kicking and waving his arms about, as he too caught fire. Then another parachute partially opened out but, strangely, nobody was attached to it. It too could be seen to be burning, and was drifting and flopping around the sky like a burning tissue. Two small dark objects could be seen falling away from the plane, they tumbled over and over.

Mrs Mace and her daughter, Edith, had been watching the whole event, but now she shielded her daughter's eyes with a chubby hand.

The two falling objects got closer and it was soon clear they were actually men; their parachutes appeared not to be functioning, or were perhaps damaged, and now streamed out, fluttering and flapping behind them. One of the men could be heard to be screaming 'Mutti! Mutti! Mutti!' as he fell, but then both were lost to sight behind some trees.

Edith, who had indeed squinted sideways, and through her mother's 'sausage-like fingers', could just about see the nearest airman. She would never forget that sight. Here was this man falling from the sky with his flailing arms and kicking legs. It seemed to her like he was almost trying to swim in the sky.

The disabled Dornier 17 descended, making a dreadful shrieking whine, until it seemed to level out. Swaying and wobbling from side to side, it was now almost totally covered in flames. And yet another tiny dark object was then seen to fall away from the flaming mass. As it did, a parachute canopy billowed out above. Then, 'Oh, thank God! At least one of them has got out alive!' was heard. Everyone looked around, but no one was quite sure who had said this. Although it was noted that Mrs Mace was now looking sternly at Edith, who had a very red face all of a sudden.

The Dornier now seemed to be gaining altitude as it shot across the meadows. But not quite enough, though, as it cannoned head-long into a mature oak tree just beside some stables, and then exploded violently in a field named Great High Pasture. The parachute of the only man to vacate the doomed bomber, and survive, was also badly damaged by fire and consequently this airman hit the ground very hard at some speed. He was later found still alive, and it was Fred Regis, of the Home Guard, and farmer, Stanley Hawkes, who had the honour of 'arresting' Feldwebel Artur Puleka, of the German Air Force.

Puleka had been the observer on board the Dornier and was so terrified that he had left it until very late to bail out. They took him up to Stanley's farm and there gave him a cup of tea, three woodbine cigarettes and a slice of bread and margarine. Then Stanley telephoned Colonel Mackey who, despite being retired, and a civilian, had recently been put in charge of the local Home Guard platoon. Puleka whose spoken English was quite good, then presented Stanley with his gravity knife and also tore off one of his tunic shoulder epaulettes, which was duly given to Fred.

This was not the first German manufactured item that had been donated to Stanley Hawkes in recent times. Incredibly, a few months earlier, a German bomber had circled round and actually thrown out some chocolate bars. Several bars had split open on impact with the ground, but this was chocolate and it was bloody scarce stuff, so Stanley had collected it all, every single scrap and broken foil-covered square he could find in the grass; even including the one bar that he found stuck upright in a large fresh horse turd.

Feeling guilty at first, he had hidden it all in a barn. His wife mentioned how she longed for some real chocolate, and went on and on about it. He wondered if she secretly knew of his discovery and was testing his honesty. Eventually, he could resist no more and finally gave her some of the chocolate, confessing that he had found it in the fields, and seriously stating she mustn't tell a soul. However, his sharp-eyed youngest son nearly caused a riot when he was heard telling everyone at school that 'Dad's got some Jerry chocolate in the last few weeks.' Of course no one really believed him. How could Stanley Hawkes get hold of any chocolate, let alone German chocolate? This 'enemy product' was summarised, some might say rather ungratefully, by Mrs Hawkes to Stanley a short while afterwards as 'being vastly inferior to Cadbury's, which doesn't have such a horse-like aroma!' Stanley Hawkes thought it best to simply agree with her, without going into too much detail.

For years Stanley treasured the gravity knife given to him by Puleka, and used it almost every day. Until one chilly September morning in 1966, he was cutting some twine and must have lost, or mislaid, it. He looked everywhere, but the knife never did show up.

Soon after the Dornier's crash, an old and rather battered Morris car, driven by two men from the local Anti Aircraft Unit, came to collect the somewhat frightened, and still very shaken, Feldwebel Puleka. As the little car departed and crunched down the flinty track-way,

Stanley looked out of the window, and then down at the knife and thought to himself, that German didn't seem such a bad lad. Bloody shame we have to be at war. Still, there you go, there's work to be done, war or not.

Sadly, a total of five horses had perished in the fire, which had spread rapidly from the wrecked Dornier to their straw-filled stable buildings. The local police constable, PC Valentine Dimmock, would recall afterwards: 'Their roasted bodies had inflated like dark crusty balloons and, to be honest, smelt almost good enough to eat. But I'm no Frenchman, of course.'

Later, PC Dimmock, with the acrid stench of roast horse flesh still lingering in his nostrils, began following up the eye-witness accounts of objects seen falling from the doomed aircraft. He went down to the meadow, and through the thin belt of poplar trees at the far end. Just as he was negotiating a rusty strand of barbed wire, a horrific sight greeted him. Two German airmen had impacted the meadow, clearly without their parachutes. One lay as if asleep, and PC Dimmock thought how peaceful the young lad looked. The other body had been decapitated, and was in a much more distorted position, with one leg bent right up under the man's body. "Oh Christ! No!' said the middle-aged Policeman, after he had initially noticed a billowing silken parachute canopy at the top of a tree.

He had also seen something else. There high up against a section of freshly shattered branches in the same poplar tree, was a man's head, with a shock of brown hair flopped down over its eyes. Some buggers going to have to get that down, he thought, and at my age, it won't be me!

As if all this wasn't enough to take into account, more German engines could now be heard in the district. This time it was a solitary Junkers 88 that also came pelting down the valley, chased by a single Spitfire. Its starboard undercarriage was already down, but the port engine was making a harsh grating noise and emitting a thin stream of orange flames and pale whitish smoke. The enemy aircraft reared up over some oak trees and impacted the side of a gentle slope leading down to the river valley, over on Fordham's Farm. It bounced gently at first and slid along the grass, swinging round on its single main wheel and tyre, until it briefly faced the way it had came. The aircraft carried on slewing sideways as it went through a wooden-posted fence, and straight into a field of wheat sheaves. These were tossed around and broken up by the flailing propeller blades, with many of them catching fire in the wake of the passing aircraft.

The Melton Briarsville Home Guard had all been watching this one and decided 'this Jerry was theirs'. As some of them later recounted, 'We weren't missing this one. Our first chance to get to grips with the Hun, or so we thought?'

Some of the Home Guard men were running, but some were simply too old to be so physical. But eventually they all met up and went down the lane and assembled by the stile. There, some two hundred and fifty metres away, lay a fairly intact example of the Luftwaffe's Junkers 88 bomber, with only a faint wisp of smoke gently spiralling upwards from one engine to indicate any damage. Otherwise, it looked to be in good condition. Oh, there would be a few pints to be drunk down the Waggoner's tonight! Cyril even pondered the local newspaper, 'Home Guard capture intact enemy machine!'.

'Looks like a bloody old Junker, or summit, to me? Like the one on our identification poster in the hall.' said Bert.

'Nope. Most likely a Heinkel bomber?' perked up someone else.

'Bloody hell! Look! Now there's a Jerry for real!' said Cyril.

As they watched amidst the swirling smoke, the bombers shattered rear cockpit canopy was noisily lifted up and three men clambered out, lifting up an obviously wounded colleague. 'That's a Junkers 88 - not a Heinkel! Look at the tail!' someone then said.

No sooner had that correct observation been stated than a terrific explosion, with a blinding white and violet-edged, circular-shaped, centre seemed to originate from the downed aircraft. The Home Guardsmen were instantly flung over by the huge blast wave that followed, which also removed all the leaves from a section of the hedge, and all the nearby trees. The entire bomb load had just exploded, rendering this Jerry to a somewhat unavailable condition to these Home Guard men. It also instantly shredded Cyril's imagined newspaper headline.

For years afterwards they would recount to all and sundry the day they nearly captured a Jerry bomber 'until the bugger went and blew up on us!' As a result of which, the Junkers 88 and its crew were scattered far and wide. However, it could be said that this section of the Home Guard did still get to grips with their German adversaries. Cyril's cousin, Albert, later found a Luger pistol still in its holster, which was attached to half a burned leather belt, a ripped pair of trousers and two separate flying boots from the area around Broadmeads Copse. The

The Swallows nest complete with three eggs on the Junkers 88 propeller blade. Fordhams Farm summer 2010 (via author)

shiny black leather boots were in very good condition, apart from the fact that one still retained the foot of its previous owner.

Two years later, in September 1942, a farm worker was repairing an old barbed wire fence some two hundred metres away from where the Junkers 88 had exploded and spotted something hidden beneath the rusted and broken wires. Clearing away the long dry grasses further, he struggled, but finally managed to pull out, a rather twisted and contorted propeller blade – complete with three bullet holes near its tip. This heavy item was destined to remain by the hedge for another year or so until it was finally taken and hung up in one of the farm barns where it can still be seen today. A tangible reminder of one of Melton Briarsville's, certainly more hectic, historical periods. Every year a pair of swallows, or at least their offspring, have migrated thousands of miles from Africa and repaired their little mud bubble crescent shaped nest delicately balanced on the front of this blade.

The current farmer quite enjoys the irony that so much new life has been created using this artefact which, as he says, was 'part of something made for death and destruction.' Many local people, even the younger ones, still refer to this field as 'bomber field' or 'Jerry Meadow'. Although those locals who know exactly why the field has earned these strange names are getting fewer and fewer these days.

Just minutes after this aeroplane had exploded yet another enemy aircraft, with its throbbing and droning engines, could be heard approaching the area. Then it too was seen right over the back and quite high up, but getting ever closer. It was another Junkers 88 that came across from a totally different direction to the other raiders. Once again, it too was obviously in trouble, and then it simply plummeted out the sky in a near vertical position. As it screamed down, part of its port wing tip folded upwards and then totally detached, fluttering away to land further down the valley somewhere. The sudden loss of aerodynamics immediately sent what remained of the aircraft into an uneven rocking motion, which then caused the entire tail section to break off.

Now looking more like some type of daytime celestial comet, the enemy plane smashed into the ground and exploded in the large field, rather inappropriately known as 'Four Acres', on Fordham's Farm, slightly to the west of the village. This farm had just experienced two Junkers 88 crashes on it in almost as many minutes!

Upon examination, the crater from the impacting aeroplane was found to be almost thirty feet across. Very little wreckage could be seen above ground. Of the crew, there was even less evidence. Down amongst the torn earthy surface of the still-smoking crater could be seen hundreds of small pieces of shredded metal and several larger sections of contorted airframe. Firstly, Bert and his colleagues, and later, PC Dimmock, made some attempts to look for any traces of the crew. Confirmation that at least one crew member had gone in with the plane came in the form of a severed finger and several small pieces of blood spattered skull, one of which even retained some traces of ginger hair. No other bodies were found in the vicinity, so it was logically assumed no one got out, and that they were all still somewhere in the crater.

The battered tail section of the aircraft had tumbled down and smashed to earth in the churchyard. The Home Guard had quite a time stopping local children from clambering all over it. There was a large white-painted swastika on both sides of the vertical stabiliser. One of these had several bullet holes in it, which certainly caused some interest. Before it was removed, Archie Klake managed to discreetly take a photograph of one of the Home Guard men standing on it, pointing at the bullet holes. Due to the wartime restrictions he knew he shouldn't have taken the photo and had to wait until 1946 to finally attempt to have the film developed. When it was, it could be seen that the cellulose in the film must have decayed years before, as not one photograph could be obtained from it.

The Human finger also caused some curiosity. The nail was neither bruised, nor had any blood on it. Strangely, it had been coloured with red nail varnish? This gave rise to a local rumour that the Germans had women flying in their aircrews. This fact in turn gave rise to another consideration: that perhaps they were very short of suitable men to fly their planes? Perhaps Hitler and his armed forces weren't such a mighty power after all?

Afterwards it was definitely confirmed that none of the crew had managed to bail out. Would any attempt at recovery of the bodies be made? was then the question. Cyril voiced his opinion by saying: 'Let the bastards stay down there!'. This statement was largely influenced by Cyril having lost an older brother in the trenches near Passchendaele. With the wartime authorities too busy for such recoveries, especially enemy ones, little further consideration given. Leaving the dead Germans down there was exactly what happened. 'Why make an effort to recover the bloody enemy? The buggers were bombing us!' was the general voiced opinion nationally. This same opinion was largely reflected around the village.

As with all aircraft crashes, it wasn't too long before an RAF crash recovery team arrived in Melton Briarsville. Over a period of a few days they managed to collect up all the scattered debris they could find from the Junkers whose bomb load had exploded. The Dornier 17 was much the same. The battered Bramo Fafnir engines, with their twisted propeller blades and about fourteen feet of one wingtip was all that remained recognisable as having once been an aeroplane. The rest was just evident as widely scattered, twisted fragments and globules of cooled-down, once-molten aluminium alloy.

For many years afterwards it was rumoured that a village boy had found one of the battered tail fins from the Dornier. Apparently later using his trophy as part of the roof for a secret den he had constructed in Beggars Wood. Other village lads scoured the wood but found nothing. Actually the rumour is in part quite true, for eighty year-old Ernest Hargreaves still has his trophy; he'd only hidden it in Beggars Wood temporarily. Today it forms part of a rabbit hutch in his garden. Perhaps yet another good use for part of a vanquished enemy bomber. But one thing is certain for sure, and that's that, even today, Ernest will not part with his trophy, whatever incentives have been, or will, be offered by interested parties.

As for the other Junkers 88, that had been seen to crash after diving vertically to the ground? Well, that was a pretty poor show for the RAF recovery team also. All that remained was a huge crater, whose edges were made of churned up chalk and chunks of soil and turf covered in shredded bits of metal with a single perfectly straight propeller blade pointing upwards, like an accusing finger at the sky from whence it came. A hot metallic smell arose from the crater and it was clear larger objects were deeply buried here. In fact, for several hours afterwards, one of the buried Junkers Jumo engines could be heard creaking and hissing as it cooled down. The rich and heady smell of aviation fuel also pervaded the air. A few of the Home Guard had to be asked repeatedly to smoke their cigarettes well away from this area.

This day had been one of catastrophic attrition overall for the Luftwaffe in making their daring daylight raids on airfields, and other targets. The Hurricanes and Spitfires, from many squadrons, had really been able to get to grips with them. Many a family in the German Fatherland would, over the next few days, receive either a knock on the door or a brief and rather heartless-styled telegram informing them of a loved one who was either missing, or believed killed, from amongst those aircrews taking part in the raids of the 26th August 1940.

Just such a knock was received on the front door of 21 Humboldtstrasse, in Lubeck. The door knocker in this instance was Emil Wielker, the Staffel Kapitan from a reconnaissance unit. He had made two similar visits to relatives of his men in the last three weeks alone. But this one was different. He knew this young lady personally, and had even admired her from some acceptable distance. The young lady who opened the door to him had only been married for six months. It would be very hard for him to have to tell Magdalene Euker that her husband, Waldemar, had been reported missing. When the door opened the serious look on his face was immediately, but briefly, mirrored onto her own and then she burst into floods of tears.

Emil longed to tell her other factors, but he couldn't. There was the account from the crew of a badly damaged Kampfgeschwader 2 Dornier 17, that had bombed Debden, which included their seeing a possible reconnaissance staffel-coded Junkers 88 crash into the Channel. The thirty year old Staffel Kapitan did not tell Magdalene this; it was not allowed, and may after all not have been accurate, or indeed relate at all to Waldemar's crew. But the real reason, as to why he didn't say this was because it would have destroyed all the hope she may have that her husband had somehow survived? He knew all too well that hope is a powerful and necessary thing in times of sadness or disaster. Perhaps if had he told her she would still have hoped? But there was no way that he was going to make that decision for her. There would be time enough for the truth to slowly dawn that she would never again see her husband.

Three days later, Magdalene Euker received a large brown package containing Waldemar's uniforms, and some documents. Two days after this she miscarried a tiny stillborn child, which the doctor, after some confrontation, finally confirmed to her had been a little boy. Weeks later, amongst the documents she found some drawings of things that had Latin writing on them, along with translations and a selection of photographs, mainly of Waldemar and his crew all standing so proudly by their Junkers 88 aeroplane. Two of the photographs were clearly official ones, taken over England. Magdalene wondered if they had been packed in here by accident? Deciding to keep Waldemar's flight book and his uniforms, Magdalene eventually gave the remaining documents and photographs to Waldemar's older brother, Konrad, so that the Euker family would also have some mementoes of their son and brother. She had at first wanted to keep every single item associated with her beloved Waldemar, but sometime later she realised that his family were grieving too, and felt it was only right to pass some items on to them.

Meanwhile, at Melton Briarsville not everything concerning the missing Junkers crew would stay unaccounted for. Unknown to his colleagues, early in the evening Cyril had gone back to the crash site and found another finger, along with the twisted centre section from an Iron Cross. He kept both souvenirs in a battered old Swan Vesta box, and never mentioned them to anyone. When he died in the spring of 1986 the Swan Vesta box was discovered, opened, and it's still-obvious contents were rather hastily burned in the garden, along with Cyril's copious quantity of newspapers. For some reason he had saved every single issue of the Daily Mirror since 1929?

The violent effects of the German aircraft that had crashed around the village would carry on for some three weeks afterwards. A violence that would still damage property, and also had a profoundly stinging effect on the back sides of two boys. For it was around three weeks later, Tommy Warner and his much younger brother Keith, crept into their fathers garden shed. They were on a mission.

Clutched in their hands were several, very much live, rounds of German 7.92mm ammunition that they had collected from one of the aircraft crash sites. Later one of these bullets, now positioned tip downwards, was being securely clenched in the teeth of a vice, as Tommy repeatedly turned, pulled up and dropped the tightening lever with a series of clanking sounds. Now, enthusiastically egged on by Keith, Tommy stood above it holding a nail to the detonator and gripping his father's biggest hammer.

Normally, this often-practiced school boy prank was relatively harmless. However, in this instance the two lads had not been aware that they should have removed the actual bullet tip. Striking the nail there was a god almighty bang and flash, and with that, the hammer flew backwards out of Tommy's hand, through the air and just past Keith's head. The boys rapidly vacated the small wooden shed, that was now filling with thick white smoke, partly from the detonated shell case, but mostly due to the smouldering, fizzling, incendiary bullet that had ricocheted around, and was now fiercely burning amongst the dust and debris of one corner. The entire shed was soon ablaze, the fire went on to consume both Dad's favourite lawnmower and his bicycle. The next associated incident, they both recalled to schoolmates, was shortly afterwards. Being in their living room, both draped over an old paisley-covered armchair, and then looking backwards to see their father removing his belt. Followed by the words: 'I'll teach yers, yer pair of bloody idiots! Yer could have killed yer bleedin' selves!'

When the wreckage, and remains, of the Junkers 88 and its crew had smashed into the ground in Four Acres field they were not the only things to break apart. Roughly two feet down, buried in the chalky clay, a large orange-coloured tile was also smashed apart by the impact of the bomber. One section from this broken tile was ploughed up sometime later from the area where the Junkers 88 had crashed. The ploughman, Bertie Edens, amidst a flurry of black headed gulls, could see from his steel tractor seat a piece of tile that had had strange markings on it. He stopped the engine and jumped down, picked it up and placed it in the tool container, thinking he had seen something similar before, many years before.

Eventually, he passed his find to Millicent Klake, who still worked as the part-time curator of the museum's collection. Millicent confirmed that she, too, distinctly remembered seeing something similar. 'And I know exactly where!' she slowly, and rather thoughtfully, said. 'It was on that tile that went to Germany. You know, the one with all the other things that mysteriously never came back, and now of course never will'.

Something about this latest artefact sort of represented replacement for the earlier loss, as well as curiosity for Millicent, and she liked that. So the tile fragment was duly cleaned and placed with the other Roman period objects in her museum display which had been slowly recovering.

Of the thirteen Luftwaffe airmen who had been in the aircraft, which had crashed in the vicinity of Melton Briarsville that day in August 1940, only one had survived. That was Feldwebel Artur Puleka. He would go on to spend a further six years in captivity, mainly in Canada, before finally seeing his wife and daughter again on the 26th August 1947. Exactly seven years to the very day he had jumped out of the blazing Dornier 17 over Melton Briarsville. Artur Puleka would live for another twenty eight years, eventually passing away, rather prematurely, in 1975 from the results of a failed duodenal cancer operation.

Over the years he had tried to make contact with farmer, Stanley Hawkes, on three separate occasions. The first being in 1954, when he wrote a letter, though he never received any reply. He would go on to write another two letters, but still never received any response. This was not due to any ill-feeling on Stanley's behalf, it was on that of somebody else's. Colin Prendergast had taken over the position of Postman from old Charlie Mayes in 1953 and, unfortunately, was not adverse to stealing the occasional item of mail, be it an important-looking letter or even better a birthday card that might contain a bit of cash.

One day Colin had noticed a foreign letter in the pile. Extracting it later on, he saw from the postmark that it had been sent from Germany. 'Well, that's not going where it should do for starters.' he muttered, as he folded and then stuffed the envelope deep into his pocket. He later burned it in his garden, and would go on stealing, as well as burning, another two letters sent from Germany some years later. Anything to do with Germans, or their country, was still despised by Colin; as he often said; 'The bastards killed my good friend, and second cousin, Tommy Warner, back in 1944, during the last war.'

Today, accompanying a hand-written eye-witness account of the incident by Stanley Hawkes, the faded shoulder epaulette of Artur Puleka can still be seen in the village museum. It was donated by the Regis family, who later emigrated to Australia in the 1950's. Of the other German airmen, who were all killed on 26th August 1940, all but one still reside in the village churchyard. This in itself is quite unusual, as most deceased German airmen were later exhumed from where they lay in the early 1960's, and reinterred at Cannock Chase, within the large communal German cemetery. Unteroffizier Sigmund Prentz, the radio operator from the Dornier 17, was, and is, the only airman from these incidents whose family requested for his remains to be repatriated to Germany in 1948, and this was duly done. The pitiful remains, gathered from the Junkers 88 that dived straight into the ground, were all buried in a communal grave with a headstone that simply read: 'Four unknown German airmen. 26.8.40.'

The ravages of the Second World War were never to visit the village again on the levels of ferocity that they had witnessed on August 26th 1940. Of course, with Bourton airfield only a few miles away, from 1940 onwards, most of the crashes and belly landings related to the Wellington bombers that were then based there, although none were fortunately that close to Melton Briarsville. Older residents still recall the 'False Sunset' that was evident to the north in November 1940, caused when the midlands town of Coventry was heavily blitzed. Once again, this had caused all the pheasants to start calling in the nearby woodlands. They called again shortly afterwards for a long period, as a series of unusual sunsets to the south east happened. This time it was London getting it; the so-called Blitz had started.

One night in 1941, the uneven throaty characteristic sound of a German aircraft could once again be heard intruding into the skies overhead; most likely a Junkers 88 C night fighter. For about three weeks it occasionally returned to the area and frequently circled the village and, on one occasion, dropped some bright white flares. One might say, rather a far cry from the chocolate bars, previously dropped over the village a year or so before. In the period that it was heard flying around, an RAF Wellington Mk1 bomber was actually shot down as it attempted to land at Bourton. All of its Canadian crew were killed in the crash. Occasionally, from then on, very high up in the night sky the dull throb of a passing enemy Heinkel 111 could be heard. And on one occasion, a string of incendiary bombs fell across the lower levels of Four Acres field, some distance from the village.

From mid 1943 there were some American officers billeted up at the Melanby's Manor house, the USAAF had now taken over control of Bourton from the RAF, and later on had installed their new P51 Mustang fighters down there. These American pilots were great fun, the children in the village could always guarantee a 'Bar of candy', or some 'Gum Chum'. And of course there were all the other fraternisations occurring in the stresses of wartime; some of which undoubtedly were linked to the birth of at least two illegitimate children in the village.

A decade before, this would have been unforgiveable, but now, although still an embarrassment to some families, the village rallied around to help. The arrival of June 1944 brought with it the great relief that the Allies had at last landed in France. But once again, there would be an element of sadness. On June 5th a small spider had begun to make a web across a place of seemingly good opportunity, a small round hole in one of the leaden panes of glass, forming the main window of the church. The web took ages to complete, and it still wasn't finished when the following mornings dew drops were swinging from it like tiny jewels. From the early morning that day the villagers noticed that the sky was absolutely full of aircraft. The ceaseless droning indicated that something big was definitely going on? Finally, by the afternoon the delicate web was near completion. Mr Pateman, the Church Warden, had previously brushed away this spider's, and undoubtedly its relatives, efforts on many an occasion before. However finally seeing the tiny creature's sheer determination, on this occasion he had allowed it to continue. For some reason it made him feel good. It was, after all, one of God's creatures, even if inconvenient, he thought. When the last silken thread was in place, both the completed web, and its tiny maker, seemed to shudder, as if in a draught. Mr Pateman noted the movement as he watched it having finally completed its task. Around the time of the moment that final thread had been joined, some hundreds of miles away on Sword Beach in Normandy many British soldiers were being killed. But only one of them had died at exactly the same time as the completion of this delicate structure and that was sadly a young Private born and bred in Melton Brirsville by the name of Tommy Warner.

However, June 1944 brought the enemy back, once again, to the skies over the village. On a fairly light summers night the sound of unfamiliar aero engines could be heard, and three fast-flying raiders raced over the rooftops. They were Messerschmitt 410's and were operating as intruders and fast attack bombers. Moment's later, three small bombs exploded on the edge of Bourton airfield. A passing Halifax bomber, attempting to land there, had a rather narrow, and very lucky escape, with a total of nine 20mm cannon shells hitting its fuselage.

Enemy activity finally petered out in this area in late 1944. Firstly there was an air-launched V1 Doodlebug that came to earth and exploded during the night, approximately two and a half miles away. The blast dislodged some tiles from the church spire at Melton Briarsville, and caused the ever suffering weather vane cockerel to spin round wildly once again. The second event, which really was the very last time wartime German wartime products would pay a visit to the area, involved a V2 rocket. This broke up, spectacularly, above the village one Thursday morning in November 1944. The aerial explosion had appeared like some huge jellyfish suspended in the sky, as hundreds of burning components fell, leaving trails of smoke behind them. The fields surrounding the village were full of bits of 'rocket'. The huge venturi outlet from the propulsion unit had been found hours later in a reed bed down alongside the river, still steaming. When it had smashed down hissing into the water it had killed an adult Moorhen, which when technically considered as the last victim of World War Two, and its effects, in this area.

The final wartime aerial incident occurred on 19th April 1945, when a P51 Mustang flew several circuits around the village. 'He came in really low on one pass and pranged his plane good and proper!' recalled Archie Klake. He was a lucky man indeed was 1st Lt Sefton Schaedel, the pilot. His propeller tips had clipped the ground and swung the little fighter right round. It spun across the field and fortunately came to a halt, more or less, in several large sections. Several villagers ran over and were in time to see a rather shaken Sefton Schaedel climb out of what was left of his cockpit and say: 'Jeez, folks, now that was some daisy cutting experience that was!'.

Little over two weeks later, the war in Europe was officially over. Soon the lanes and surrounding areas became much quieter as the Americans finally went home, leaving a few villagers treasuring their stockpiles of chewing gum and nylons. This war, like the last one, had arrived and was now over. But for every villager it had been a time, a massive event in their lives that would most certainly never be forgotten.

CHAPTER TEN

TWO MYSTERIOUS VISITORS

The year of 1945 was also a time for reflection. For the duration of the war, SS Obersturmfuhrer Bruno Prussmann had been involved in a wide variety of responsibilities whilst working for the Reich. For a short period he had been employed in a team that were cataloguing looted art works from various occupied countries. Then he had found himself more securely employed in the Rasse und Siedlungs Hauptamt (RuSHA) section of the SS. This was a section that was concerned with protecting the racial purity of the SS within Germany, and later extended its influence to the entire Reich. This had brought him into occasional contact with some very senior SS personnel, which wasn't exactly to Prussmann's liking at all. Such activities usually meant photographs being taken at high level functions, despite his moderate rank this was an activity that he felt threatened his own security.

Towards late 1943 he had concluded that the war was not going exactly as he, and many others, had originally assumed it would. Photographs were indisputable evidence that he was at a certain place at a certain time, with certain people. Making it potentially very problematic to deny knowledge of certain, as he put it, 'happenings in the Reich'.

Always cautious, Prussmann would hedge his bets. He would, where ever possible, adhere to the best opportunity of the moment, but had always analysed its implications. So far as he knew there were only two photographs in existence of him in uniform, and he had deliberately kept moving on one of them in order to blur his face. On the other, a saluting arm covered half his face. But one could never be totally certain, could never guarantee, that other images unknown to him were not in existence? He had also signed documents with a very erratic signature that, unusually, had no under-typed clarification of who this was. Truly, he was a clever man.

It had been Prussmann who had assisted with the overseeing of the construction of crematoria at Auschwitz, and who had earlier assisted with the implementation of carbon monoxide gas trials under SS Obersturmbannfuhrer Walther Rauff. Prussmann had also been heavily involved with supplying slave-labour workers to a variety of armaments concerns within the ever-expanding Reich. So astutely had he done such tasks, leaving no known identifiable trace of his involvements, surely he was safe?

Having had a pre-war interest in archaeology, he had worked closely with Professor Harald Seiffert on several archaeologically-based racial excavations, in the hope of providing data on the establishment of the Aryan race in Germany. In 1943 his colleague Seiffert had taken over control of an Einsatzgruppen Unit in the East. Having no time now for previous involvements, Seiffert had then handed Prussmann several confidential documents. These included Frederick Pearson's original notebook and the copies of all later research completed by Waldemar Euker. Amongst these donations was also the single Roman tile looted from Britain just before the war. For a brief period both men had discussed the notebook and its implications. Prussmann was fascinated and, like others before him, had read the contents over and over again.

By 1944, having always been careful to avoid promotions and attention were proving to have been the right decisions. Had he accepted what he was definitely entitled to, this would for certain now have found him in a position of some interest to the Allies. However, the Allies, even at this stage, already had several references to a certain Prussmann having worked in various SS offices, but had hardly any associated details pertaining to what he actually did?

Prussmann had always completed his projects keenly stating: 'It was an honour to work for the Reich, and needed no reward.' His seniors had keenly interpreted this as loyalty to the Reich, without the desire to seek personal gains, and were quite content to leave it at that. After the war he intended to sink quietly into obscurity and, if at all possible, eventually make his way to England and continue investigating what had then nearly become an obsession. He believed that this Waldemar Euker had indeed been on the verge of discovering something valuable, that could be a potential source of wealth and therefore it was quite natural that he, Bruno Prussmann, would at least be interested in such. He would not have minded being known for making such a discovery, that was a totally different issue. However, it would not be Bruno Prussmann that would be the name involved with that. It would be a Kurt Empfanger, as that was his new name, already arranged on his 'Post-War documents', as he referred to them.

Having been such a meticulous planner and given everything his utmost attention, Bruno Prussmann now considered it was almost providence that he would survive this war. On the 20th January 1945 he was once again poring over Euker's original notes, when the dreadful wailing whine of the air raid siren sounded off. 'These damned American raids are so numerous now. But I've been safe so far.' he considered, and then decided as usual to remain at his desk. Normally he would get up and watch the scurrying citizens below, but not today. He stood up and closed the slightly-open window to drown out the noise from the anxious bustling crowds in the streets below. The decision to remain there that day was indeed one that definitely merited more time in its making. Five minutes later the ornately patterned plaster work ceiling, exactly fourteen feet above him, cracked and then burst open like a giant chrysanthemum of dust. A fraction of a second later Prussmann saw a huge splinter-edged hole just appear on his highly polished mahogany desk top and that was the last thing he ever saw. What had wrecked his desk now impacted the hard marble floor beneath it. The huge USAAF 500lb bomb instantly exploded in a terrific magnesium-white flash and rush of an immense blast. Prussmann's body was never found, or at least anything substantial enough to merit the actions of a burial. The same blast also vaporized an example of ancient ceramics, the tile that Velas had so carefully made so long ago was turned to dust

Just thirty seconds after the salvo of bombs, which included the one that would kill Bruno Prussmann, left the bomb bay of the B17G bomber twelve thousand feet above the city, someone back in England was also to lose their life. A small rat-like featured man named Oliver Brillo died just as quickly as Prussmann would, as the thick braided noose tightened round his neck in Wandsworth Prison. He had been arrested five weeks before, at his home address in Bourton, Oxfordshire. Ironically, Prussmann had been extremely concerned for some time, as his most senior agent in Britain had mysteriously stopped transmitting his usual messages. Brillo's arrest, and later trial, as Britain's longest resident German spy was a shock to his fellow villagers, amongst whom he had been living for some twenty years. The explosion from this one 500lb bomb, and another that fell close by, demolished sixteen houses and sent some of the contents of Bruno Prussmann's office files over four hundred feet into the air. From here they fluttered down, dispersing for over a quarter of a mile around the adjacent suburbs. However, explosions can have strange traits. Though Prussmann's body was vaporised, paper in bulk, even when burning, has a strange tendency to survive such blast effects.

Being subjected to aerial bombardment had a wide variety of effects on many individuals. Seventy two hours after the raid a small dirty child, ferreting for clothing and scraps of food in amongst the rubble of a nearby bombed out street, had a very lucky day indeed. For he found a gold wristwatch blasted onto the side of a brick and, although damaged, it bore the inscription; 'To Bruno, from Mother and Father 1929'. The boy and his family would now eat for at least a week or two from selling the watch.

Later, Prussmann's secretary, Magdalene Triebel, could be seen almost daily gathering up as many notes from the ruined office, and surrounding streets, as she could. She was always fastidious in her nature and without her life being in order, and with no Prussmann and no responsibility, she attempted to re-create the filing system and bring back some organisation into the chaos. Amongst the masses of papers she had collected were several pages ,torn from the Pearson notebook. Back in her small flat the situation was now actually becoming a total reversal of what she was striving to achieve. Piles of paperwork were everywhere, each one topped with broken bricks and all manner of heavy objects being used to keep them steady. One tottering large pile was actually kept in place by a section of 500lb bomb nose cone she had picked this up in the street outside. Not knowing of course that it had originated from the very same bomb which, ironically, had caused so much to change in her normally organised life

One person who, unlike Prussmann, had not only desired to disappear, but subsequently did so very successfully in the chaos-ridden aftermath of post-war Germany, was SS Obersturmbannfuher Professor Harald Seiffert. It was rumoured that he had used an escape network and travelled down into Italy, staying for a while in a small coastal fishing village. Finally, with the help of a local Catholic priest who assisted with the provision of false paperwork, he had apparently been living in a safe house near the coast, awaiting a ship to take him to Chile. This had been the similar course of action for many of Seiffert's ex-colleagues, such as Adolf Eichmann and Dr Josef Mengele. However, unlike them, Seiffert eventually abandoned the entire system and its network. Thinking that the Allies would obviously be looking for him elsewhere, he decided to head straight back into Germany. This proved to be a very good move, and he eventually managed to open up a small chain of optical shops centred around Munich. This proved to be yet another fortuitous decision and was of such a profitable nature that Seiffert later sold the entire business to a large French optical manufacturer, who wanted an ready -established retail outlet in Germany. His wartime days now seemed very far off indeed.

In December 1947 the snow lay thick and crisply across much of Britain. A truly harsh winter had fallen across the country, and much of Europe. Melton Briarsville had been cut off for about two weeks, which was one of the occasional bad weather hazards of only being connected to the outside world by a series of deeply-sunken, and very ancient, lanes. Millicent Klake, though, had marvelled in the snow and the delights it had brought, spending much time observing the local wildlife. Everything now seemed so easy to see through her binoculars against the intense white back drop. On one such nature foray, after noting all the usual tracks, she spotted a flurry of feathers and several spots of fresh blood on the snow. Sparrowhawk? she guessed. Then a far more interesting flash of white and grey caught her eye a hundred feet or so down the hedge, through her binoculars she spotted something with which she was unfamiliar.

A large bird that looked like a small pale magpie had alighted on a hawthorn branch, creating a flurry of falling snow. 'What are you then?' Millicent said softly. The bird continued to observe Millicent as she watched, and then it flew off further down the hedge, sitting on another prominent small branch just above the hedge line. That evening sitting down by the fire Millicent consulted her bird spotting guides and at last could put a name to the strange bird; it was a Great Grey Shrike. A 'rare and exotic visitor from Europe', the books had said. Millicent, very lucky to see such a scarce bird, was enthralled. The shrike returned for several winters, and was seen by quite a few other people. But then it came no more. However, it was not to be the only unusual foreign visitor that would eventually find their way to the village in years to come.

It was in the Waggoner's Inn around or about the spring of 1967, locals still recall, that the tall well-educated man who always had a camera with him, had first been observed. He spoke with a distinct Bavarian accent and claimed he was very passionate about bird watching. However, his knowledge on this subject seemed somewhat limited, and somehow he always managed to get the conversation turned around to local archaeology. Sam Frost was suspicious about something. The man seemed strange, and he didn't think he knew anything about birds whatsoever? Sam had actually told the foreign visitor that he had just seen a Siberian Bluethroat in the churchyard, which resulted in no response at all. Sam knew that any birdwatcher worth his salt would want to see such a rare visitor; something just didn't seem right about this man.

The suspicious visitor had eventually departed from the village after staying in a small room at the Waggoner's Inn for some two and half weeks. A year or so laterm Simon Wiesenthal, the famous Nazi Hunter, had appeared on television and radio claiming that he had been successful in tracking down ex- SS Obersturmbannfuher Professor Harald Seiffert. The notorious Nazi had been living in Hamburg under the false name of Emil Broger, and even owned a small industrial works which manufactured chemicals for the petroleum refining business. When the newsflash covered the court prosecution case, several Melton Briarsville locals excitedly claimed that this was the very same man who had stayed at the Waggoner's Inn a year or so previously. Despite informing the local Police station of their experiences, no investigation ever resulted. What could such an undertaking really achieve? So it was never considered by anyone else further, or ever proven that former SS Obersturmbannfuhrer Heinrich Seiffert had ever visited Britain at all - let alone sipped a beer of two in the Waggoner's Inn at Melton Briarsville? But in fact, he had done just that.

About twelve years prior to what locals referred to for a while as 'The Seiffert Affair', another foreign visitor, a medium-built balding man, approximately in his early forties or so, was having a pint of Cranbourne Brewery bitter in the Waggoner's Inn. Apart from pulling a nose-wrinkling face when supping the area's finest ale, it was quite obvious to the locals that the man was foreign. Even without speaking, his mannerisms were clipped, and almost military. Sid Shreaves reckoned, 'It's another Jerry again! Them buggers, they are always snooping around our village. Remember them sods up at the villa dig those years back?'. Indeed it was true, this visitor's accent certainly did remind several locals of the German youths who had something to do with that archaeological dig on the Roman villa. The scars of the recent war were most definitely not yet healed in the village and consequently several locals had become rather hostile, and none too pleasant, to this lone man who had invaded their pub. George Stannish, the publican, whilst agreeing with what he calls 'his locals', would entertain no problems in his pub and had made this well known.

George was a master of social observation, and could tell when a conversation, or action, was heading too far and always nipped it in the bud with his 'OK lads, quieten down, or take it outside please'. But on this occasion it seemed to be more jeering, and the making of quiet, snide, comments that was happening. The man did ,at one time, actually say rather embarrassingly: 'Look, I'm very sorry if being German causes so much offence?'. Some regulars then took great delight in informing their visitor that the village took part in the destruction of three Jerry aeroplanes in last war. They rather over -optimistically claimed to have been a part of the actual demise of these aeroplanes, as opposed to more honestly just having been around when they crashed.

Apart from the occasional statement the foreign visitor seemed to be a quiet man. If anyone had cause to stand up and argue the point it was him. But no, he just remained, silent observing and occasionally making a comment. Eventually the locals involved gave up on baiting him. He just wouldn't respond.

Ironically, it could be said that Konrad Euker was rather like his dead brother on one issue, and that was that he, too, was on a reconnaissance mission. He had decided to pay a visit to Melton Briarsville to see what it was like. Being in possession of his dead brother's copied notes, he had of course read them many times over the years. Konrad had known his brother had been up to all sorts before, and during the war, but had never questioned Waldemar about anything. Asking questions, even from close family, back then could have been a rather dangerous affair. Konrad was basically just curious, he was certain his brother had a great interest connected with this village and of course he knew that this interest had been archaeologically-related. However, some of Waldemar's annotations indicated that there was something either buried, or positioned, near here that could be of great significance.

On other issues, it must be said Konrad wasn't like his brother at all. He had seen through the war as an auxiliary fireman, and his only action had been just two days before the war had ended. Konrad had spotted a Russian T34 tank that had just crushed a woman with a pram against a section of broken wall. It was now having problems traversing over a pile of shattered bricks and girders, so he had aimed and fired his newly issued Panzerfaust, and had scored a direct hit on the tank. He then ran off, looking back just the once, to see the whole turret of the tank being blown off and upwards. He also thought that in the flames, just for a split second, he had seen a burning body that was still moving.

Amongst the bullets and shell bursts, Konrad was damned lucky to get away from the scene at all. But he did, and not only that, he would go on to survive the war. After his tank-wrecking episode he packed a few belongings from his relatively undamaged house and went to stay with a distant cousin somewhere near Bremen. His trip to England was also to see, of course, if he could establish where his brother might possibly be buried, he had tried several methods of investigation.

Some months earlier he had received a letter from one of his brother's flying comrades suggesting he should also examine the possibility of Waldemar having been shot down into the channel, or perhaps the English were unable to identify his body? After one uneventful morning walking around, and being the recipient of the occasional 'Jerry-based' comment, Konrad found himself in the village graveyard. There were several military graves here, one to a very young soldier named Tommy Warner, killed in 1944. An isolated cluster of grave stones over at the back, that he saw, all related to German airmen. He was visibly moved when he saw the two single headstones with details including the words: 'Unknown' on them.

Bending down uncomfortably, he touched both headstones and thought how his brother Waldemar might also be officially unknown too? How ill-fated that would be, to have given your life and be unrecognised. Unhappily, Konrad finally returned to Germany, no closer to finding his missing brother, or to what that brother had thought so curious about the village of Melton Briarsville? Perhaps one day he would go back, maybe when things were all the more peaceful and settled?

Two decades later found Konrad attempting to supplement his meagre pension by trying to sell the same documents and photographs to a newspaper. The newspaper editor had responded with a letter to the effect that could see something of possible interest here, but Nazi treasure? Or whatever it may be, wasn't quite perhaps what they were

142

looking for just at that moment, or so the editor had indicated. As a result, Konrad decided that after all these years the issue just wasn't worth pursuing any longer, and he considered burning the documents and photographs to affect some sort of a closure on the whole thing. But he knew this would also permanently destroy the last links he had to his long lost brother Waldemar.

After a period, his neighbours had observed Konrad became unshaven and rather dishevelled in his appearance, and on some occasions had been verbally rude to them. These same neighbours later told the two policemen that this was 'so unlike him', as he had previously been such a kind man. But recently, he had also refused any assistance, or offers, to talk about his circumstances. Or any assistance that he might need? He had remained in his small flat for days without anyone seeing him, all his neighbours at this stage had long ceased to ask about or offer him help.

Finally one day, Frau Irma Schemmel, who lived next door with her husband and two children, had had quite enough. 'Bottles of rancid milk all over the landing! It's dangerous for the children. For some reason, he's simply not taking the bottles indoors. And then there's that awful smell?' she said.

The fact that the milk bottles, some forty in number, hadn't been collected was Konrad's fault. The strange, sweet, sickly odour that combined with the smell from the rotting milk, well that was also Konrad's fault too. When finally the police broke down his front door down they found that he had been dead for at least three weeks. His relatives later cleaned out and sold the flat, sharing out between themselves, or selling, all Konrad's other belongings. It was decided to retain some of his paperwork and also that of his brother, who had been killed in the last war. 'Who knows,' said one Konrad's relatives, 'one day someone might actually be interested in this sort of stuff?'

CHAPTER ELEVEN

IS IT VELA, OR VELAS?

One sunny weekday in September 2001 Kelly Morton, an agricultural student from Loughborough who was temporarily working at Fordham's Farm, ran into the village museum, very much out of breath. Kelly visiting the museum was not an unusual occurrence at all, as she seemed to be as passionate about history as she was agriculture. She was always popping in with Belemnite fossils and bits of this and that she had found out in the fields. But what was unusual this day was that she had run here from over quarter of a mile away. 'I was just ploughing up near to where the old Villa site is and my plough has just smashed a load of old pots, damn it! Looks definitely like they are Roman, and it's quite possible that I've just brought up some evidence of a small cemetery?' she gasped.

Kelly was only twenty years old and had been sent to Fordham's Farm to train as part of the personal experience section for her agricultural qualifications. After finishing the acreage that she had been asked to plough that morning, she was going to be assessed by her trainer, and seemed very excited about this. Having been lodging in the village for some seven months now, she was known for being polite, very helpful and was generally well liked by everyone she encountered. Kelly had gathered up as much of the broken urn fragments as she could find. In Kelly's opinion, many were quite well produced, but made of a well known local fabric, she delighted in telling everyone. However, there was one pot, she keenly pointed out, that was very different to all the others, as it had been rather finely decorated, and so stood out from the rest.

Sitting down on the freshly-ploughed soil, that now had that fresh earthy smell to it, Kelly had begun fitting the pieces together. Her attention focused on the different, cream-coloured, decorated urn fragments. Try as she might, she was now quite tired and decided, 'Nope, this is a job for the Museum.' Grabbing a carrier bag, and shaking out the strands of grated cheese, she literally filled it with all the pottery fragments she could find. At the museum a volunteer was tasked with seeing what Kelly had found and to assess whether some of it could be displayed.

Elderly Eric Parry was that volunteer, and also the conservator. Rather cringingly armed with a tube of superglue and charged with, when he had the time, reassembling all such finds. Despite his arthritic and trembling hands, old Eric managed in just over a week to re-assemble four bases from the grey ware urns, and a few other sections. He also separated what were clearly some small fragments of burned bone from amongst the pottery shards. Looks like Kelly could be right in saying they are cremations? he thought.

His final attempt was the coloured pottery fragments, that he had been saving for last; they looked more exciting as they were parts of a much larger cream-coloured urn. It was clearly evident that there was a lot of it still missing, but he did manage to re create pretty much three quarters of the vessel and, on one side, the decoration clearly showed the figure of a man feeding what appeared to be a young deer. Above this, in two inch-high letters, could be seen the letters 'VELA'.

When Kelly next visited, Eric proudly showed her the reconstruct-ed pottery. 'Tell you what, Kelly, why don't you ask that Jonathon man, you know, the metal detectorist around here, to have a look where you found all these? I bet there's some coins and things up there too?'

Eric noticed a brief flash of what looked like embarrassment on Kelly's pretty face. Unknown to Eric she had already met Jonathon some while back, and she didn't quite feel comfortable just yet in ask-ing him to look for coins. After all, that's exactly what he was doing when they had encountered each other previously.

The coloured urn was still very much incomplete, but where the letters ended only a small section was missing. Eric considered that there could possibly be space here for one more letter, given the size, unless of course 'VELA' was all that was present in the first place? 'Well blimey. You are something else, Kelly girl!' he said a few days later, as she handed him another two large pottery fragments, one of which was most definitely from the cream-coloured urn, and bore the letter "S" on it. It fitted perfectly: 'VELAS!' exclaimed Eric, who would later wonder 'Is this the name of a God, or some other local deity? I don't think so, I've never heard of one with a name like that, it's not a known inscription or common abbreviation for something that I can find, I wonder if it just might be the name of a person? Now that seems quite plausible to me".

CHAPTER TWELVE

JONATHAN PEARSON – METAL DETECTORIST

Just eighteen miles or so from the village of Melton Briarsville, Jonathan Pearson and his wife, Christine, were at last finally moving into the new house that they had bought in Charleston. It was May 1995 and they had always wanted to live here, and so had been saving for years. But with current house prices it seemed for ages that it would only ever be a dream. However, for both of them it was a dream that would be realised with the help of Jonathan's recent, rather well paid, promotion in IT communications, which now involved him working away in London. Charleston was also very convenient, in Jonathan's opinion, as it was also situated directly on the commuter link to the City, thus avoiding the dreadful urban drive from their previous address that he had so disliked, and which he knew had always been a concern for his wife.

Jonathan came from the large Pearson family, who were perhaps better known for being involved with 'Pearson's Bakeries of Cambridge Ltd', until fairly recently that is, when after ninety one years of family involvement, the entire company had been sold to a large supermarket chain. Not that any of that particularly concerned Jonathan however, as he had never been keen on the idea of bakery management. Despite mild family pressure to join the business he had decided otherwise, and had sought alternative employment elsewhere. Between them Jonathan and Christine had developed more than a passing interest in genealogy. In the last two years they had completed what was believed to be the most comprehensive, and largest, family trees that ever existed for both their families to date.

As always there were some inter-family disputes about certain things, such as birthdays, exact names and in Christine's case, amusingly, for Jonathan anyway, three queries as to legitimacy. Most of the Pearson genealogical issues on Jonathan's side were supplied, and corrected, for him by his Aunt Hilda. Jonathan had seen that amongst his many relatives was a Frederick Pearson ,who had been killed in World War One. Somewhere, vaguely, he remembered seeing a rather blurry sepia-toned photograph of this very same Frederick, but he could not recollect where? Most likely at his Aunt Hilda's, as she kept all sorts of similar things. Working in the city had certainly brought its benefits to the couple, but being born in the country, Jonathan often desired to spend as much time as he can out and about. Just like his great uncle, he too has long been interested in archaeology, militaria and ancient coins; in fact anything to do with history would attract his attention.

For many years, on and off, he had thought about 'giving that metal detecting thing a try after all', he thought, quite innocently . 'I could find my own things, and need not always go to museums. It must be great to touch and feel objects from all ages that can be identified?' However, like many things, the years flew past, and what with one thing and another, getting a detector just never seemed to happen. Recently, though, he had once again seriously started to think about metal detecting, and had at last decided that this time he was definitely going to give it a go and actually invest some hard-earned cash in a brand new detector.

Actually, the final decision and investment side of things, so to speak, were initially Christine's idea. She thought it would match up perfectly with Jonathon's outdoor activities and who knows, he might even one day find something of value or interest? So it was that Christine finally ordered a detector called a Minelab Musketeer, from a company down south called Joan Allen's. That name had amused Christine, as her research showed, she had a great aunt born in Poplars around 1893, and her name was also Joan Allen. She had no idea what it was all about but from the write-ups she had read through had at last concluded this model of metal detector looked the best. Of course there was small level of additional influence here, and that was something about the name 'Musketeer', which smacked of dedication, commitment and success, and that in turn had in some ways reminded her of Jonathan.

From the initial period of bursting open the packaging; Jonathan then spent quite some time asking for permission to search various areas around his home town. Most of the land, as the land owners informed him, already had people on it who detect, and they wouldn't like anyone else being there too, he had been told. Not put off at all, Jonathan was determined, and finally gained permission to search some meadowland and a small farm to the east of Charleston. It was on one of these meadows that he experienced the thrill of his first coin find. In his hand had lain a dark green glossy Victorian penny dated 1869.

Further searches introduced him to the Eley shot gun tip, and lead in the form of once-molten droplets and off-cuts in every shape and size. At this stage he was enthusiastically fired up with that beginner's eagerness, everything, no matter what, was true treasure to him. Christine had even found out that there was a local metal detecting club that he could join, and after a short wait he was able to join the Midlands Detector Researchers. Jonathan wasn't able to attend all their outings and meetings, but he found their experience and helpfulness really useful. After the Victorian penny, further coins would follow, but they were mostly corroded Georgian issues (dating from 1741 to 1807). But one Wednesday in April he had taken the day off work and headed out, driving off to the small farm.

He had the whole day ahead of him, de-bagging his detector and setting down his packed lunch beneath an ancient gnarled oak tree. Then he was quickly off detecting. Whilst searching alongside an old ditch later that day a loud and clear signal came from the Minelab Musketeer. Digging down very carefully, but excitedly, he saw a large uneven grey coloured disc in the dark sandy soil, stuck amongst the tangle of nettle roots. Thinking at first its irregular shape meant it cannot be a coin, he was very surprised, as well as delighted, to find that he was wrong. Wiping away the mud with care he saw a large horse and some lettering emerging. 'This is definitely something good!' he said out loud.

Unable to detect any more, he then walked back to the car at a rather brisk pace. Occasionally stopping, just to feel the reassuring shape of the coin in his pocket. When he arrived home he looked through his copy of Spinks coin book, and was delighted to discover that he had indeed found something good. It was a Charles 1st Half Crown, dating to 1642. This was one of those discoveries that Jonathan would never forget and, decades later, he would still recall every detail, as well as the excitement he had felt when making this find. However, as the years passed, his finds from the same old searched areas became fewer and fewer, something he always knew would happen. 'Well it has to, doesn't it? Laws of logic and statistics tell you that one,' he would say. 'There are, after all, only so many losses per search area.'

The dawn of the New Millenium would find Jonathan considering extending his permission-seeking ventures once again. He thought, what a great idea it would be to just see if he could get any land around the village of Melton Briarsville? This was the very village where his Great Uncle, Frederick, had once lived for a short period. Who knows, if he could find some old pennies around the actual house? Or if he could just locate where it was, or still is, then it's possible that his Great Uncle may once have actually touched them, and later probably lost them of course? Jonathan loved this sort of time line connection that can be made with the previous owners of coins and artefacts, especially the ones he finds.

He decided the best approach was to ask the land owners of the surrounding land. Then, if he wasn't lucky on that account, he would concentrate on getting permission from smaller local areas within the village itself, such as the gardens of any large houses, the village green, or maybe even the cricket pitch? He had a friend who had once found numerous Victorian and Edwardian silver coins on an old cricket pitch, but who had finally been very curtly asked to stop his activities. The reason being that some moles had also recently started to show an interest in the finely manicured grass of the pitch, and several players had suggested that the disturbed soil was due to metal detecting? And that was that.

'Perhaps I'll give the cricket pitch a miss for the time being?'

Jonathan considered. He just could not get the feelings of anticipation and excitement out of his mind. Just imagine finding something that once belonged to my great uncle, he thought. Just like his great uncle, it seemed to Jonathan that Melton Briarsville could be a very interesting pace to investigate. Reading the UK Guide to Metal Detecting Sites book, Jonathan had discovered that this village even had a local legend attached to it, concerning a battle that allegedly took place there in ancient times? That's even better, he had thought. All things aside, all he had to do now was get permission.

Although quite unlike his great uncle, Jonathan didn't suspect that there was ever anything particularly noteworthy about this village? To him it just seemed a very interesting place to visit, and hopefully metal detect around. Jonathan ended up being very fortunate indeed. After a long conversation he was finally given permission for the entire area surrounding the village by Craig Melanby. Who, along with his sister, Candice, now owned and farmed the entire estate. They had also po-litely notified all the tenant farmers on their land that they had given this permission, and had kindly arranged for Jonathan to actually meet them all. Provided of course it didn't interfere with any of their agri-cultural plans.

Craig very much enjoyed acting the traditional landowner and made it known that he wasn't really to be disturbed on matters relat-ing to Jonathan's searches, 'Unless of course, you find that pot of gold!" he had said. Jonathan was uncertain as to whether Craig was trying to be humorous here, or had been stating the obvious. At one time rather unnervingly for Jonathan, Craig had mentioned, 'Now don't you go bringing any ruddy archaeologist people, or that English Heritage lot up here with your finds, will you? A good friend of mine, over at Bourton, has a scheduled Saxon burial site, as well as a priory, on his property and has had enough trouble with: "you can't plough this! You can't do that! What are you doing to control, the moles and rabbits?"

Jonathan considered that, if ever applicable, and it was probably unlikely, then he would cross that bridge at the time. But he knew that should he find something significant he would, without question, inform the relevant people, no matter what results. Between them all they did, however, agree to drafting up a metal detecting contract. This stated that if Jonathan ever did discover a major find, and if any monies were payable as a reward, then fifty percent would go to the estate. Another twenty five per cent would go to Jonathan, and the final twenty five per cent to be divided between any charitable organisations that both parties elected to choose. It was also clearly verbally established that Jonathan must be the only detectorist to search this area. 'No friends at all, Jonathan. OK? I don't want armies of people treading all over the estate!' Craig had ordered.

'At last! I'm one of those detectorists who actually has some land like this!' Jonathon thought. He actually wouldn't have minded sharing this estate at all with other like-minded individuals, as it was huge. But it was clearly stressed that he must not invite, or have any guests detecting, and so that's the way it was. This was of course Craig's suggestion, and there was seemingly no doubt that he would be sticking wholeheartedly to it. I bet some of the people in my detecting club won't be happy about this? Jonathan thought, but then again, they must all have their own private non-club sites too?

Craig Melanby's sister, Candice, on the other hand was quite dismissive of her brother. 'Oh, don't get all tangled up in this and that. You go out there and enjoy yourself," she had said, further revealing, 'I once thought about getting a detector myself, but simply can't find the time these days. But how very fascinating it all is".

She also asked to be shown any finds of interest that were made and had enquired, 'Despite what Craig says, don't you have to report them, or something?' Jonathan replied that it was voluntary, but that yes he did report all such finds to the Portable Antiquities Scheme, and other recording resources. He added, 'Although if I did find something major, or very significant, I am legally obliged to report it under the Treasure Act. I must make that clear Miss Melanby'. She had replied: 'It's Candice, Jonathan. Please, I'm sure my brother will not object, especially where there's money involved.' she added with a knowing smile.

In the first couple of weeks, Jonathon didn't find very much at all.

Twisted scraps of aluminium kept popping up from almost all the field he investigated. He had later found out from several people that these pieces 'probably came from one of those German rocket things that blew up over our village in 1945?' These finds were, of course, liberally mixed with the usual worn Georgian coins, similar period pewter buttons and ,without exception, copious quantities of shotgun cartridge tips. No matter,though. Being in no way put off, he was simply in awe of just how much land he now had to detect on.

Now and then the occasional surprise hammered silver coin popped up, giving Jonathan small glimpses of the potential that could lie here? He then decided that perhaps it was time to apply far more research, and a more methodical and organised approach to his searches. During this time, when he had planned to take this more methodical approach, instead of randomly searching all over the place, he was slightly distracted. Several villagers had asked him if he wouldn't mind running that 'thing' over their gardens? He had of course willingly obliged and, as a result, had found many further mostly Victorian coins, several long lost old Dinky cars as well as several much-corroded cap firing type toy guns. Although this could be frustrating at times, in Jonathan's mind it all helped to give metal detecting a sound positive promotion in the locality, and that could do no harm at all.

To be fair, had he not got the Melanby's permission it would have been these sort of requests he would have been resorting to anyway. In the garden of one cottage, that looked to be of rather more recent construction than the surrounding ones, he had found a blackened and corroded George 1st silver shilling. Apparently there had once been a fire here and the cottage had all but burned to the ground, eventually being rebuilt many years back. In the garden of the same cottage there was also an old well. Jonathan peered over the moss-clad crumbling brickwork and looked down into the gloomy water. He was unable to resist dropping a five pence coin into it. Several seconds later he heard the coin make a plopping sound in the dark waters below. There must be a wealth of stuff down there? he thought to himself. If only it could be drained?

153

The tiny five pence coin settled into the sludge at the bottom at the bottom of the well. Amongst other things, it now accompanied a broken, armless, doll, some toy cars and a pram wheel. In several feet of leafy muck below these modern items lay a solid bronze eagle that had been there for a considerably longer period.

On one of his first short forays over the main estate pretty much all he had found were several buried, and burned out, wartime German incendiary bomb cases down at the bottom of Four Acres field. He had read somewhere that the Home Guard, in some cases, were only issued with five rounds of live ammunition each. If that was true there must have been a contingent of several thousand for this village, some fields seemed to be full of fired 0.303 cartridge cases. Despite his desired change of approach, one result of his initial casual pottering around and assessing the estate approach was the discovery of an unusually large type of penknife. It looked to Jonathan to be in very good condition. He had found it beside an old gate post, three inches down, amongst the dry oak leaves and tangled spaghetti-like roots of some ivy. If only old farmer Stanley Hawkes had still been alive. He would have been so very grateful for the return of that cherished German gravity knife that he had carelessly lost, way back in 1966.

Jonathan was delighted when Candice suggested he should have a stall at the village fete, showing people some of the things he had found around the village. Once again, he had thought this would be a superb way to promote metal detecting, and maybe get some more information on local areas or even permissions to search?

Jonathan continued to metal detect the entire estate and in the following years began to hear about illicit metal detecting by people called 'Night Hawkers', and all its bad consequences. This aspect of such a great hobby really annoyed Jonathan, as did the negative press that metal detecting always seemed to receive as a result of it. Didn't these people realise just how much history passed through their finger tips? And, more importantly, when something was sold on to oblivion without being recorded, everyone loses out. However, there was good and bad on both sides. As he gained in experience, Jonathan was also qualified to express his opinions on a wide variety of detecting -associated issues. For example, Jonathan didn't go along with the regularly-made statement that his finds should be officially interpreted as an 'exhaustible resource'. He felt that it was clearly an obvious statistical issue that hardly needed declaration, as it was applicable to all collecting hobbies, and was only usually made by those who were trying to stop people like him from enjoying metal detecting.

Someone was trying to get people to imagine that this limited stock of coins, and things, was being 'pillaged', when in fact they were actually saving them. Jonathan considered it ironic that, in many cases, the very people in authority, as well as those outspoken, self-elected, custodians of our heritage were actually condemning thousands of coins and artefacts to gradual destruction. He failed to see why these so-called heritage organisations consistently failed to utilise detectorists in order to rescue that very same heritage they declared to be so concerned with protecting? In some cases they of course do protect heritage, such as architecture, etc., But scheduling vast tracts of land, much of which is subjected to agricultural activity, and not allowing anyone to metal detect on them has very grave consequences. The primary one of which is that coins and artefacts, which are part of everyone's heritage are continually bathed in acidic rain, pesticides and fertilisers, and are thus condemned to corroding away, if not recovered.

It was fair to say that Jonathan was often quite positive, and sometimes even outspoken, when coming forward to defend his hobby. The other statement of which some aspects rather galled him was 'This heritage is all of ours. it belongs to all of us!' Jonathan regarded this as totally true in principle, but felt he would like to see a greater effort made by such critics to participate themselves in the finding of 'our heritage', not just sitting back and criticising people like him at every opportunity. At least he felt secure in the knowledge that he was making a small, but significant, contribution to the recording of his nation's history, and that such was accessible to all for educational purposes. How could anyone find fault with that? Furthermore, Jonathan pondered the statistics of the whole issue and concluded that almost all his finds would never have been found anyway had it not been for his actions with a metal detector. So what factual base did some of this criticism come from was a bit of a mystery to him?

Certainly night hawks did little to ease the situation, and fed ammunition straight into the critics mouths. But all this aside, it certainly did feel on a few occasions that some people had adopted the attitude: 'I prefer to think, and know, that these coins and artefacts remain buried, and should stay so.'

Jonathan shared his opinions with other detecting colleagues, and became all the more concerned when on some of his sites the effects of organo-phosphates, and other chemical additives, were clearly destroying the very coins and artefacts he was attempting to locate, record and conserve. The idea that our heritage was condemned to lay buried, decaying in the ground and lost forever was a major pre-occupation in Jonathan's thoughts.

Fortunately, being a small village, it seemed everyone quickly knew everyone else's business and it seemed that Melton Briarsville had so far got away with little attention paid to it by these so-called night hawks. Certainly, in all his years there Jonathan had never seen any unexplained foot prints, or holes, on any of his sites. But from what he continued to hear he considered it was perhaps only a matter of time before he would encounter the results of such undesirable night time activities? He thought about letting Craig and Candice know that such an event could be a possibility? But he could just imagine Craig saying: 'Well, that's it then, Jonathon. Thanks, but no thanks. I don't want anyone detecting here if that's likely to happen, and that, my friend, includes you!'.

Jonathan naturally wanted to protect his interests for searching in this great area, and cautiously decided not to mention it. Unfortunately, though, Jonathan had but a few years of this trouble-free enjoyment remaining, before the first evidence of possible nighthawks in the area would be noticed.

This so-called first evidence in the district came in the form of several unrecognised cars that had been seen parked in lay-byes, or sometimes rather carelessly on verges along the lanes. Admittedly, these incidents took place on very rare occasions, but once a group of three suspicious looking men had also been seen. A sharp bend on a winding lane had caused a car headlight beam to flick out across a field and three men were illuminated, who instantly all dropped to the ground and lay flat. So from their actions alone it was clear they were up to no good?

Next morning, thankfully no signs of poaching were evident but there were foot prints all over the field, and quite a few freshly-dug areas of soil in one particular area. With no knowledge of metal detecting, the farmer wondered what the hell had been occurring on his fields? And with that wondering unsatisfied he went on to call the police. This would later be considered to be the first known incident, but initially the farmer involved then got a bit flustered and started to wonder if perhaps he had been a bit rash? Perhaps after all, if they had only been a group of visiting poachers trying their luck, no real harm done, eh?

The police had arrived at the farm house and, from what they said, they seemed far more concerned with an event that had just taken place outside a pub in Bourton. Their ever-crackling radios confirmed those concerns, and they clearly couldn't wait to depart. So it was the first recorded incident of this 'night hawking' just passed by.

From the autumn of 2005, Jonathan did begin to notice the occasional sets of footprints, and unfilled holes, on some of his sites around the village. Maybe, just maybe, he had left these holes in a moment of excitement at a find? However, this as Jonathan really knew, was fantasy. The track prints on the shoes were definitely not his, and anyway, they had strayed off any footpaths and went across fields where he hadn't yet searched that season. All in, all it was indeed minimal evidence, but it did really annoy Jonathan. Naturally at this stage, Jonathan was rather irritated, but he had no idea that very shortly this so called night hawking and all its effects would seriously affect Melton Briarsville, and he would be involved with a lot more than just the feeling of being irritated.

CHAPTER THIRTEEN

THE ARRIVAL OF UNWELCOME INTRUDERS

O ne cold and drizzly night, seven years later, in January 2012, found a certain Peter Ellis crouching down in a damp ditch at the base of a dense hawthorn hedge near to the village. Carefully he removed his headphones and clutched his metal detector tightly. He could hear the haunting melancholy exchange of the wheezy shrieks and screams from a Little Owl, and its partner, further down in the valley. Right now, though, he was concentrating on a far more serious issue.

Peter had been a metal detectorist for a fraction over two decades now. In that time he had made some astounding finds, which kept his fascination and passion for metal detecting burning. 'What the hell am I doing here? I'm getting too old for this lark!' he grumbled, as he settled deeper into the crackling crunching, thorn-ridden hedgerow. He had often been in situations like this, where he would firstly reflect upon his age and ability, as opposed to the fact what he was doing was, in effect, illegal.

Peter had started off fascinated with this hobby and was a dedicated collector of Roman coins. But his passion had developed into an obsession, and that was dangerous. On many occasions this obsession had led him to break the law and take great risks, although it was this risk-taking that Peter found created suspense in his, otherwise rather mundane, life. Peter, in effect, was one of the very people that Jonathan had heard referred to as a 'Night Hawker', and consequently would often take many dangerous risks to find ancient coins and artefacts. This of course did not always work out; there is no quantitative advantage as opposed to daylight searching by going out in the dark. However, it did of course have one distinct benefit, and that was without any permission-seeking being required, Peter could literally go anywhere he chose to.

Several times he had been chased off land, and on several occasions he had been stopped by the Police late at night when he was driving home. 'One young copper got really narky with me! Reckoned I had guns in my car boot? Bleedin' detectors in bags, was all they were!' he would gleefully recount to his mates.

Peter did once have a permanent night hawking colleague for some six years who would often come out with him. But they had ended up having a big disagreement over the selling of a George 111 guinea. So for some time, Peter had operated as a lone individual. Recently, though, he had made three more acquaintances of what he termed as 'fellow brother nighthawks'. But, although pleasant, Peter considered them to be idiots. They just did stupid irresponsible things and took far too many unnecessary risks. Peter considered himself to be far more professional in his attitude and performance, but even he couldn't deny that the occasional camaraderie, and shared costs of petrol, was welcome. Anyway, for this night Peter had decided he would prefer his own company again; far less hassle, and only himself to think about if things got a bit out of hand.

The fact that this very night he was again thinking that he was too old for this lark was largely influenced by the appearance of a small red light, along with a larger white one of a much brighter intensity. These had suddenly appeared in the corner of the field he was crouching in and, in his own words: 'Gave me a real bloody scare!'

Just twenty minutes earlier he had been cursing at all the fragments of aluminium he was finding, along with the odd exploded bullet casing. Having gone nearer to the hedge, he had found nothing but a few Georgian coins, which felt crusty and rough, and many more of those damned shotgun cartridge tips. So he had moved away once more, retrieving several pieces of twisted aluminium and some bullets. Whilst he was considering that this hobby was sometimes a real pain in the backside, he then had a clear double signal in his headphones. 'Now that does sound different!' he muttered to himself.

Using his steel spade, he dug into the soil. Eventually he could hear from the signal in his headphones that whatever was causing this crisp signal was now out. He crouched down, looking furtively around. Whilst thus engaged, he knew he was at his most vulnerable. Grabbing handfuls of chalky soil he passed each over the search coil. Nothing! Where the hell is it? he wondered. Then, in the last handful of soil, the signal returned. He looked down and saw a pale disc; quite a large pale disc at that! It looked bright, but then again so does lead, or aluminium, in the moonlight. Despite the accompanying soil, he could sense the weight of the object; it was as heavy as lead. Experience suggested it was most likely a large mediaeval leaden token, at the very best? But as usual, curiosity was more intense than experience, and he just wanted to check. Slowly opening up his jacket as a shield, he shone a small torch into the palm of his hand. 'Jesus Christ! It can't be! What the heck is this?' he excitedly blurted out, as the tiny, but powerful, light beam

Sketch of an example of the magnificent Bodvocca Double Stater found in January 2012 (Courtesy of the very lucky anonymous finder)

revealed the detail of not one, but two, disjointed prancing horse images, and other animals too.

'Oh my God, yes! Brilliant! Boring old lead, my arse! I've never seen a coin like this before?' he joyfully exclaimed. 'It's a bleedin' huge Celtic gold stater thing! And this has to be a well rare one too?'

With trembling hands he couldn't resist a last look. But, just as he turned his little torch on again, something else had caught his eye. Just a momentary flash of light, or was it? Perhaps it was the dim sky-lightening effects from a distant thunderstorm? The tree tops further down the field, had he thought, just flashed paler. Definitely! There it was again.

Quickly stuffing the coin into a separate bag, and then into his finds pouch, he snatched up his detector and ran over to the hedge. Crikey! There it was again. Yes, very definitely now, he could see a red light with another huge white searchlight beam probing around the far corner of the field. He had just got to the hedge when the larger light beam suddenly flicked about all over the field. Was it looking specifically for him, he wondered? He thrust himself backwards, deeply into the hedge, and crouched down, trying to keep an observant eye on whoever this was.

Knowing exactly where they were was useful, particularly when planning a hasty exit from the field. He had no intentions of running about blindly, and possibly straight into whoever had the torch. Being polite to a late night dog-walker was one thing, but some of these farmer types could get a bit aggressive. Had someone seen him recently? Or maybe even spotted him park up his car and get his detector out? Or was this just an innocent rabbit shoot? He couldn't be sure for definite. Earlier on he had been crafty, and driven into the car park of the Waggoner's Inn, placing his car amongst all those of the regulars. But you never know with these villagers? Crafty folk, he thought. Had someone begun to get suspicious about his car, and started asking questions?

This was not the first time Peter had been here. He had only found a few hammered coins and mediaeval belt fittings before, but intuition told him this could be a good site. He was now in a tricky situation and had to assess, as quickly as possible, whether he was now accidentally caught up in a rabbit shoot? Or was this a group of angry people intent on finding him? Perhaps, he thought, it was a pre-organised village posse, hastily gathered from the pub to catch this so called 'heritage thief'?

Peter got down further. Damn it! The lights were now coming towards him along the field. Often, he had found it was best to sit tight, rather than run away without assessing what was going on. Just then, when they were only about sixty feet away, there was the loud, thin, crack of a 0.22 rifle being fired, followed by an agonising squeal from a rabbit. Peter was greatly relieved. It was definitely a shoot, but he was now getting a little panicky about how close it was getting. He looked up, very carefully, and saw three men get out of Land Rover-type vehicle. They were looking around, but then one of them said: 'John, Kev, it's OK. I've got the bugger. It's in the nettles here'

Clambering back into their vehicle, they started to come even closer. The bark of a dog brought it home to Peter that he was very likely going to get caught this night. And with a bloody gold stater on me as well, he thought. The light flicked here and there, and then with blinding intensity, exactly where he had earlier laid. Cripes! I hope they haven't spotted the crushed nettle area where I came in here? thought Peter, worriedly.

A wood pigeon flying over was then illuminated, and one of the men had a blast at it with his shotgun. Peter heard the man exclaim: 'Missed the bloody thing! Charmed life that one, eh?' This was followed by the clicking sounds from the odd spent lead shot, that now tumbled down into the hedge, falling onto the surrounding damp leaves. Then the sharp crack from a rifle split the night again, and was followed by another thin high pitched scream, and then a flurry of activity. Just ten feet away from Peter, a young rabbit lay kicking, and making a wheezing noise. The vehicle stopped again.

The men were no more than twenty feet away from Peter, who was now panicking and sweating profusely, hardly daring to breathe. He could hear his heart pounding in his ears. How was he going to explain this, a grown man hiding in a hedge? Perhaps he may be lucky - they may not even be locals? Maybe he would just get a severe ticking off? 'We could have bloody killed you mate!' sort of thing.

'Not another nettle job, Frank?' said one of the men.

'It's worth it, mate. Get in there and grab it.' said another. 'Have you seen all the bloody holes these little sods dig in the fields?'

Despite his serious predicament, Peter chuckled. They're not the only digging holes in your fields, matey, he thought to himself. All of a sudden, the shielding nettles parted in front of him and something damp and warm thrust itself into his ear, and then sniffed loudly. The youngest Labrador, named Barley, was not quite trained enough to find the rabbit. But she had found something interesting and started barking. Peter was just about to get up and call it a day, when a voice shouted: 'Barley! Come on, you dopey sod. Get over 'ere!'. Barley dithered, wagging her tail, and then loped away. She attempted to bound back to her find, but was then restrained on a leash and placed back into the vehicle.

As Peter lay, crouched down further, he then heard something much larger crashing into and forcing itself into the hedgerow right next to him. It was the robust wax jacket-protected body of Frank Scullins, who was determined not to lose any rabbits that night, particularly the ones he had despatched. 'Gotcha, you sod!' said Frank, which a few feet away, nearly made Peter need a change of underwear. Fortunately for him, the comment was in relation to the rabbit, that Frank could just make out in the bottom of the hedgerow ditch. The rabbit now retrieved, the men stopped for a cigarette, leaning against the vehicle. Peter was only a few feet away, and lay listening. I wish they would put all those bloody dogs back in, he thought.

For ten minutes at least Peter lay, and listened, to the men discuss various things from previous shoots, to what they thought about various young, and not so young, ladies in the village. Then, after several cigarettes, which seemed to take an absolute age, it finally looked as if they were getting back into their vehicle. Just before, though, one of the men opened a door and then looked all around him saying: 'Funny old area this, Kev. Gives me the creeps when I'm out here on my own. Always get the feeling others are about around here, or I'm even being watched'.

Their departure was now frustratingly delayed, as all three men now started talking about similar experiences, and all lit up yet another cigarette. From the ditch Peter observed, hidden, not daring to move, whilst wishing these guys would hurry up and get lost. One of the men then started to slowly walk towards Peter, whilst still talking to his mates. This individual then stopped, flicked away his cigarette end, which spun away in a shower of sparks, hit a twig, fell down, rolled off a nettle leaf and then landed right onto Peters hand. Hardly daring to move, Peter very carefully, and painfully, flicked it away. But not before the acrid smell of his scorched skin and hairs had hit his nostrils.

With a burst of diesel exhaust fumes, that hung around like a giant bulbous, blue-grey ghost, the vehicle and its occupants slowly moved away. Christ! That was miles too close for my liking, thought Peter, as he reached down and felt the reassuring shape of the coin in his finds pouch. Thank God! he thought, as he then gave a large sigh.

He stayed put for over an hour, hardly daring to move. Perhaps sneakily they had left someone behind, concealed, in order to catch him out, you never know? Very slowly, he extracted himself from the ditch and the hedgerow, as thorns and briars rasped and grabbed at his coat and head phone cable. Peter looked around, he was keen to do some more detecting, but he decided to get out whilst the going was good, and head back home. It was too risky in this area now.

Getting to the edge of the field, he quickly cleaned his wellington boots on a patch of rough grass. The last thing he wanted was a trail of mud leading down the lane from his field. And it would also be a lot quieter when walking past the cottages.

Back in the car park, he slid the keys in to his car door, as quietly as possible, and looked about. For just a second he was certain someone was watching him from the upper window of a small cottage just over the road. But they had turned the room light off, making the details hard to see. Anyway, Peter was keen to leave, as it was late.

As he drove home, the fairly long journey back seemed to take no time at all. He always found the journey back from where ever he had been seemingly went quicker if he had made a good find; and tonight he certainly had! He couldn't wait to get home and see this most unusual coin. Then to clean it, admire its beauty, and see exactly what it was that he had found? That night, Peter's sleep was interrupted by periods of intense excitement. Waking up repeatedly and turning the light on. He simply had to keep checking that it wasn't all a dream? It wasn't, of course. There for real, on his bedside table, lay the huge golden coin.

The next morning Peter slowly washed his find, and removed all the ingrained soil. Examining in detail what was surely his latest, and most exciting, find ever. On one side it had the word 'BODVOCCA', which was above a tablet that also contained the words 'CAMU', 'LON' and 'VER'. Above this, in Celtic style, unless he was mistaken, was a design that seemed to represent flames leaping upwards with a wheel-like design. There were also what appeared to be spears and a single shield? He had a term for a coin like this, that had so much detail included in its design. He called it 'busy'.

Peter could not help but wonder at the seemingly 'aggressive' design of the coin before him. What did it all mean? However, the other side, Peter considered, was really something else. It had two prancing horses above each other. And, on each side of these, featured a winged hare, or maybe it was a rabbit? Apart from these stunning designs there was something else most unusual? Weighing in at thirteen grams, it was twice the weight, and size, of any currently known Celtic coins. Peter squinted as he examined the hare, or rabbit, motifs. 'Now that is rather ironic, I suppose? As it was one of you sods that nearly got me caught last night!' he said.

Reaching over to the bookshelf, he took all his Celtic coin reference books down. Spending ages, thoughtfully turning each page, but he could not find any reference to the design, and style, of his coin in any of them. For a while he felt annoyed. Some of these books cost me over forty quid! he grumbled. Then this attitude was shifted by an excited thought: What's the matter with me? If it isn't in these reference books, then it must be rare?

Peter's main interest was the coinage of the Roman Empire. So this unusual Celt would get sold, or perhaps swapped, for certain. But with something so unusual he had to be very careful on who to approach, or who he can trust? After some serious consideration, he realised that he had little option but to show the coin to one of the 'idiots', a man named Tony Creasey.

Tony may well be what Peter classed as an idiot, in his opinion, but the man knew his Celtic stuff and, with little other option, Peter finally phoned him and arranged a meeting. They met up in Larameys Coffee Bar, in Stretchley, a small town not far from where Peter lived. A dreadful, gravelly-voiced 'You alright then, geezer?' announced the arrival of Tony. Peter took no time in discreetly passing the coin to him over the table. Tony took a sip of tea, that dribbled down his chin a bit. Using his arm to wipe the dribble away, Tony accidentally dropped the coin onto the table top. I was right. This guy is a total idiot! thought Peter.

No one noticed the coin drop, and Peter quickly grabbed it back to check for any damage. 'You're lucky, Tony.' he said, and slowly passed it back. Taking another sip of tea, Tony then asked: 'Where in hells name did you get this thing? I have never ruddy well seen, or heard, of anything like this ,Pete! It's gotta be unique for starters?' he went on, 'It's like a bloody double-stater, or something?'

'So, what do you reckon its worth?' asked Peter, optimistically.

The reply of 'anything from thirty to fifty, possibly even sixty thousand quid, mate?' was like a tonic to his ears. He stood up and dropped two crumpled twenty pound notes onto the table, flicking them towards Tony. 'Cheers Tony. That's top dog!' said Peter, gratefully. 'Perhaps see you, maybe in a few days then, for a run out somewhere?'

Tony grasped the notes and replied: 'Don't forget, Pete, where there's one there could be a load more of them?'

In fact it wasn't a few days at all. Peter had been considering his position on this one, ever since the words: where there's one, there could be a load more? had echoed in his head like a sweet poem. However, with the size of the field involved there was no getting away from the fact that he was definitely going to need some like-minded colleagues to help him work the site properly. He reluctantly picked up the phone to Tony, and said: 'Wanna come stater hunting then?'

Peter indicated that it would be a good idea if Tony brought along the two other as well. Reluctant phone call then over, Peter sat back and considered how unusual it was what he had just done. Who would believe a nighthawk actually sharing a site, a site that could be potentially highly productive too? Only time would tell if he would have any cause to regret this? Six hours later, a far too loud banging on Peter's front door announced the arrival of the 'idiots'. 'Okay. I'm coming, I'm coming!' shouted Peter. Opening the door, he met Tony and the other two, who had arrived with balaclavas, camouflaged jackets and trousers; and as usual, not carrying bags for their detectors. 'I see we are easily going to pass along Melton Briarsville's streets unnoticed then?' Peter stated, sarcastically. But the hint appeared not to be understood, nor appreciated.

That night Peter's car quietly pulled up once again into the car park of the Waggoner's Inn. Inconveniently, a group of teenagers just stood around outside idly smoking and chatting. Annoyingly slow, they finally all returned back inside the pub. Fortunately there was no one else with him in the car and he managed to carefully shut the car door, and slink away into the darkness unseen. Ten minutes later, from just over the road an old man was watching through his curtains, thinking 'It's that damned car again!'

As usual for such missions, Peter had dropped them off with all the equipment in a gateway, some three quarters of a mile outside the village. Anyway, it will only take a matter of minutes to meet back up with them.

As he walked down the lane and got nearer to the gateway he saw two small glowing lights with faces illuminated for a second. Arriving, he said; 'What have I said before about fags? Cover them up, I could see you from hundreds of feet back up the lane!'

However, Peter was not the only person to have seen them so far that night. For some weeks now, eighty five year old Albert Dyce had been watching out for the strange car that occasionally parked in the pub car park, from his cottage window. What was the driver up to, he wondered? He never him enter the pub. He just walked off up the road each time. So one night, a few weeks back, Albert had followed the man. And in the light of a good half-moon, all had been revealed. The mysterious individual was in fact a metal detectorist!

Of course old Albert knew who owned this land, in fact when it came to Melton Briarsville, Albert Dyce knew most things. He knew that only one person had permission to metal detect around here and that was Jonathan Pearson, who lived some distance away. This other man wasn't Jonathan that's for sure. Why did he keep returning here at night? Was he finding valuable things – stealing them and creeping away in the night? Previously Albert had watched the local news with interest, a month or so previously, when they had a section on illegal metal detecting. he had been quite shocked at the huge loss of local history that was taking place. 'Bloody night owls, or whatever they call themselves?' he muttered, as he had continued to watch.

Meanwhile, down the road, things had not got off to a good start. One of the 'idiots' had forgotten to recharge his batteries, and the other had brought along no headphones at all. Fortunately, Peter and Tony carried spares of most things, and so the illegal search could finally now commence. After about an hour the four night hawkers met up alongside the hedge, where Peter had been hiding just some twenty four hours before. Hands thrust deep into pockets and pouches, and the gentle clink of metallic objects being sorted could be heard. Things they had found were roughly cleaned in the grass, and held up to the moonlight to see what they were. So far, it would seem that only lead scraps, bits of aluminium, some shot gun tips and a smooth, green-patinated Victorian penny were to be the haul of the night.

Setting off again, it was some thirty five minutes before one of the 'idiots' began shouting out something. 'What the hell was that?' thought Peter, frantically. As his eyes adjusted, he could see three men grouped together. Fortunately the glint of moonlight reflected from one of the detector stems revealed instantly that they were his colleagues, or at worst, another group of detectorists.

Having removed his headphones, and now walking over briskly, he noticed that their conversation was far too loud. Someone is going to hear all this noise! What have I done, inviting these buffoons here? he angrily thought to himself.

Arriving amongst the three, highly animated, men Peter demanded: 'What the hell is all this fuss about? Someone is going to hear all this chatter, come on what are you lot playing at?'

Without saying a word in response, Tony held up something to the moonlight and slowly said: 'Pete, you know your gold stater thing, mate? Well it isn't unique anymore! Karly boy here has just found another one!'

Although pleased, frustrated, and slightly annoyed, Peter examined the find, and to be sure it was another huge double-size stater, exactly like the one he had found here the night before. They carried on frenziedly searching for hours, but no more staters, or indeed anything else of any consequence, was found. They finally called it a day (or a night as a critic might add). A short time later, it was nearly two o'clock in the morning and pensioner, Albert Dyce, once again peered through the curtains. He had been awoken by a familiar car engine starting over in the pub car park.

Next morning, a tired Albert was walking his dog, Percy, a small white rather nondescript Jack Russell cross, when he spotted Greg Phillips, the tenant farmer from Fordham's Farm, along with Jonathan Pearson. They appeared to be having quite a heated conversation and, as Albert approached, the conversation toned down. Sensing awkwardness, Albert said: 'Morning gents. You found anything interesting then Jon boy?'

Jonathan looked embarrassed, and Greg Phillips replied: 'No, he hasn't, and won't likely to be either, I'm off up to the Manor to complain to Craig'. 'What's all this then?' Albert enquired, and managed to find out from Greg that someone had been digging all over Four Acre field, and worse, had left holes everywhere.

'Yes, but as I was saying, I haven't been here for a week, Mr Phillips. You know I always fill in the holes that I dig.' Jonathan replied.

'Greg, it ain't Jon boy whose causing all the damage down there. Someone's been detecting around here for some weeks, at night! I've been watching them, and was going to tell you soon, once I knew it was a really regular thing.'

Jonathan looked relieved, but also angry. 'Why, whenever I find a good site, do these people either already detect on it, or sooner or later, find out about other areas I research?' he said. As soon as he made that comment, Jonathan regretted it. It looked like he was used to being followed by a gang of thieves, and was not the impression he wanted to give. Greg seemed to settle down and was reminded by Albert of the good relationship that he and Jonathan had over the time Jonathan had been searching his farm.

'OK, Jonathan. My apologies.' said Greg. 'But you can see where I'm coming from, can't you? Of course you can carry on detecting. I'm sorry for accusing you, but I'm gonna have to catch these night hawks. On my farm in the dead of night, are they? We will see about that one!'

Albert then made a strange comment. 'Something about that Four Acre field, ain't there?' he stated, 'Just before the war, I saw some bugger out in it at night. I reckon it was one of those German lads?' He continued, 'You've heard, you know, the ones that were up at the Roman dig. Bloody Germans, out there in the fields at night. We had enough trouble with 'em later on, flying over here in the night. Anyway, whoever it was, they was certainly digging away for something. Might 'ave been burying a radio set out there for all I know? Spying load of sods! I went to look later and you could see where the turfs had been ripped up. Digging away he was, just digging away all night.'

This made both Greg and Jonathan just look at him. There wasn't really much that they could add to that. Jonathan offered to help Greg with the problem, and it was agreed that on a few nights over the next few weeks they would carry out searches of the area to try and catch the culprits.

Next night, and for three consecutive nights, found Jonathan and Greg taking flasks of hot coffee and going out checking the fields. One night they were crouched in the hedgerow alongside Four Acres, when they spotted a movement out in the field. Slowly Greg raised his powerful torch and switched it on, only to reveal four fallow deer that looked rather surprised, and trotted off at some speed.

Weeks passed with no success, and it was concluded by them that the nighthawks must have given up for some reason? Unfortunately, however, this was most certainly not the case. They had simply been operating somewhere else; an archaeological dig close to Peter's home had simply distracted them.

A medium-sized Romano-Celtic shrine, and temple complex, had been discovered. And although a security company was employed to look after the site, Peter had met the two guards down his local pub, when they were supposed to be up at the site. For the daily sum of twenty-five pounds each they were prepared to not check the site quite as securely at night as they were employed to do. Paying out fifty quid a day was not a bad fee at all, considering Peter and his colleagues found some three thousand four hundred and eighty six coins in just over three weeks. The vast majority of which were all sold on for a good profit. However, the dig co-ordinators were soon very concerned that, despite the security guards being there, night hawkers were still breaking in and looting the site. They assumed, correctly as it happened, that not all was as it seemed with the hired guards. So it was decided to maintain security at the site themselves, and dismissed the contracted company in the light of so many thefts.

Unknown to Peter this change of policy speedily resulted in both he and Tony very nearly getting caught the next time, but they escaped after a lengthy chase. And they were damned lucky, as eventually the police, and even a helicopter, were called in. These were very high risks indeed. Peter consequently decided that he was going to resume hawking the fields up at Melton Briarsville again, but he was now going to park somewhere different from now on.

On the 27th January 2012, Albert Dyce was being driven home by his granddaughter when, as they passed round a bend in the lane, Albert spotted a car almost hidden behind the gateway hedge. The very same car as he had frequently noticed being parked in the pub car park.

'Hold up, Ellie.' he said 'Slow down just a bit'.

Some way out in the fields Peter, Tony and the other two, had noticed the car headlights slowly passing the point where they were parked. They all stopped, crouched down and watched, but thankfully the car had carried on. Half an hour later, Albert phoned Greg saying; 'Greg. I think them night owls are back in your fields? Just seen their car parked down Holly Lane behind a hedge.'

After two hours of searching, Tony had become rather unwell and was violently sick out in the field, just after finding a superb silver Celtic unit. (Author's Note:- a Celtic unit is a general term applied to mostly silver or bronze examples of coins from that period) The others suggested he should go over and lie down by the hedge and rest. They didn't want to quit yet; the find of the silver unit had inconsiderately spurred on their enthusiasm. A few minutes after Tony had headed off to the hedge Peter got a really sharp and crisp signal with a double-blip sound; soon he was holding two more mint condition silver Celtic coins. At this stage they discovered Tony really wasn't well and after some deliberation it was decided to take him home. 'Oh well, this stuff has been here for two thousand years. I suppose it can wait a few more days?' considerately piped up one of the 'idiots'. Back at the car, Tony was violently sick again said he felt even worse, it was definitely time to depart.

The back ground clatter of spades and machines being deposited into the boot masked the faint sounds of another car engine coming down the lane some way off. 'Sounds like some trade coming our way?' said Tony, noticing the distant head lights. The sound of the other car was then totally blotted out by the crunching sound of grit and sticky clay trapped in the tyre treads, as Peter pulled away sharply.

Despite Tony feeling so unwell, he glanced backwards to check his machine was there, and as he did so he glimpsed the increasing glow of a pair of headlights behind them. So what? he thought, we ain't detecting now, so no problem! I'll soon be home in bed.

The headlights pulled over and shot into the very gateway they had been parked, just some thirty seconds before. As Greg pulled over to the verge he noticed another pair of headlights a few hundred metres down the lane. Stopping the Land Rover with a harsh jolt, Greg jumped out and instantly turned on his powerful torch. Out in the crop could be seen a few clumps of soil and some dark patches, 'Someone has definitely been here tonight" he said, quietly. Shining the torch downwards, he looked at the bubble-covered, coffee-coloured, water in a freshly disturbed puddle and saw the muddy wet tracks leading out from the gateway, and down the lane. He remembered the other headlights. 'Just bloody missed em!' he cursed.

Meanwhile, back in Peter's car, Tony mentioned that he reckoned the site they had just done was one with damned good potential. 'But something just spooks me about it? It's got a really bad atmosphere, anyone else think so?' The other two 'idiots' simply nodded in agreement.

CHAPTER FOURTEEN

HAROLD FOSTER – ANTIQUITIES DEALER

After handling, and repeatedly admiring, the huge gold coin for a short period Peter had decided to make arrangements to sell it and, after informing Tony of this, was put in contact with a man called Harold Foster. Harold was a dealer in antiquities but, unlike many other dealers, he chose to purchase and deal in both legally found items as well as those of a more suspicious nature. The living to be made was good, particularly relating in his dealings with night hawkers. Such dealings had taken him, and his business colleagues, deep into Europe and, on occasion, even further afield.

Harold was a collector by nature. As a child, it had all started with collecting wild birds' eggs, then stamps - but only good quality Victorian issues. Finally, he turned to ancient coins and artefacts. His trade mark saying was: 'If it's good and old, then it can certainly be sold!' often adding: 'And I'll have it'.

His interest in coins and artefacts had begun in earnest by his late teens, and had led to him achieving a university placement to study archaeology, where he would eventually go on to achieve a first class honours degree. Things were definitely on track for Harold, and he was overjoyed when he finally secured a job as a field archaeologist working in Cambridgeshire. Here he was involved in several excavations, and experienced first hand the joy of finding, seeing, and handling ancient objects. The salary wasn't brilliant, so Harold had also worked part time in the local museum as an archivist, to earn some extra money.

One day he was discreetly approached by a man enquiring as to whether Harold might just be able to get him some cheap examples of Roman coinage? Harold certainly could, but knew this was totally out of his remit, it was wrong and so had politely refused. The man had then suggested 'Perhaps we shouldn't be wasting time with the cheap end of the market.' And had then asked about any quality coins. Again Harold refused, and had walked away, but not before taking a business card from the man, who had said; 'Please. You never know? Take it, just in case.'

However, upon reflection, the man had offered such a handsome financial incentive that Harold began to have second thoughts. After all, he thought, it's only the once! Harold hesitantly did the deal, and from then on, unable to resist, driven by the money, he had steadily supplied the man with whatever he could reasonably remove from excavations.

After a while, with a good steady sub-income, Harold began to have even more thoughts. He both considered, and knew, that the man he was selling to was then selling on to others for a handsome profit. So why did Harold need him? Why not cut him out and sell directly to those willing to pay a higher price? So he did just that, becoming further obsessed with making even more money. Soon afterwards, he discarded his archaeological career, now looking upon such people as 'standing in the way of his profit margin'.

Harold obtained the freehold ownership of a small premises near Biggleswade, in Bedfordshire, and with his established contacts, began an outwardly seeming, very respectable business. In the 1970's, with the progressive development of the hand held metal detector, Harold of course had not looked upon them as potential scientific instruments to assist archaeologists, those days had long gone. He viewed these new searchers as a damned good source of new coins and artefacts, and therefore income. He had not the slightest care, of course, where they had procured their finds from? However, Harold now found himself being actually assisted by the very people he now despised, namely the archaeologists.

In the 1970's, fortunately for him, hardly any of them were far-sighted enough to see the metal detector as a useful addition to their tools either. They isolated the metal detector, and consequently, anyone who even used one. Hence they missed a vital opportunity to integrate the new availability in its infancy, and subsequently created a massive division between themselves and detectorists, that in all probability could never truly be resolved.

This division created a gap that Harold had elected himself to fill. Where archaeologists didn't want to give credit to any detectorist, then he certainly would. Not only that, but Harold would also give them something else for their troubles – and that was hard cash! However, despite all things considered, Harold had made a good living out of this trade, although not quite as good as he would have liked.

He knew many detectorists were now becoming knowledgeable in their own right. The days were quickly disappearing when he could fob off most people, claiming their rare find was so common that it almost wasn't worth him buying it! Not only that, but soon Harold was in direct competition with those detectorists who collected coins and artefacts themselves, those who donated to museums and those who never sold a single thing that they found.

Times changed fast with modern technology. But, as with Human nature, there would always be those who would sell, whether for a love of money like him, or in some cases simply to survive and pay their bills. But Harold also knew things could change for such people like these detecting collectors and 'never-sellers'. He knew well that there would be a few recessions, hard times, and even a few divorces no doubt in the future. From experience he also knew that when such people turned up at his shop looking embarrassed it was a sure sign he had got their collection at last. He gave a kind, if only very brief, thought to giving thanks to the government for the redundancy, or to the wife for the divorce.

Tony became acquainted with this man when, a few years ago, he was lucky enough to find a partially scattered hoard of Roman anton-inianii coins on a building site, mostly from the reigns of the Emperors Carausius and Allectus. Tony had actually asked the site foreman for permission to metal detect, which was a rare occurrence. And, when granted, had later given the man a few Roman coins that he began to find there.

Two days later, Tony found the hoard – just a fraction over five thousand two hundred complete coins, with eighteen broken pieces. Cunningly, he acted as if he wasn't paying too much attention to the area. He collected as many coins as he could locate and took them home. He had wanted to sell, but to who? Such a vast amount of coins on the market would surely arouse suspicion? he guessed. He couldn't use the Internet auction sites either, he had heard that people checked them. So he needed a person who was either a major collector themselves, or had safe established contacts with those who were. But Tony himself simply didn't have such connections, or knowledgeable associates.

After a while he excitedly told a few chosen trustworthy people about his find but, although they were keen to see and touch the hoard, none of them could help him out. A group of coins like this was very much out of their league also, and simply far too hot to handle in an amateur manner.

Just how trustworthy some of the people he chose to inform of his find actually were, was reflected within two months when his telephone rang one evening. A man stating he worked for a company called Fosters Antiquities enquired about the rumours of the hoard? Had Tony found it? Or did he know who had? Tony was a bit cleverer than this, just who was this man on the phone? He could be from the authorities hoping to rumble him? He arranged a meeting.

After several meetings, where Tony illegally sold him several undeclared silver and gold finds, this pretty much convinced him that this man was legitimate. So he revealed that he, himself, had indeed found the hoard of rare antoninianii, and of course, they were for sale for the right price.

The right price was finally agreed, at twenty seven thousand pounds, and both parties were happy. After that Tony remained in contact with Harold Foster, he always gave a fair price, well most of the time; apart from the Coenwulf penny incident, but that's another story.

Harold Foster was suspected of being involved in many illicit antiquities deals, not just in the United Kingdom, but extending as far afield as Russia. But there had, so far, never been enough evidence to prove his direct involvement.

So it was that Tony had no hesitation at all in recommending Harold Foster to Peter, and that's how the two men would eventually meet. Peter was reassured in the safety of the deal, in that Tony had said 'On the whole, mate, Harold ain't bad. He should offer you a fair price. I've been dealing with him for ages, no worries it'll be safe.' So it was in London, a few days later, that Peter finally met the highly-recommended Harold.

Harold was a professional, always conscious not to show any sign of emotion that might make his clients think they had something of value. Some people of course knew what they had found, knew exactly what it was worth and what they wanted for it. Peter knew that around four weeks previously Harold had purchased, for £45,000, the other rare gold stater that had been found at Melton Briarsville, from one of the 'idiots'. Peter had only ever seen this other stater at night, and had not had the chance to closely examined it, so was not even sure it was the same as his?

The price now offered by Foster for this second stater was £34,500. Peter questioned this figure, as he was fully aware of the previous price given. 'Excuse me, but why is this not as much, or nearer, to the price you paid for the other coin you have just bought?' he asked.

'Coz when I bought that other example,' explained Harold, 'its status was unique. But now, with this one on the scene, it's not. Take it or leave it. But you do have the opportunity to make some additional money out of the situation - if you were to let me know where both these coins were found?'

After just a few cups of coffee, and about half an hour, Peter left the fast food restaurant where the meeting had taken place, with £36,5000 stuffed into his coat pocket. For just an additional, and rather paltry, two thousand pounds the site at Melton Briarsville had been disclosed to the notorious Foster. For just two thousand pounds the village, its heritage and ancient history, were now all put under threat, placed into the hands of an unscrupulous antiquities dealer. A man who was very well-known in certain quarters and yet highly suspected by others for stopping at no length to acquire coins and objects.

In Peter's opinion, the meeting had gone reasonably well, although one thing had rather unnerved him. This had been when Foster made it quite clear, in a very arrogant fashion, that from the point when he passed over the money for the information, he had in effect now purchased not just the site but the entire village and surrounding area of Melton Briarsville. Peter and his colleagues were no longer required, or welcome, to carry on night hawking there. Foster had his own team of 'professionals', who would take over and deal with the issue from then on.

Unknown to Harold, some nine hundred miles away, a rather extraordinary discovery had just been made, or perhaps more appropriately, it should be termed as a re-discovery. A relative of the long -deceased Konrad Euker, a certain Franz Stihlmann, who lived in Augsburg, had just found something rather curious. It was a discovery that Harold would certainly have been most interested to be aware of.

Franz was a mature law student but his dedication to the subject, and associated study, had long been called into question by his tutors. Any easy option, or fast way to make a buck, and Franz was on it. One of his tutors reported that 'wherever there is trouble, Franz Stihlmann is always in close proximity. Never directly accusable or, seemingly involved. Often just a face in the surrounding crowd, but nonetheless he is always around.'

This was in fact quite an accurate assessment, Franz's main haunts were the seedier wine bars around the city centre where he was involved, allegedly, in no end of minor dubious dealings. Not exactly the rumours a law student of any standing would particularly wish, or needed, to be associated with. But that's how it was and so long as he never got caught, or too closely linked, that's the way Franz liked it.

Franz was nearly twenty seven years of age when a distant aunt had passed away. The family were busy and so decided to call on Franz to sort out her estate, and perhaps finally do something of some use. Travelling to the small town of Buren, he located the address of the distant aunt with the help of a taxi driver. Quite an impressive district, he thought, and then immediately considered what lucrative antiques or furniture he could remove, so to speak, from the chattels. Franz spent a week rummaging around and assessing things. Strangely, apart from some Dresden china dolls, there didn't seem much of note. And as for upstairs, all the rooms were stuffed with brown paper-covered old seventy eight style records, boxes of oddments and suitcases of all descriptions. It was after some lengthy deliberation and none too few cigarettes that in a cloud of swirling smoke Franz stood up. It was time to sort all this out for good.

God, there was tons of it. Whilst about half way through he came upon a pile of old photograph albums. Inside them a few faded photographs showed several past family members in Nazi Party uniform, as well as that of the Luftwaffe. 'Right that's definitely going out in the dustbin!' he considered. "I don't need that sort of association.'

Amongst the albums was a large dark brown envelope with Berlin University stamped on it in violet coloured ink. Sliding his fingers into the age-stiffened envelope, he managed to pull out a sheaf of thin papers. Some had hand written notes on them. Others were typed, and also there were two Luftwaffe reconnaissance photographs, dated 1940. Reading the notes he saw that they related to a certain Waldemar Euker, who it seemed had been the pilot of a Junkers 88 aircraft during the last war. However, it appeared that before the war he had apparently been an archaeological student of some sort. Apart from being present on a number of excavations in France and Spain, he had also been leading a team of students on a major excavation over in England. Exactly where this had taken place was given as Melton Briarsville, a small village in the Midlands. However, reading the other notes and printed sections, it certainly seemed that this was no ordinary dig Waldemar had been involved with?

As Franz read more, he felt a close association with this Waldemar relative, he seemed to have been quite a devious fellow indeed. One note however, did bring back that feeling of distaste, at the bottom in Waldemar's own hand writing was a brief annotation: 'Today, I, Waldemar Euker, was the subject of a great honour, for I met our SS Reichsfuhrer, Heinrich Himmler.' Franz was certainly very intrigued as to how a low ranking bomber pilot anywhere would have got the opportunity to meet, and be involved, with so senior a figure. Unless of course there had been some exceptional circumstances to have merited it?

There was definitely far more here than meets the eye, Franz considered, who then also thought it very wise to get these documents photocopied. The originals he would secure in a safe at his university. The copies he would keep on him at all times, ready to hand for the in-depth research he knew was most likely to result from his discovery of these documents. The estate now sorted to Franz's satisfaction, if not to that of anyone else in his family, he now headed back home.

Franz was basically a decent fellow but perhaps not what one classed as a trustworthy individual, by any measure. He was handicapped by one aspect of his personality, and that was his susceptibility to telling people about his exploits and successes. He liked to gloat, but the law of averages can come into play here. Sooner or later, if you were involved in clandestine things, this wordiness would fall upon the ears of the wrong person, or persons. True to form, in Franz's case, this is just what happened. Although he was useless as to recollecting just how this had happened, when he was later interviewed by the police. This was mainly due to the fact that at the time he had been too drunk to remember very much at all.

One morning, after a particularly heavy drinking session, he couldn't find the document copies anywhere. In the hall, at last he thought he had found them, same colour, what relief, but it turned out it was just a motley collection of blank papers. His flat was in its usual total mess and in his half still -drunken state, Franz looked around and made the hasty assumption that he had been burgled?

The police duly arrived, wading through a layer of discarded boxes containing old dry curling slices of pizza, brimming ashtrays along with discarded half empty cans of very stale lager. They were puzzled how on earth Franz could have deduced he had been burgled in all this mess, which was clearly of his own making? They left shortly afterwards, with a stern reminder to Franz concerning the value of police time, and how not to waste it. Later when he had sobered up somewhat, Franz pondered as deeply as he could, he definitely had those notes with him last night, of that he was certain.

He looked everywhere, retracing his steps as best as possible, but no bar staff at any clubs or bars had anything that matched his documents handed in to them. True enough, he considered, perhaps they were just mislaid under a table, or in a toilet somewhere? Fortunately, the latest research which Franz had done, which wasn't much, had been placed with the originals in the safe. Hopefully the copies were still somewhere in his flat or, failing that, would preferably end up crushed in some municipal out-of-town refuse dump.

Franz had no idea that the previous evening someone had overheard one of his drunken conversations where most people were quickly bored. 'Yes, yes, Franz, we know, your father, or whatever, met Heinrich Himmler, and together they planned to find a great treasure!'. Franz had then at that stage usually got very perplexed and abusive. 'You all think I'm just a drunk? But I will show you fools that the village of, whatever it's called, will hit the headlines one day!'. However, on this one occasion there was an individual sitting close by who, for a change, was most interested in what Franz had said.

Watching and waiting, this individual had closely monitored Franz. At first there didn't seem too much point, but as he was staying in the area anyway, it might prove to be fruitful? A few days later, another drunken conversation erupted in the same bar. This time Franz gave the name of Melton Briarsville for the village in question. The observing individual had then nearly choked on his cold lager. This was really interesting to the man who had been watching Franz, because that name had stuck in his mind, and back in England he knew someone else who would also be very very interested in anything to do with Melton Briarsville.

That someone else just happened to be a certain Harold Foster. The watching individual here was actually a man named Malcolm Collins, who was sometimes employed as a potential scout by Foster, for any undercover antiquities, or coins, that may be present and obtainable in

Europe. Foster's particular concerns at present had focussed on Bulgaria, from which there seemed to be a never-ending supply of good quality, rare, Roman silver coinage. In fact Foster had so flooded the UK market with this Roman silver, it had devalued the book price by some fifty percent of some issues. This in turn had led to a growing concern amongst both legitimate UK detectorists and night hawkers, who sold coins to Harold, because they simply could not compete with these high quality imports.

However, returning from Bulgaria, Malcolm had found himself in Germany, following an evidently factless trail concerning an extremely rare gold coin, purportedly from the Roman Emperor, Severus Alexander. This had allegedly been a 'Colosseum Aureus' example, which, if it could be purchased from the rural farmer alleged to have found it, would sell on for a huge and handsome profit. So with this failure under his belt Malcolm had slumped into a wine bar and, by pure luck and fate, had happened to encounter Franz Stihlmann, and his paperwork.

Always watching, Malcolm had to find just the right time to get hold of those notes, as well as the right level of drunkenness of this Franz Stihlmann to offer no resistance to, or awareness of him taking them. This requirement didn't take long. One night, 'It was clear old Stihlmann boy was really going for it again!' as Malcolm had later recalled. He had verbally abused this girl, whose boyfriend subsequently then catapulted Stihlmann through the door, into the street outside. Gathering himself up Stihlmann came back in to the bar again.

'Huh! Now that takes some doing. Is he brave, or just a fool?' Malcolm commented quietly, as he observed further.

The young couple complained, but the owner weighed up the few Euros spent by them, against the many that Stihlmann had ,and would continue, to spend and so asked the couple to leave instead. Here we go, thought Malcolm, and gently ran his fingers over the look-alike pieces of paper, secreted in his inside pocket. As always, he was meticulous in his planning was Malcolm. He had already prepared rough-looking copies of the documents that Stihlmann always waved around his head when drunk. All he had to do was wait, and wait he did for exactly one hour and twenty three minutes.

By now Stihlmann was thoroughly inebriated, and had just started to wave the documents around again. Some people moved aside, or even departed, looking embarrassed, and now even the bar owner had got involved. Then it happened. Whether Stihlmann had attempted to strike out at one of the young bar staff, or had simply made an alcohol-enhanced gesture, was uncertain. But he toppled from the bar stool, and the documents slid out of his hand and into the air. They had fluttered for a second and then, as if in slow motion, fell separately all over the bar floor.

This was it, just what Malcolm had been waiting for, he extracted his copy documents and rushed forward as if to assist Stihlmann. He then feigned a trip, quickly gathered all the original documents from the floor, stuffed them into the other pocket, and then offered Stihlmann back the replacements already in his hand. It was as simple as that.

Malcolm then made a quick mobile call to Harold, informing him that he had not been able to secure the Roman gold coin after all. Harold was not happy, in fact he was decidedly off-hand. 'You told me that was almost certain to be a definite job, Malc!'.

The lengthy reply Harold had received, beginning with: 'Harry, if anyone in our line of trade knows that nothing in life is guaranteed, then it's you!' was totally unexpected. Unexpected as it was one of the few times Malcolm had defended himself, and also because it contained two words that totally stunned Foster and they were 'Melton Briarsville'. 'You still there, Harry?" asked Malcolm.

Seconds of heavy silence passed and then Harold replied hastily: 'Yes, well best you get back here soon then Malcolm. Well done. It sounds quite interesting does all this.'

Not wishing to sound too enthusiastic, Harold had added, and hopefully not sounding too impractical: 'But if you have time can you just pop in and collect those French staters from that dealer down in Amiens?'

Malcolm wasn't easily put of,f or fooled. Yes he would go to

Amiens, as requested, but he had his own contacts and recently Melton Briarsville had frequently cropped up in several of their conversations too. Quite possibly something was in the offing and Malcolm also wanted to be part of it. He knew from experience when Harold tried these bluffs. After all, he had seen him do it enough times when buying coins and artefacts from detectorists, always careful not to reveal how superb or valuable he thought something was.

However, three days later Harold was holding the documents, which Malcolm had so deftly removed from the possession of Franz Stihlmann. He took time to read and re-read them and to also to compare the diagrams of the tiles with the sharp quality copies of the wartime photographs. He was going to take his time on this one, he would prefer to digest and research all the information by himself. If what the documents and recent finds clearly indicated was true, then that quaint little village could be the making of him. His newly acquired contacts in the United States seemed to have unlimited supplies of ready cash in exchange for ancient British coins and artefacts. If what Harold suspected lay in the ground at this location truly did exist, and this whole thing was not in itself a complex elaborate hoax, then these American collectors were going to need their so-called unlimited cash to the absolute maximum.

So such are the dreams of acquiring things shared by many people, detectorists included of course. But as detectorists know too well only some of these dreams might ever come true. As months dragged on, and became years, Harold 'invested much effort', as he put it, in Melton Briarsville. But overall it was to achieve surprisingly few results. Ever-determined, Harold's dream of course survived these setbacks. He was not giving up so easily and was now convinced, if not obsessed, that something was linked to that village, something that he believed was only just out of his reach for the time being. His dream after all, was based on successful metal detecting, and he knew only too well how fickle that could be.

It just so happened that it had not only been Harold's team of 'professional' night hawks that were operating around there. As a result, and also by a sheer quirk of fate, his dream would receive some further, and very intriguing, encouragement. One of his contacts had recently revealed to him that there was another person who had done some hawking around that village some time back. Just a few visits, he reckoned, nothing really serious. But now this bloke was involved in very messy divorce case and needed to get some cash together. As a result he was now offering to sell his entire collection. Amongst this so Harold was told were some bits and pieces from around Melton Briarsville, which he might find very interesting indeed.

'Oh thank you, divorce lawyers – and you courts as well!' Harold rejoiced, and now pursued this new opportunity vigorously.

A short while later he had already managed to set up a meeting with this person in the forecourt area of a large motorway service station. Plenty of people in cars munching burgers and fries, or walking piddle-bloated kids to the toilets, perfect for concealment, no one will notice a person get out of one car and into another. So it was that Harold Foster finally met Danny Wilcox.

Danny gave the entire story, but was clearly keen to do business, get his cash and go. Danny had brought along the usual bags of 'tat', as he described them, as an introduction. 'Sorry no market with me for that lot.' said Harold, looking at the bags of broken buckles, corroded Roman coins and lead bits. 'What else have you got for me?' he then asked. 'I heard you may have a gold stater or two up for grabs?'

Danny then brought out some rather scratched and battered coin display trays, which contained various Roman and medieval hammered silver coins. The guy is holding onto the best stuff until last to make a greater impression on me, and hoping to get more money. The fool! thought Harold. Making out he was reasonably impressed, though, Harold had bought them all.

He was especially pleased, as they had included a slightly worn silver penny of King Offa, which Danny seemed to be unaware of. Some of these people are just so remarkably stupid! considered Harold with glee.

Danny revealed the last coin tray. Wow! Now that's more like it.

Just look at that little lot! thought Harold, again careful not to give the slightest indication of his true feelings away; and in this case that commanded a great deal of personal skill.

Just then, a car was being very badly parked, brightly illuminating both men several times in its head lights. This seemed to make Danny rather nervous. 'Look mate, do want the stuff or not? I aint got time to waste, if you know what I mean? he blurted out. The headlights illuminated the coins in the tray. And from what Harold saw, there were two true prizes indeed. He simply must have them.

'Now those are quite nice!' he said, picking up one of two massive double-sized gold staters' Both were identical to the two exceptionally rare ones that he had purchased some time previously.

'Yeah, they seem to me to be a bit bigger than usual, eh?' Danny replied.

Harold actually told the truth in part, 'Well, not really. I've seen examples like this before, just a slight extra flan size, the blank caster probably made an error?' he bluffed, confidently. 'I bet it was caused by to too much wine eh? Not bad, though, where did you find them?" asked Harold.

'Oh, up at that Briarsville place, or whatever it's called, mate. Nice them, ain't they? Gotta be worth something pretty tasty? I'd say'.

Harold took his time and then said: 'Tell you what, I'm going to have a problem selling some of these coins - just no market at all for them at the moment! But I reckon it should pick up sooner or later? That aside, though, I'm prepared to take the chance anyway, as I'm actually a collector of such things myself, so I will keep one or two of them myself anyway".

Harold then skilfully left a long silent pause in the conversation to emphasize that he was thinking about their value in great detail. 'If I give you three grand for the lot Danny, does that sound fair?' said Harold.

'I was really looking for around the five mark, mate?' Danny replied.

'Ok. I can take the loss.' agreed Harold. 'Shouldn't really, but, oh go on then five grand it is'

Five thousand pounds in twenty pound notes was then laboriously counted out by Harold, 'Please count it too, Mr Wilcox.' he said formally, ever perfecting the kind considerate and concerned business man image to his new client.

'Looks good to me, cheers mate" said Danny as he deftly flicked the door lever and got out of the car.

'Stay in touch Danny.' Harold said to the dark shape, now flitting away between the cars. Bloody hell! thought Harold, he had forgotten to ask this Danny fellow if he would make a quick sketch of the stater find spot.

Huffing and puffing, Harold opened the car door quickly and swung his large bulk sideways and stood up looking over to where Danny had been heading. Walking over, he spotted a man in a car, fortunately it was Danny, who sitting there was rather carelessly counting out his money into piles on the front seat. Harold moved exaggeratedly to make himself obvious, not wanting to startle the young man. Danny glanced up quickly, winding down his window, looking a bit flustered. 'OK mate? What's up?' he asked.

'Nothing, it's all fine.' Harold replied. 'But I meant to ask you if you would be so good as to draw me a sketch map, if you can remember exactly where you found those large-flanned staters?'

'Yeah, sure. I can do that for you, as I doubt I will be going back there, the site was surrounded by stacks of crap anyway, aluminium bits and all that sort of dross" Danny replied.

Looking down at the crude, almost childish, sketch it was quite clear to Harold that the find spot for all these rare gold staters was once again confirmed as being one section of the very same field. Despite his results of searching so far, there simply had to be something else to be found? Harold pondered thoughtfully, was it indeed a burial or maybe a large Celtic temple? If so why was it then that the finds were so sparsely distributed?

Over the next few months Harold's team waited for the crops to be harvested. But once again the sole finds of any significance were several small Celtic silver coins. I'm so bloody near to this thing now, I can feel

The two double staters originally purchased by Harold Foster
from Danny Wilcox.

it, thought Harold. However, as he well knew he had a 'business' to operate. Other people would continually have to be sent to the area on his behalf, and at his expense, to see what they could find. Then there was of course the trust thing. Could Harold trust those who he employed? Would they tell him about everything that they found, or would they perhaps keep the best stuff back to sell on themselves to someone else? Suppose they actually found what I am actually looking for and were intent on just fobbing me off with rubbish, he wondered? No, they can't be. This final thought wasn't based on any element of trust at all for his fellow colleagues. It was simply that Harold kept a critically close eye, enabled by his well established grape vine, on what was going on everywhere. If there was ever to be a huge number of illicit coins or artefacts coming onto the market then Harold Foster always knew about it. In fact he reassured himself further by acknowledging his belief that only he could ever be possibly involved directly with happenings of such magnitude anyway.

CHAPTER FIFTEEN

DEDICATED TO UNCOVERING OUR HERITAGE

By the year 2018 it seemed incredible to Jonathan that he had been metal detecting for over twenty three years now, with eighteen of them spent searching as often as possible around Melton Briarsville. There is no doubt that he has been well and truly 'bitten by the bug'. For him very few things can beat the excitement, anticipation, and sheer great fun of metal detecting.

'It's so variable - one minute you are holding a fragment from a three thousand year old Bronze Age axe-head, the next a Victorian pipe tamper.' he would often inform the many intrigued listeners to his exploits.

Although as he progressed he had sometimes wished he could return in attitude to the days when he first started. Back then a few pewter buttons and a half handful of Georgian coppers seemed like true treasure indeed. But as is normal with metal detecting, and similar activities, in time he developed a quest, in fact a passion to find more and more intriguing and fascinating finds. Jonathan is also a great believer in sharing his finds and his experience, and achieves this in many ways. As well as still having his regular ever-popular stall at the village fete each year he also gives talks to local schools and societies, always bringing with him examples of his discoveries. He has submitted regular articles for many years to a magazine called 'Treasure Hunting', which is dedicated to supporting metal detecting in the UK. He was often in friendly competition with writers for another detecting magazine called 'The Searcher', some of which were in his own club.

Jonathan likes writing these articles, as he knows it allows people to both read about and actually see the finds he makes, which includes people who perhaps have not got access to, or choose not to use a computer. This is somewhat proven by the frequent letters he gets from more senior persons who express their delight at seeing his finds in the magazine. Jonathan is one of those detectorists who is always looking at parish records and buying those little historical pamphlets that are produced by dedicated like-minded local persons. Such documents can be invaluable for indicating potentially good areas to ask for permission to search. His experience has also helped him interpret the land. When he glances at a secluded corner of a field now, he can literally see the Georgian farm workers having a break there. With their cider flagons tilting, coarse bread loaves being broken apart and pieces of cheese being stuffed into grateful crumb-covered mouths amidst much chatter. Often such thoughts are mysteriously transformed in to a pocketful of Georgian coins and thimbles. He has had these feelings and observations on many types of site, and is delighted when such thoughts are solidified with finds from the activities he knew or had even imagined took place there.

With the ongoing development of computers and information availability Jonathan was fascinated when Google Earth had become available. Any opportunity he got he was upstairs on the computer, looking at field layouts, dark patches and crop marks. In fact, on occasions, when he had sloped off from some household chore, Christine would now listen for the faint sounds of keyboard tapping, purely out of habit and instinct.

Google Earth was a brilliant tool, and Jonathan had consequently located many more sites, ranging from mediaeval manorial areas to small Roman farmsteads. So enthusiastic was he that he would frequently find that, without knowing it, he had drifted on the screen, and was searching areas hundreds of miles away. Areas that he would, in all probability, never even get to metal detect on. One of the aspects of metal detecting that Jonathan particularly enjoyed was when he had identified a small area of crop marks in a field. After obtaining permission to search these they were then revealed to be a small Roman settlement or farmstead. True enough many of these were late third and fourth century sites often revealed nothing more than a handful of corroded coins, often referred to as 'Grots', and perhaps a lead steelyard weight or maybe a brooch or two.

But Jonathan loved the idea that people had once lived here and he was finding evidence that, in his eyes, made these people come alive again, through finding their lost coins and artefacts. Once he had put in a five-hour search on just such a small Roman site, and had only found nine small corroded coins and a broken section from a fibula brooch. But for him that was enough, he and his faithful detector had found yet another previously unknown site.

Naturally, metal detecting wasn't all seriousness, there was a lot of associated variety too. Already having an interest in wild life, Jonathan had seen some remarkable sights. There was the day when he had seen his first Red Kite flying high up in a thermal over the village. He would never forget the time when he had found his first Bee Orchid, and had marvelled at the clever deception it played on the local bees in order to survive.

Another time during the winter he had been sheltering against a tree from the wind when he saw a strange bird. This had turned out to be a Great Grey Shrike, which apparently, he later found, out had not been seen in this area since around 1949. The only mistake Jonathan ever made was actually connected to this bird, as he told a friend who was a keen birdwatcher about it. The friend was actually not just a keen, but almost a fanatical bird watcher and via the Internet went on to inform hundreds of fellow watchers about the bird's presence. The very next day the lanes and lay-bye's were full of cars, and people called 'Twitchers' with binoculars and scopes were all vying for the best vantage point. Craig Melanby wasn't too happy about all the fuss. But as usual, Candice thought it was all rather fun. Jonathan just hoped the bleeding bird flew away before Craig associated the whole event with him. Fortunately for Jonathan, it did.

There were also some humorous incidents and sightings as well, one in particular was firmly stuck in Jonathan's memory. This had occurred down by the river, quite a few years ago now. He had been detecting alongside the grassy bank where, at one time, there had been an old boat shed. All that remained now were a few moss covered timbers jutting out from the river bank and a crumbling concrete floor base. The surrounding area was good for Victorian and Edwardian silver and bronze coins and on one occasion had released an 1857-dated gold sovereign into his finds pouch. However on this particular day, as he had approached a thick patch of bracken he heard some noise. Getting nearer, it sounded rather like a courting couple. Just then a head suddenly popped up out of the green undergrowth partly confirming his suspicions. Then the head had just popped back down. All of a sudden a young lad with an armful of clothing sprang out of the bracken like a flushed partridge and ran off holding up his trousers with one hand. From deep in the undergrowth came an alarmed female voice: 'Oi! Lee, you can't just bloody well leave me here. What's going on?' But Lee had well and truly gone, as he could still be heard crashing through the undergrowth some distance away. Blimey! and there was me thinking chivalry and honour were all but gone, Jonathan thought?

Anyway the long and short of it was that Jonathan had quickly found out there was a rather scantily clad young lady concealed in the bracken a few yards in front of him. Her head had popped up too, accompanied by a startled, but drawn out, 'Bloody Hell! Who are you?' And then this head too went back down again into the bracken. Jonathan stood back some distance, and when she was dressed he looked back to see a pretty young girl, who was clearly very embarrassed. She asked if he could possibly guide her back to the roadside lay-by that she had parked in? It seemed she had no damned idea where she was? Jonathan felt awkward, but said of course he would, after all he couldn't leave a young lady stuck out in the middle of nowhere for a second time could he?

Walking back he discovered she was working temporarily at one of the local farms as a student, in order to get some agricultural experience, and that her name was Kelly. The 'brave' lad named Lee, who had run off was apparently her boyfriend, who had come down from Durham to see her. She then rather mildly, given the circumstances said: 'Durham is where that sod is going right back to, today for all I care! I mean, he left me there all on my own, and you could have been anyone, couldn't you?

Halfway up the woodland path she seemed to have calmed down considerably and said to Jonathan 'So what's all that about then?' pointing at the metal detector. He explained briefly how it worked and that today he had been looking for some old coins down by the river bank. Later Jonathan reflected and thought that Kelly, after everything, seemed quite a level-headed young lady? He considered it would amuse Christine when he told her about this. He could just hear her saying: 'What? Naked ladies in the undergrowth? Right you can stay away from that place from now on!' and he smiled to himself. He had often told people about this incident, and even just thinking about the young lad high-tailing it through the bracken still brought a smile to his face, seventeen years or so after it had happened.

It was now 2018. On several occasions over the last twenty three years Jonathan had encountered criticism from what he called 'those ignorant parties'. He was amazed by some of the attitudes that he truly believed almost seemed to want such things as he finds to remain buried. Once, whilst involved in some TV promotional work, he overheard an amateur archaeologist state: 'Oh, yes indeed. It is basically preferable to me that things remain undisturbed, and unseen, rather than they be found by one of those metal detectorist people'.

Unable to resist he made his way over to this outspoken lady, who was now loudly proclaiming her latest successes on a recently-undertaken site excavation, that she had supervised and had only just completed. This had been carried out on a small Roman settlement site that was also well-known to Jonathan. When he was right next to the lady in question he asked her, 'That all sounds really interesting? I take it that the site has been thoroughly excavated, and all of the finds recorded?' to which she replied: 'Oh, yes. You're that detectorist man, aren't you? Well you lot won't find much up there now. We excavated it traditionally, and sieved everything!'

Jonathan smiled, somewhat revelling in this delightful situation, and enquired: 'How could it possibly be then that he and his friend, Colin, had in the last four weeks found over one hundred and fifty Roman coins, and five brooches, on that very same site?'

Jonathan added that the find spots for these objects were mainly in the spoil heaps, that she had so kindly left still in situ for them. She looked flustered, as indeed she was, and then she made a hasty move away. Apparently someone had just come into the room that she knew from her university days. This confrontation was actually recorded by the film crew and went out on air eight months later, much to the amusement of many a UK detectorist.

Jonathan was to encounter this woman again a few years later, just after the finding of the Crosby Garrett Roman helmet. Apparently she was concerned that the helmet had been finally purchased by a private collector, and had not been placed in a museum. Jonathan could see her point to some degree, but was angry when she had announced: 'Metal detectorists are in it purely for the money! This time, and at all times!'

That was a foolish comment to have made, especially as the relationship between archaeologists and metal detectorists had by then greatly improved to the benefit of everyone. Eventually he had managed to contact her via an Internet forum and challenged her with the following statement:

'I appreciate your concerns madam. However, one of many points you neglect to consider is that:- such a wonderful object would never have been seen at all had it not been for the diligent work of a fellow metal detectorist. Now that it's in a private collection does not mean it will not ever be allowed to be studied further, or even publicly displayed in the future? However, one related point really galls me. Whenever some multi millionaire tycoon, etc., sells a famous painting or vase, it may as a consequence go abroad. Our museums, therefore, have to try and raise the capital in order to acquire it. There never seems to be any negative press, or apparent problem with this? But when a plain old detectorist is involved with a major discovery there is always a hoo-ha about the public purse, and what a struggle there will be to raise the finance involved? This has developed further into a sub-culture opinion that seemingly expects, and politely puts pressure on all detectorists to consider donating their finds for free?

This is great in many circumstances, and indeed often occurs, due to the consideration of the detectorist. However, at the end of the day it's the law that detectorists have to comply with, and that treats everyone in the same manner. So perhaps we could see some evidence of this being fostered by those people who believe we should offer everything for no reward? Do these people, who are so generous with their opinions on the rights and wrongs of others' possessions, go to work and not expect to receive a wage then? In today's tough economic climate we would all dearly love everything to be free. But that's not going to happen, so why should any detectorist be criticised for receiving a reward for, or making some money from the sale of something that they have found - especially when he or she has probably already spent hundreds if not thousands of pounds on a detector, batteries and petrol?'

Funnily enough, he never received a reply.

Jonathan had also been involved in several local amateur archaeological excavations, including a ploughed-out Bronze Age burial mound and the search for a long-demolished row of early Victorian farm workers cottages. He was also primarily responsible for the extensive geophysical survey near the village of Walkern, in Hertfordshire, where an interesting field had revealed the remains of a substantial Roman villa.

From its very conception, he had also been an avid supporter of the Portable Antiquities Scheme over the past decades, and had seen this grow into one of the most detailed research facilities in Europe. However, this was not the only recording scheme that he supports. There are some other superb Internet-based recording sites, and he used many of these to ensure that his finds receive the widest audience possible, and he encourages other detectorists to do the same.

Many detectorists specialise in trying to find types of objects, or series of coins, or maybe artefacts that relate to a particular period in history. Whilst some just love finding anything. In Jonathan's case, he just felt that the finding of Roman coins and artefacts was something that just could not be equalled. The coins and associated objects from

Sketch produced from a recent photograph of Jonathan Pearson whilst detecting. This is titled "Honesty in January 2011" as it was taken in exactly the same place where Joshua and Ezekiel had been 192 years earlier.
(Via the author)

this period are his true detecting passion. For him nothing quite equals finding an area of pottery shards, oyster shells and scattered stones and then digging into an area of darkened soil, and finding a coin or artefact with a deep green-coloured glossy patina. 'Straight away,' he says, 'your brain kicks into that ancient bronze mode.' The delightful arch of a fibula brooch, or that stunning thick edge of a Sestertius coin just before you recover it is about as good as it gets in Jonathan's opinion. Over the years he has made some astonishing finds ,and of course some that are not so astonishing, such as the various sized small lead shot balls that he finds everywhere.

Unknown to him, many of these that are now residing in his odd-ments box, were once fired at pheasants, and other winged or legged countryside edibles, by the two ambitious local poachers, Joshua Klake and Ezekiel Foukes.

Over the years Jonathan had extended his searches westwards to the extreme boundaries of the estate, and in one large area of meadow and arable land had made some very interesting discoveries. In the same area are some curious humps, bumps and a huge linear depression, cre-ated, so it was said, by some previous land owner who, in or around, the mid-eighteenth century, had wanted to drain the land around here. It was also rumoured that he engaged the services of a local vicar, or cler-gyman, to conduct some type of excavation at around the same time. But nothing was now known of what was found at the time?

Parish records show that the large meadow here was known as 'Tur-vey's Holt' at one stage, and then curiously in records thirty years af-ter it seems to have been renamed 'Bullocks Pasture'? Although it was possible some of the rather crude early drafted estate maps and field boundary diagrams might have been misinterpreted by Jonathan? What was curious, though, was that on one of these older maps, just beneath the name, Turveys Holt, someone had neatly written in pencil: 'The field of the Devil's work'.

Perhaps they burned witches there, Jonathan considered? Or could it be that during the Great Plague it was the site where those locals who had succumbed were buried? Whatever, it did seem rather a curi-ous thing to write. Try as he might, there were simply no other records available that indicated why this field should be associated with the dark doings of the Devil. Jonathan had searched where he considered the field to be on several occasions, but it was mostly established an-cient pasture, and those grass roots could defeat the sharpest of spade blades, especially in summer.

Why, when you dug a hole on meadowland to retrieve a target, did there always seems to be one and half times the amount of soil to fit back in? Finds that Jonathan had made here amounted to rather a lot of fired 0.303 bullet casings, plus far too many of their seemingly modern counterparts made by Eley. He also found modern coins, some of which, unusually, were French francs. However, by now Jonathan knew that to write off a site after a few searches was foolish. In his experience, good finds were often made in areas that he least suspected. For example, one year a promising new field can be rather devoid of finds, yet return next year and it is packed full of coins and artefacts from all ages.

One clue that he had found, which hinted at the potential for the area, had been made much further down the slope. A good clear signal had resulted in a small Roman silver coin, which was unfortunately very badly damaged. Something had obviously struck it at some speed to make such a dent, thought Jonathan, as he imagined some Edwardian men on a partridge shoot placing it on a fence post for a target practice-based wager. In fact it wasn't shooters in modern, or even fairly modern times, that had damaged this coin so. It had in fact been damaged as a result of the actions of a young man named Curnos, whose arrow had made this mark upon the coin almost two thousand years before.

So it was, as his metal detectors got increasingly sophisticated and more capable of even greater depths and discrimination, he returned back to this area. Slowly he began making finds of far more interest, and at much greater depths than ever before. One of his best finds was a large Celtic chariot lynch pin - and boy was that at some depth, ten or eleven inches down at least, he reckoned? The lynch pin was a magnificent crescent of bronze inlaid with yellow and red enamels, with a good length of the iron pin still present. Ironically, nearby to this equine-related find, Jonathan found a large modern horse brass with a floral star shaped cut out design.

A hundred or so metres away came even more horse-related artefacts. Jonathan found a group of Celtic terret rings. Tnd these surprised him, as before, the area had seemingly been infested with iron, or so he thought, and he'd had very few positive signals. That day no interference or scratchy sounds at all came from this area. Just goes to show how environments and conditions, even on a single field, can always change.

Later finds included some very good condition Denarii, four of which were from the reign of the Roman Emperor Claudius, although one of these was later confirmed as a plated copy. He had also located quite a number of the larger bronze Roman Sestertii coins, several of which were worn smooth, as well as a sizeable selection of very scattered corroded fourth century coins. Jonathan knew that some detectorists can become complacent with these small Roman issues and think: 'Oh no not another rubbish Grot!' But not him, he delighted in crumbling away the adherent soil and seeing yet another small greenish or black-coloured coin.

However there were always surprises in store, for example once when flicking up a four inch thick piece of turf and topsoil, which unusually revealed many shards and splinters of bone, there sitting right on the side was a true prize indeed. A tiny Celtic coin known as a quarter stater, made of the purest yellow gold, which had been cast and struck over twenty centuries before.

Rubbing the little coin between his thumb and forefinger caused the dark soil to become ingrained into the detailed design, enhancing it even further. As always, Jonathan stopped and wondered who had lost, last touched or seen this small coin? How had it come to be where it was found? In fact all the usual detectorist type of wonderings.

Carefully, he placed his find into a plastic seal top bag, where immediately it created a little circular patch of condensation. Later he was to discover it was quite a common coin of the Celtic king known as Tasciovanus. But who cares, he had thought? Common or not, it had been found after being lost for so long, and that's what is important. On the far side of the meadow he found many of what appeared to be small thin bronze hinges, some of them still had crusty iron deposits attached to them. He had thought they were of some age when he had first found them, but had no idea just how old they would prove to be? It was a chance visit to Verulamium Museum, in St Albans, that identified what, and just exactly how old they were for him.

Whilst looking at the superb displays, Jonathan spotted a mock-up Roman soldier cut-out in a case. Placed onto this, in their correct positions, were examples of all the associated parts of military armour that had been found in and around the site of the Roman City. There on the appropriate sections of armour right before him was a clear example of one of his hinge things.

As his finds increased, it seemed that the Celtic finds were mainly on one side of the valley, with Roman things at the farther end, but centrally, it was a total mix of both types of finds. To all intents and purposes, logically, it looked like there may have been some type of conflict, or even a battle here? But Jonathan was unable to precisely date his finds into that context, it could be that the Celts lived and worked in this area in the first place? Then later, a detachment of soldiers may have been based for some years, perhaps in a temporary fort as yet undiscovered?

There could be hundreds of years separating the loss of the artefacts and coins that he was finding. Jonathan was only one detectorist, though, and although he had made this presumption, he knew what was really required was a good search over a long period of time by many more detectorists. Unfortunately with Craig's attitude seemingly unchanged, he knew that was not likely to happen in the near future. Whatever Jonathan considered, his finds might just reinforce the battle section of the local story he had heard years back, and why not? Certainly something had occurred around where he was searching?

Jonathan had stayed with the Minelab brand of metal detectors, ever since his first machine back in 1995. He still liked their build quality and superb accuracy of performance; they are the detectors that he believes in and consequently have in turn delivered the results. Over the years several detecting friends from the club have attempted to persuade him to try other manufacturer models when out searching, and on several occasions he has done so after persistent pestering. But try for short periods is all he has done, and then these other detectors have always been returned back to their owners, sometimes very very quickly.

However, by now Minelab have upgraded many of their established models, having had a major product launch in 2017. This as a result released a series of totally new highly sophisticated metal detectors onto the market. But Jonathan has stuck with his CTX 3030 detector for about six years now. He is sure that one day something will tempt him to upgrade, but not for now. His CTX 3030 detector had after all been responsible for the vast majority of the finds that he considered impressive. Just like all of his detectors before his CTX 3030 is referred to as "she" or "her" with quite some considerable degree of affection. In fact, unknown to most people, a ritual often occurs when he gets a good signal and has dug it out, as he kneels down to grab each handful of earth to pass over the coil, he actually pats his metal detector like a dog and says: 'Nice one old girl!' every time.

A recent find of note was a German Luftwaffe pilots badge from near the ancient oak trees up in Great High Pasture Field. An enemy aeroplane had crashed up there, or in the same area Jonathan had been informed some time ago.

Another find, that his wife thinks is 'cute', and that strangely he also particularly likes, is a tiny silver bear which has German hallmarks on it. It could well be from one of the air crashes around the village, or

The Pilots badge found at the crash site of a Dornier 17 bomber (Courtesy of Jonathan Pearson)

This is the little silver bear charm that was given to Unteroffizier Edourd Poschenhalter in 1940 by his wife and daughter. It was found sixty nine years later by metal detectorist Jonathan Pearson. (Courtesy the author and J. Pearson)

perhaps lost by of the German teenagers who, he had been told, had actually helped excavate a Roman Villa here just before the last war. Since it was located amongst a few bits of crumpled airframe, Jonathan reckons, chances are it most likely belonged to one of the aircrew, but who knows?

He has also briefly searched around the area where another German aircraft supposedly had come down in the last war and made a few intriguing finds there. However to be honest Jonathan is simply not that interested, personally, in World War Two artefacts. Although he still has great respect for these fragments of aviation history, and has saved the majority of interesting and curious pieces that he has found. Experience means Jonathan is fully aware that you just never know into what area of new research metal detecting might take you next?

Being a well known metal detectorist, he also frequently received phone calls and emails from people asking for assistance, be it helping to locate a lost wedding ring, to checking that someone's beloved pet has not swallowed the front door key again. One area he has tended not to search so much, though, is where yet another German aircraft crashed during the last war. The ground here, as always, is so contaminated with bits of crumpled aluminium alloy that even most of the night hawkers, that Jonathan knew were occasionally visiting this area seemed to be avoiding it too.

Although recently this seemed to have changed a bit, as he had noticed more unfilled holes and soil disturbance appearing in this area. He considered that it was perhaps more likely to be a novice, or maybe a night hawker who had some interest in wartime relics? With his lack of particular interest in war-related things, Jonathan had never got around to researching any of the the history of aviation -related finds. He didn't even know what types of aeroplanes had been involved? Although old Fred Clements had once told him that the pilot's badge he'd found came from an old 'Jerry Heinkel' that clapped down up in the fields in the last war.

Jonathan had often reflected how variable this hobby can be, one week researching a 19th Century military button, the next a small corroded Celtic unit, and then heading off to buy or ordering a book on mediaeval spoons. So you never know, he considered perhaps, one day I will start to hold all these tiny shreds of aluminium alloy in better regard. The day when this would happen was from this point actually not all that far off.

The East Midlands Aviation Group, better known as EMAG, had been established in 1980, under the auspices of Peter Felston, a dedicated aviation enthusiast. At that time many aviation excavation groups had quickly been formed all over the UK, each one competing to do as many digs as possible. Later on, as this aspect of what some term as archaeology-developed, many former excavations were re-dug ,and the pace of these excavations slowed down somewhat.

EMAG was a group of dedicated aviation historians, researchers and archaeologists. Not archaeologists in perhaps the normal understanding of the word, or sense. EMAG are people who always use metal detectors, and who occasionally delve deeply into oil-soaked craters to recover wreckage and artefacts for conservation. The efforts of such dedicated people largely result in the preservation of our aviation heritage for the future and for all to see. The group's slogan is very appropriately "PreservingYesterday Today for those of Tomorrow". Its members come from as far afield as North Wales and Kent.

Over the years, EMAG members have conducted some astounding excavations of World War Two aircraft and on occasion have been instrumental in finding their missing pilots, or the remains of aircrew that still remain trapped in the wreckage of their wartime aircraft. Normally this results in the remains of those pilots being honoured, and accorded a decent burial, which is a befitting finale to those who gave their lives in such a tragic manner. It was members of EMAG that discovered Pilot Officer, Harry Bracey's remains, that had been rammed fifteen feet under a Chiswick pavement, and made it possible, after six decades, to finally inform Harry's one remaining sister that they had found her 'missing brother'. It was also EMAG members that originally found the remains of the sunken German Dornier, that was eventually raised and conserved for display in Hendon Museum.

The group held monthly meetings, to discuss potential sites and associated eye witness accounts. At one of these gatherings it was decided to start investigating what looked to be a possibly good crash site of a Junkers 88 over at Melton Briarsville? Tentative investigations had revealed that the Melanby's, who own the farmland where the Junkers crashed, might possibly be quite receptive to a search for the plane.

The normal routine, once permission was granted, was that the group visit the area, and try to find eye-witnesses to pinpoint the crash-site, if possible? If there are no surviving eye-witnesses then they adopt methodical metal detection or field walking surveys over the suspected crash site. EMAG members also normally try to find local metal detectorists who know the area and can perhaps pin point an impact area through finds that they have made previously. On occasion this has saved many weeks of sometimes fruitless searching in unfamiliar areas. One of the villagers they have contacted had stated that there was a man who had been coming here for years and metal detects all around Melton Briarsville village. This was great news, and a few days later the name of Jonathan Pearson had been given to EMAG, along with a contact number over in Charleston.

So it was that Jonathan arrived home from work one day to find yet another answer phone message asking for help. But this was no missing betrothal ring or door key suspected to be lodging in the stomach of Sam, the golden retriever. It was from a Simon, who was a member of some sort of club, or something that called themselves the East Midlands Aviation Group. Apparently they went around digging up the remains from crashed wartime aeroplanes. The caller had asked if he would consider assisting them in locating a crashed German bomber? Could he possibly call back at his earliest convenience?

Jonathan had to go to a three-day training course, which started the very next day, and consequently forgot all about the call. Returning home he had several more messages that he listened to and the message from the aviation archaeologist was played back once again. Returning the call, Jonathan apologised for the delay and was fascinated to learn that the proposed crash site for investigation was at Melton Briarsville.

'I know that area really well.' he explained, 'I think there were a total of three German aeroplanes that came down around there? I will try and find out some more details for you. In the meantime what are the chances we could meet up? I have some aircraft bits I can show you in my collection of oddments bags and boxes.'

A week or so later Simon, from the EMAG, arrived outside Jonathan's front door. Jonathan had already conjured up an image of what this Simon would look like? quite short perhaps, middle aged with a tweed jacket, a typical archaeologist. He was therefore surprised to find the denim-clad, bearded thirty something on his doorstep announcing: 'Hi! You must be Jonathan? Pleased to meet you, I'm' Simon.

Trying to hide his look of surprise, or guilt at having stereotyped someone, Jonathan invited him in and then rushed off to get the pieces of aircraft. They both sat down to examine some of these finds. Simon showed Jonathan some copies of original wartime documents, that clearly indicated there could still be a lot of aeroplane wreckage buried in the field. Rummaging through the carrier bags and small boxes of twisted metal pieces that Jonathan had collected, Simon suddenly exclaimed: 'That's what we are looking for! That's definitely Junkers 88, brilliant!' He held up several small pieces of crumpled, gold–coloured, anodised aluminium alloy and asked, 'Jonathan, does this all come from one particular area?'

'To be honest I'm not sure? replied Jonathan, feeling more than a little inadequate. 'If I recollect correctly, I think those bits may have come from two of the crash site areas? But I can certainly show you the area where the majority of these pieces came from.'

Simon seemed to become animated with interest, "See the yellow gold anodised colouring? That's classic Junkers factory manufacture!' he explained. However, trying not to dampen all this enthusiasm, Jonathan pointed out that it may be quite some considerable task just to get the Melanby's to agree to a search, let alone a full on excavation. 'Let me discuss it with them, and see what happens?' he said.

The EMAG group considered that with two Junkers 88 crash sites in such close proximity it may be somewhat difficult to pinpoint, and distinguish, which is which? Simon had also said; 'There does appear to be some confusion in the wartime records as well.' He went on, 'It seems only partial human remains were found at both sites, but in both cases the aircrews seem to have been accorded full military burials. However, further confusion emanates from the fact that of the two Junkers 88 crews, only have two headstones in Melton Briarsville churchyard, each recording the crews involved as 'Unknown German Airmen.'

CHAPTER SIXTEEN

EXCAVATING THE JUNKERS 88 CRASH SITE

After some considerable assurances on Jonathan's behalf, Craig Melanby had finally consented to a search for the crashed aeroplane to be conducted over his land. He mentioned that if they find what they are looking for then the matter, and all its implications, will have to be discussed in much greater detail at a later date. From that point it took several more months to arrange all the final details. Finally, an official-looking brown envelope arrived at Simon's house. This contained a licence, giving legal permission from the Ministry of Defence to search the crash site, and potentially excavate it if EMAG considered it worthwhile? Although they had applied to excavate a specific aircraft it was still not known which Junkers crash site was which? That was something the group would definitely have to clearly establish before they could even consider an excavation.

Jonathan was very surprised that Craig had finally allowed anyone else to search around the village; and was quite proud, as he had obviously put forward a very good case from the historical aspect for him to have agreed to this.

On a fine Saturday morning, Jonathan, and five EMAG members, arrived in the gateway to the field, in which Jonathan was fairly certain that most of the unusual yellow-coloured aluminium had been found in.

Seeing the passion and dedication of the EMAG members, he too can feel the anticipation building up. Here he was helping to possibly find a crashed Second World War bomber; he considered metal detecting certainly does take some rather unusual twists and turns. Jonathan pointed out the approximate area and the search commenced.

Within a few moments one of the EMAG members, a man named

Ed, shouted out: 'Got some!' Another piece of the yellow alloy had been found, and everyone ran over to examine the find.

After a few hours, a definite concentration of twisted metal could be determined, and was accurately plotted and marked out. Ed and Mark, another EMAG member, headed back to their cars to get their Forster deep seeking metal detectors. Having found the impact point of an aircraft crash site these detectors will reveal if any substantial wreckage remains deeply buried in situ?

A search was conducted, and after about an hour the news was not good at all – there were no responses from any deeply buried items, such as engines, etc. A rather disheartened discussion was held by the cars about what to do next? 'It looks like we have found the site of the Junkers that went bang and exploded?' said Ed. 'Well I guess that's it for the time being. It's getting on now, I suggest we all head back home and re-assess the other possible area up by Four Acres field in a week's time, if that's OK with everyone?' said Simon. Jonathan added; 'Anyone who wants to is welcome to stay here and have a look around for a while longer?'

However, looming clouds and a slight drizzle that had started resulted in no takers for his kind offer. In the meantime, he decided that a few days later he would have a little search of his own up in Four Acres. It would be great if he could pin point the exact crash area, and then let the EMAG lads know before they up came next week.

Up at Four Acres field his search with the CTX 3030 quickly revealed more small pieces of yellow coloured metal which, Jonathan now knew, came from a Junkers 88 aircraft. He even found some exploded bullet cases, dated 1939. These worried him, as he was sure he had heard Simon and Ed say the crash had taken place in August 1940? Was this the aeroplane they were all looking for?

Just as he was about to go home he had another clear signal, some way from the main concentration. Deciding to dig it, yet another crumpled piece of alloy was unearthed. But this was different, it had partially visible lettering on it, and the torn rivet holes showed it had once been attached to something. Definitely curious? But it did little to alleviate

Jonathan's seemingly dashed hopes of finding EMAG's 1940 bomber for them. The dates on the bullet casings kept nagging at him.

Back at home, Jonathan cleaned the crumpled yellow artefact, and managed to gently straighten out its creases with a dinner knife handle. He gave it one final rinse, to remove the traces of long trapped and compressed soil. A stamped inscription was clearly visible: 'JUNKERS FLUGZEUG BAU IM DESSAU, TYP JU 88, WNr 659'.

Jonathan cannot resist making a telephone call to Simon: 'I'm just checking, Simon. You did say the plane we are looking for came down in 1940 didn't you?'

'Yes it did. It crashed on August 26th 1940, why's that?" replied Simon.

'Then there's some bad news, I'm afraid. I've been searching up there today and the bullets recovered from the site are all dated 1939. I guess that sort of blows us out of the water again, doesn't it?'

'Hey, Jonathan,' Simon replied, 'easy mistake to make mate. On some early German crashes, like this one, it's possible to find bullet casings dated as far back as 1936, which we presume were surplus stocks from the Spanish Civil War period? Initially, the Germans had millions of rounds of stock, and it took some time to use up as the war got started.'

Jonathan was greatly relieved, but now wished he had researched the issue before highlighting his ignorance. Never mind, though, he had learned something, and that's what it was all about.

'In that case, Simon, something else was also found today that I think may be quite useful to you guys? I reckon you'll like this.' added Jonathan. Whilst reading out the details from the small square of metal, he can hear a rustle of papers at the other end.

'Hi Jonathan, just checking something, although pretty certain, hold on....yes..... oh, great stuff! That number '659' is what the Germans call a Werke Nummer, and normally relates to only one particular aeroplane.' he explained. 'In this case, that's the number of the aeroplane we are looking for. You did mark the exact area where it was found, didn't you?'

'No problem.' replied Jonathon, 'I've located a scatter of bits, but this find was some distance away from them. No worries, I can take you to precisely where the scatter is, and where this thing you say is a manufacturer's plate was found as well.'

A few days later the same EMAG members as before, along with Jonathan, find themselves standing around in the field known as Four Acres. 'Mmm! Looks a lot ruddy bigger than four acres!' stated Ed.

Jonathan showed them where he earlier found the concentration of alloy fragments, and it was not long before several EMAG members, with their metal detectors, declare that the impact point has been located. Like the week before, the Forster deep seeking metal detectors were brought into use, and after a short period are classed as 'Off the meter.'

'Ed?' quietly whispered Jonathan. 'What does 'off the meter' mean, when it's at home?'

Ed replied with a beaming smile: 'It doesn't get better than that! Iit means there is still a mass of buried wreckage remaining on the site. One thing is for sure, though, something large is certainly buried right under here! We need to go and see Craig as soon as possible.'

Conveniently the next afternoon, Craig had fortunately agreed to meet and discuss the next phase as it was then called. At the start of the meeting Craig seemed quite positive, until the method of excavation was outlined; he had previously imagined a group of men armed with spades digging a hole some four feet deep. Craig's eyes had bulged, and his skin colour changed a bit when he was told the wreckage could be up to twenty feet down? 'You think that a JCB-style digger will be needed? Bloody hell! I don't know about all this?'

Things then looked to be on an extremely delicate balance. 'What about my mole drains, or any water pipes?' Craig asked.

"We can fix all those, if necessary, when the dig is finished and we start to back fill.' chipped in Simon reassuringly, and added: 'That's no problem to us. We have done it many times before.'

"OK. But what about all the top and sub soils being mixed up when you excavate?' Craig had then wanted to know.

It was at this point that the normally over-chatty and loud Ed simply, and for a change, quietly, added "Mr Melanby, whatever we do, I don't think the soils will be half as mixed up as they were in August 1940, and to be fair still are.'

Simon shot Ed a glance. What he had said was true of course, but perhaps not the most tactful, or diplomatic, approach that could have been applied to the situation. But Craig saw the logical side of what Ed had suggested and replied: 'Well, so long as you put the soils back then as best you can, and the land surface is returned to the same appearance as it was before your dig, I agree in principle, go on then, dig up your bomber.'

September 27th 2018 was the date that EMAG had scheduled to excavate. And on that morning its very keen members started turning up at around 6.30am for a final metal detecting survey, to see if they could locate any interesting artefacts before the main excavation. This resulted in the finding of many more pieces of metal, several small pieces of shattered Plexiglas and one exploded bullet, again dated 1939.

Two hours later, the satisfying chugging sounds of the mechanical excavator, that had kindly been supplied as a generous afterthought by Craig Melanby, could be heard rumbling down the lane. With a mighty burst of power, and black exhaust smoke, it launched itself up the sloped field entrance, trundled down towards the group of assembled men and stopped.

'What ho!' shouted the driver as he jumped from the cabin. 'I'm Mr Melanby's driver, Jack. So, what can I do for you?' he asked, joyfully. 'Digging a hole to get something out is a change for me, I must say. Normally on this estate it's the other way round!'

Listening to what was required, Jack soon had the mighty clawed bucket in operation, scooping out great scrapes of soil. Within minutes EMAG members held up their hands and Jack stopped. Already, there were signs of something interesting? There were dark oily streaks in the clay, and powdery blue deposits, nick-named 'Daz, owing to its resemblance to a well known washing powder. This 'Daz', as several EMAG members explained to Jonathan, was the corroded deposits of Aluminium Oxide from aircraft alloy.

As the digger bucket bit ever-deeper, the ground became a mixture of chalk and clay. 'That's a good sign. Definitely disturbed backfill! Shows something has at least penetrated this deep?' said Simon.

The rich, pungent smell of aviation fuel now became evident and, like the Home Guard some seventy eight years before, various EMAG members were now asked to smoke their cigarettes well away from the excavation. Some very large oil-soaked sections of compressed airframe were now being brought up in each bucketful. One, a large girder-like object was pulled up and was delicately balancing on the teeth of the digger bucket. They were really reaching dense wreckage now, as each bucket scoop crunched and crackled as it ripped through the metal-packed soil.

Simon then requested that each bucket load was placed to one side and carefully metal detected, or hand searched, for smaller items that might be missed. One sharp-sighted EMAG member held up a partially melted green rubber Luftwaffe oxygen mask for everyone to see. This resulted in even more clicking and flashes from mobile phones and cameras. Aircraft wreckage seemed to be everywhere and small groups of people were checking, searching, and examining as much as possible.

As the excavation became deeper the sides were shored up with scaffolding and planks. The sections of compressed airframe started to become even larger. There was some evidence of severe burning at this depth, some of the surrounding clay had almost been fired with the heat, and had turned an orangey brown colour. It was probably when the digger bucket had excavated down to a depth of around fifteen feet the first signs that there was a problem were seen. A shout: 'Simon! Jack! Stop everyone! Look at this - it's a flying boot!' was heard above the roar of the digger engine.

Ed was heard to say: 'Oh heck! That's the last thing we wanted to find. But to be honest, it's not totally unexpected.'

Simon examined the moist leather boot. Amongst the chunks of adjacent oil-streaked clay it was clearly evident that the lower portion of a human leg was still contained in the shrunken leather tube that formed the upper boot section. The bones were brown and greasy-looking, kept in place by the shrunken flesh, and decaying remains of a woollen sock. Jack was asked to take Simon down into the hole in the bucket to conduct an examination; it was wide enough, so there was little danger of a sudden infill slide.

The dig would have to be stopped, and would be delayed until the authorities had been notified, and taken action. At fifteen feet down the bucket stopped and Simon looked around. Pulling at the odd piece of jagged metal, it was clear that there were at least two fragmentary bodies down there, or possibly three? It was very hard to be precise as the remains were just a jumble of shredded Luftwaffe tunic fragments, and shattered bones. 'Sorry everyone, but it's the end of this one too I'm afraid.' Simon shouted up from the hole. 'Someone had better inform the Police, and the Coroner.......... like right now please!'

Simon was correct of course. Under the Protection of Military Remains Act, 1986, if human remains, or unexploded ordnance, etc., are found, the excavation must stop immediately. Some sense of humour was derived twenty four minutes later, when the loud sirens of the Police cars could be heard down the lanes. Swinging into the field, one of them appeared to slip, then slide and lose control. Then, when both cars finally managed to get to the crash site, a young policeman literally flew out of the car and breathlessly asked where the air crash was, and how many passengers were hurt? The flustered guy obviously thought that the air crash had only just happened, and was some type of modern passenger aircraft from Bourton, or close by. Tactfully, but sarcastically, he was informed that 'As for the persons on board, mate, you are just a little late to offer any assistance. Late in fact by some seventy eight years!' The situation had to be explained several times, before it sank in just what the Police had been called for to attend.

Shortly after this, the Ministry of Defence (MOD) excavation team arrived and closed down the site from a civilian angle. As they skilfully excavated, each small fragment of bone was carefully pin pointed with a little red-flagged stick to see if a body-part density could be established? All personal finds were logged and photographed as found. Two Luger pistols were unearthed, three Luftwaffe flying caps, buttons, one wallet containing a bus ticket, a car key and five French coins. The barrel of one of the Luger pistols had been snapped cleanly off in the force of the impact. Particularly poignant were the two twisted Iron Crosses, located amongst some neck vertebrae and skull fragments.

It took them just over a week to painstakingly remove all the fragments of tunic and human bone that they could locate. Eventually the local Coroners van could be seen in the field, also. From out of this appeared two men, who removed and placed on the ground three tiny coffin-shaped boxes in which to collect the remains.

Simon was contacted to say that as far as the MOD were concerned the site was as practically clear as it could ever be. However, should any further human remains be located then, as on this occasion, he must notify the authorities immediately.

The Coroner laid out all the tiny fragments and started to work out how many individuals were evident in the mass of uniform and bones. It took him and his team two weeks to establish their findings. Having assembled two incomplete, but separate, skulls, associated with two virtually complete skeletons. Another series of fragmentary skull sections had included a broken lower jawbone, with perhaps the most awful dental bridgework the Coroner had ever seen completed. There was also a considerable section of spinal column, to which there was evidence of some tissue preservation. But the strange thing was that, despite some bones forming another pair of legs, the Coroner also had additional bones and tissue that indicated a total of three further arms? One was preserved very well in an oil-soaked section of tunic, and was still bearing what appeared to be a thin gold wedding band on one of the shrunken fingers. Upon examination this ring was inscribed around its inner side and related to a wedding that had taken place in 1940. To all intents and purposes it would appear that one of the aircrews' remains had either been consumed by fire at the time of the crash, or possibly still lay undiscovered back at the site?

In the meantime there was a lack of communication between the Coroner and the MOD. Not aided by the fact that the Coroners hand writing had been so illegible that the poor woman, who had later transcribed it for the official report, had simply done the best she could with the details. The MOD, now being satisfied with the forensic report that had confirmed, in their opinion, that all the human remains relating to the crew had been recovered. This resulted in Simon and EMAG being given permission to complete their excavation.

The Coroner's team also had in their possession a crumpled fire-damaged identity tag, found amongst the remains, and had managed to trace this as having once belonged to an Unteroffizier Edouard Poschenhalter. This had then enabled a positive crew identification to be made, and this information was later forwarded and confirmed to EMAG.

Ed was delighted with the identification confirmation as he had been researching the crew members of both Junkers 88's for some time now. It was good to know definitely which crash site related to which? Even with the manufacturers plate that Jonathan had found, he had been slightly uncertain. It was possible that anyone could have picked up, dropped, or relocated the artefact from a crash site in the years since the war? However, a dog tag, in association with actual human remains, was pretty much irrefutable evidence as to the identity of the aircraft involved ,and of course the rest of the crew contained in it.

Ed had also been trying to trace relatives of both aircrews, but so far has had very little luck, only obtaining an address in Germany for a very distant relative of one of the airmen involved. He knows that it is not really appropriate to contact relatives of deceased aircrew personally, especially where there is concern about definite identification. But now, seeing that had been confirmed, Ed saw no harm in pursuing, and contacting, this relative in Germany. Who knows, perhaps they would be interested in attending the finishing phases of the excavation? After all, everyone seems to be interested in their family genealogy these days! Whatever, Ed considered that it's got to be worth trying. And had it been his missing relative buried deeply in a field, he would have appreciated someone trying to find and inform him if they had finally been located.

That evening he tried telephoning the number again, but all he got was an engaged tone, and then the line seemed to get cut off totally. Ed was not one for giving up and tried again the next day as well. Finally, in the evening he got a connection, and heard a voice reply in German. After Ed spoke a few slow words the voice had responded in broken, but reasonably good, English: 'Good evening. Now this is Augsburg 201471. How I may help you?'

Initially, as Ed went on to carefully, and still rather slowly, explain the situation the phone call was punctuated by great lengths of silence from the recipient. Then he replied: 'You say to mean that someone has the very aircraft found that my relative flew back in the war? How incredible that is? I simply cannot believe it!'

Ed thought that, above all the excitement, the man who he is talking too seems quite possibly to be a little drunk, his speech has just that slight giveaway slurred sound. However, to be fair he seemed cognisant of all the facts, so Ed proceeded. Ed had certainly been correct in this case, with his previous assumptions about relatives being interested. Despite still feeling the German relative, whom he was talking too, was perhaps slightly under the influence of alcohol, the man confirmed he would be very interested in coming over to England and seeing the excavation. Ed passed on the details of the location, along with dates and timings for the proposed last phase of the dig.

When Ed had mentioned that the crash site was at Melton Briarsville there was another long silence. Ed thought he detected a very faint but sharp intake, then exhalation of breath from the man, followed by him whispering: 'Melton Briarsville?' Finally a reply came: 'Sorry about that,' the man said, 'all this just has come as rather a shocking to me!' Ed apologised for the intrusion and stated he looked forward to their meeting at the village next week.

Once again, hopefully for the final time, everyone was gathered back in the field at the site, and Jack began to operate the digger. Down at seventeen feet there was a huge 'graunching' sound, that everyone felt the vibrations from through their feet. There was no mistaking this; the digger bucket had just made contact with something very large indeed.

Examination revealed it was the back end of a Junkers Jumo aircraft engine, and with little effort the giant digger bucket scooped around the edges, until it could finally be lifted out. As the bucket creaked and groaned, bearing the weight of its load, everyone was delighted to see that the propeller boss was still attached, along with two very contorted propeller blades still in position. Roughly the same time as this huge lump of aviation history was being hauled to the surface, a taxi was just pulling up outside the Waggoner's Inn.

Out clambered a fairly young man with a rather large rucksack, who then went inside heading to the bar. He looked totally lost and asked the barman, in heavily accented English: 'Does anyone please know where these people are who are digging up the.......um 'flugzeug', apologies......I mean aeroplane, are?' He was taken outside where several villagers pointed over to the direction of Four Acres field. From the general area came the distant tractor like noise of what sounded like a digger. After thanking his helpers, Franz headed off towards it.

Finally lifted to the side of the crater, Jack repositioned the JCB digger and safely placed the huge engine assembly as far away from the excavation as he could. Simon looked up, and pointing said to Ed: 'Hey up! Who's that coming over here?' Ed followed his stare and responded: 'I think this could be my surprise for everyone here today?'

Walking over to the figure, Ed stuck out his hand. 'I'm Ed. Hi there!' The young man stopped, looked at the crater and then replied, in broken English: "Hello Ed, I'm Franz. Thank you so much for inviting me. I believed never this would happen. So tell me, what's going on?'

Franz was given a tour and a full explanation of events so far. At mid-day Simon announced they were all having a lunch break, and anyone was welcome to join him up at the pub. When they were all seated in the ancient wooden-beamed saloon bar Ed had stood up and explained about the research he had been doing. How, frustratingly, he had only managed to trace a single relative from either of the two Junkers 88 crews. Then he introduced everyone to Franz, 'And this, my good friends, is Franz, who just happens to be related to a certain Waldemar Euker, who was the pilot of our Junkers 88.'

Franz was informed again that, although due to all the remains having been so fragmentary, it was impossible to determine exactly which, but the remains of his relative, Waldemar, had certainly been recently located. These, along with his fellow crew members, will at some time very soon be accorded a decent burial in the churchyard at Melton Briarsville.

It was then that Ed also let everyone know that Franz was not the only special guest he hoped will be attending the dig that afternoon, as he has also traced another man. This other person wasn't a relative, but when it came to aerial history relating to the Second World War ,and in particular that of the 26th August 1940, then he was a true expert. Everyone just sat open mouthed in disbelief when Ed mentioned how he had traced this other person and finally persuaded him to come along to the day's event.

Franz then opened up his rucksack and revealed all he knew concerning Waldemar Euker, and also how he had amazingly been an archaeological student here; actually in this very same village back in the 1930's. H revealed that he had participated in some type of excavation and archaeological investigation. Jonathan was absolutely fascinated, especially as this village had once seemed to hold a certain captivation and interest for a relative of his too. Jonathan sat and quietly thought, just what is it about this village? Now here was a German fellow who was in exactly the same position as he was, in having a relative closely linked to the history of this same village.

Jonathan waited until an appropriate gap in the conversation and then sat down next to Franz. 'Hello again Franz, this is a real coincidence. Incredibly, I have a relative also, that had a very closely involvement with this village. It was around the time of the First World War period. And, like your Waldemar, he was interested in archaeology as well. Sadly, though, like your relative he was killed in combat due to a war, such a waste of life wasn't it?'

Franz had over the last week or so been doing some considerable thinking about his own life, which would explain the half pint of fresh orange juice he was now drinking. 'Jonathan, that's incredible, truly.'

replied Franz. 'To now discover, and know, we both have a link to this area. What was your relative's name?' asked Franz.

'Oh, he was called Frederick, Frederick Pearson.' answered Jonathan.

Franz looked puzzled and slightly uneasy , 'Frederick Pearson!' he exclaimed. 'I too have seen that very name mentioned in my relative Waldemar's notes.' Franz then began to rummage around the cavernous rucksack interior and finally brought out a creased piece of paper. Sure enough ,there in the text was the name Frederick Pearson. After some minutes Franz carried on and revealed that, as far as he could make out, Waldemar had been responsible for coordinating a student excavation of a Roman Villa here and had been close to finding something either very rare, or perhaps very valuable?

Franz brought out some more of Waldemar's original notes, and also some diagrams of two curious Roman floor tiles. In addition to these were two aerial photographs of this very area that Waldemar had taken whilst flying over here on operations in 1940. 'These are what it is all about, have a look yourself.' said Franz, as he held up the notes and diagrams. 'Please do have a look at the translations; my relative was fixed on something that they mean. Look also at the map along the bottom. I don't think this is a hoax, by all accounts my great uncle was quite a serious man and would never have dedicated so much time had he believed there was the slightest chance of it not being fact?'

Jonathan leant over and examined everything without saying a thing. He recollected that several older villagers had told him before about these Germans, and how they started wearing Nazi armbands at the excavation, and that it had all started to get rather unpleasant. Jonathan had never thought that one day he would be sitting in a pub with the descendant of one of those very same Germans.

Meanwhile Ed made a humorous comment, suggesting: 'Do you know why the German aeroplane bombed this village? Because the pilot was at school here before the war and the head master caned him severely one day. So he thought he would have his revenge on the village.'

There were many similar tales and local legends like this, very few were ever proven to be factual and yet here they all were sitting and listening to a version of it that was for real. But there was more to it all, Franz had suggested, 'My great Uncle, Waldemar, had certain information that led him to thinking, and believing, there was something buried near this village of great archaeological importance? I'm sure he was near to the finding of it? I really believe my great Uncle Waldemar thought he was on to something?' he went on, 'This does not end here either. He was but only a pilot in the Luftwaffe but he was called to a meeting once with Heinrich Himmler, and other senior Nazi Party officials, what on earth could that all be about? Most people back in Germany make the fun out of my beliefs, and some of this is my fault, but I have always felt there was a thing of truth about all this. I have always wanted to come here and just to look at the area. Incredibly, here I am right now. It seems that the stupid wars we have each other fought have always got in the way of much research that could have been done here, just like it got in the way of the lives of millions of other people.' Then there was a rather awkward silence as everyone present gathered their own thoughts and opinions on war, and most probably about Franz too.

'Well,' said Simon, finally attempting to break the awkward silence, 'Franz, you are here now representing your great uncle's determination, some eighty years afterwards. We can't promise you something valuable, or rare, but we can show you more of what remains from your great uncle's aeroplane. Talking of which ,I suppose that we had better start again.'

Jonathan stayed back a while to chat with Franz further. 'Simon, I'm just taking Franz to the local museum. Can you delay by say, half an hour?'

Jonathan had wanted to show Franz the section of Roman tile that was held in the museum. Provided of course this Waldemar had made accurate original drawings of the tiles he found and saw, then the scratched writing on the fragment, up at the museum, looked to be almost identical. This was something that Jonathan wanted to look at, and resolve immediately.

Moments later they both walked into the museum and began closely comparing the tile fragment on display with the drawings Waldemar had made back in the 1930's. 'Unless this is one massive joke then I'd say that the style of writing on the diagrams and the writing on this tile in front of us is possibly that of the same person?' said Jonathan.

Franz once again got out all the paperwork he had. 'Jonathan, look at the tiles, at the map, does it not look quite similar to this section shown on my great uncles photos?' he suggested. 'I have not noticed this detail before.'

If you took into account the landscaped lake to the west, and some other minor changes around village that have occurred in centuries past, and since the war, then it was true, it did bear a great resemblance indeed. On Waldemar Eukers wartime photographs were evident the very faint crop marks of what appeared to be a cluster of three possible round barrows? When compared to the so-called map on the two tiles they did seem to line up with three circles, that had been incorporated into some type of winged animal. On the wall to the side of them was a copy of a large aerial photograph that the Melanby's had taken of the estate in the mid 1960's. This clearly showed some extensive tree-felling had then just taken place in Pickard's Wood. This clearance revealed a huge circular earth-work formation from the air, which then had been assumed to be something to do with drainage, or perhaps the original site of another ornamental lake? Whatever, when this aerial photograph had been taken it was not recognised as being any impor-tant archaeological feature.

As Franz and Jonathan compared all the diagrams and photographs it was clearly evident that this formation was the same as that depicted as the head of the abstract animal shown on the drawing made of the first tile to be found. 'Whatever that thing is,' said Jonathon, 'it was definitely part of the landscape of this area two thousand years ago! Look, it lines up almost perfectly when you examine those three bar-rows, or whatever they are. I'm hazarding a guess, but it looks like the person responsible for making the tiles utilised the landscape that then existed to create an abstract type of animal? It looks like a giant hare or rabbit to me?' Jonathan became excited, 'Franz, we are going to need time to study and assess all this properly. Here is not the place.'

Franz agreed and replied: 'Jonathan, we may not have much time to assess. Where the aircraft dig is going on seems to be the approximate area marked with this square shape that has a letter 'B' above it. Don't you see, Jonathan?' said Franz. 'It is just possible that where we are digging right now is very near to this burial, or whatever it is? he deliberated. 'The disguised animal map and the photos, Jonathan, they cannot be a hoax? Now I am here, I can feel that this is all very important. I feel something is about to happen?'

'This is certainly exciting enough, Franz, but we should get back to the aeroplane excavation for now anyway. Otherwise, my friend, it will all be over and you will miss what you came over here to see. I'm sure we will have the time and opportunity to assess and plan our research later this evening.' Jonathan suggested. 'Are you are staying at Simon's tonight? Or has someone booked you a room in the pub? He enquired.

'In a room at the, as you say, pub. I've decided to stay until Waldemar's funeral.' Franz explained. 'Right now, Jonathan, I do not know what exactly I did come over here to see? But I felt I simply had to be here. For whatever reason, or what might happen, I know somehow I made the decision correctly.'

Just as they were about to leave the building, Jonathan stopped to look at the display of Roman urns and pots. 'Franz. Hold on.' Jonathan said. 'Just get those diagrams out again, can you. Look at that.'

There in front of them was a pale fabric fragmentary Roman-period cremation urn with a slip -decorated design on it of a man feeding a deer. 'Look at the lettering above the deer. It reads 'VELAS'.' said Jonathan. 'I wonder if that's any connection to the person referred to as 'VELAS' on the tile diagrams? It seems everywhere we turn another clue is appearing, but a clue to what?''They discussed the matter as they quickly headed back along the lane and down into the field towards the excavation.

At the crash site Simon had been as good as his word; further excavating had only just started when Jonathan and Franz finally rejoined everyone. Both of them seemed rather preoccupied with chatting and pointing all around them, rather than watching the actual proceedings, this factor being briefly noticed by several people. Then everyone's attention was totally distracted by Ed, who suddenly jumped up said: 'Oh yes, this is brilliant! Makes the day! History can really come alive, right now and right here!'

'What on earth is he on about now?' half whispered Jonathan to Franz. But before Franz could reply it was all made clear. The guest that Ed had mentioned earlier in the pub had just arrived at the top end of the field. At a fraction over one hundred years old, Pilot Officer Kenneth Lumsden could now see where the German aircraft that he shot down, nearly eight decades before, had ended its days.

Although this was one of seven enemy aeroplanes that he had shot down during the war, he had stated he had always meant to pop up and take a look at this one. After the war things were a little hectic and Kenneth never found the time, too much was happening then and it all started rather quickly to feel so long ago anyway. He had questioned as to whether there even a point to visiting here back then? After all it was just a phase in his life; just Kenneth Lumsden basically doing the job he was paid to do at the time. His son had been the one who had taken the call some months back from Ed and then passed the information to his father, for whom the whole event had suddenly sprung back into crystal clear sharpness.

As Kenneth's wheelchair was somewhat awkwardly pushed over the last remaining few feet of stubble, he obviously doesn't quite know what to make of it all. He was amazed at the size and depth of the excavation, 'I always thought it just crashed onto the ground.' he commented, 'I never even considered it would go down to such a depth?' He was there to witness several large sections being unearthed and seemed to relish in all the attention. It wasn't too long before a faint moistening could be seen around Kenneth's eyes. 'Such a waste of young life!' he kept saying.

He brightened up a whole lot when Ed brought him a little souvenir. 'Here you go sir, a section of airframe with two bullet holes evident in it. To think that it was you that personally fired them all those years ago, and now you are here today, what a brilliant timeline!' said Ed.

The airframe wasn't the only souvenir Kenneth would take home from that day. Jonathan also gave him three fired brass 0.303 cartridges. When Jonathan had first started metal detecting around the village an elderly man named Alf Symons came up and said: 'Here lad, you like history. You'd better have these,' handing the cartridges to him.

It transpired that Alf had also witnessed the aerial dogfights back in August 1940. Years later when he was cleaning out his guttering, that had got so choked and clogged up in the early 1960's, the three shell casings were found amongst the moss and decayed leaves. Now Jonathan didn't know if they were directly attributable to Kenneth's actual action, but they did relate to the 26th August 1940, when a much younger Kenneth Lumsden had put his life on the line. He deemed them a suitable present to give him.

There was something else that the aged pilot would take from the site, that would remain with him for the last few years of his life. This was something unseen, a raw emotional experience that only someone who has ever been in a similar situation can perhaps describe. Franz had discovered who this elderly man was, and wondered if he should introduce himself, or would it be too embarrassing for them both? Eventually he decided the opportunity should not be missed and strode over and shook the elderly man's hand for a few seconds. He introduced himself as Franz, and then just held the old man's hand tightly, released it and walked away. "Well who was that polite young German fellow?" Kenneth Lumsden had asked. When it was explained, Franz looked over to see the old man pursing his lips and squinting as if in deep thought. Then he had looked over at Franz and smiled warmly, no words needed to be said between them; there was an instant understanding forged between them. An understanding and an experience that both men would indeed remember forever. So it was that a young German man actually met the man who had killed his great uncle nearly eighty years ago.

After an hour, Kenneth's son indicated it was perhaps time to go, as a slight breeze that had sprung up was 'making Dad a little uncomfortable'.

Pilot Officer Kenneth Lumsden was watched by everyone as he was finally driven away, a quick visit, but as Ed said, 'He was here. Kenneth Lumsden was actually able to see the very aircraft he destroyed so long ago being excavated today, how brilliant is that?'

Another aircraft engine, some fifteen feet to the side of the previously found one, had now been located. This example was not in such good condition and fell apart as it was removed, forming a sloppy cascade of clay and metal. Once a powerful and superbly engineered German power plant, it now lay as a mass of fractured engine casing with its pistons sticking out at all angles. Once recovered, many sections of the engine casing were seen to be badly scorched, and there were even several bullet strikes that could be seen.

In the centre of the two engines, and about two more feet further down, the shattered remains of what was once part of the forward cockpit area was found. This was very carefully removed, so as to avoid any damage to the instruments and controls. Huge amounts of wiring and compacted panelling were found, along with several large crushed sections of the frontal glazed section. A violently folded piece of airframe from this area had red painted lettering on it, but only the letters 'Ma' could be distinguished. Amongst all this was found two very battered MG 15 machine guns, one of which had been bent into almost a complete circle so violent had been the impact. Another hour saw what Simon and several other EMAG members announce to be the 'Bottomed out' stage of the dig. Further scoops revealed the soil was devoid of any discolouration, disturbance or wreckage. 'OK, I think that's it!' announced Simon.

CHAPTER SEVENTEEN

OLD LEADEN SHEETS AND DEAD AIRMEN

At Simon's request, Jack then backed the JCB away a short distance, as EMAG now needed to run the Forster metal detectors over and around the site to complete a final check. Several times in the past it had been these final checks that had located another patch of buried wreckage. Blast from impact can do strange things when an aeroplane hits the ground at three hundred miles per hour or more, and not everything is always located where it is logically expected to be. It had been just such a final check on the Sombourne Heinkel 111 dig that had revealed four buried SC50 bombs, quite some distance away from the main wreckage. The same final checks had revealed a detached engine from an RAF Short Stirling bomber over fifty feet away from the other three engines.

Ed was painstakingly searching around the area when he said: 'Nope! Nothing left here. Looks like we got it all? Well done everyone.'

It was at that point Simon asked if Ed had previously checked the area where the JCB was now positioned? 'Good point there, Simon, ooh, err... sorry about that one!' and Ed commenced the last section of his search.

Only one or two people noticed the slightly puzzled expression on Ed's face as he asked Jack if he could possibly reverse back further, just to make sure the detector wasn't picking up the digger. Ed adjusted the controls and walked backwards, forwards and backwards again. As always there was the hope that the day's activities were not quite over, that the soil had one last secret to reveal. This hope was to be realised when Ed said: 'Sorry Simon, but the Forster is kicking off big time again. I'm still getting another reading here, and it's really big, and very deep.' continued Ed, 'Anyone know if this bugger dropped all its bombs? Or did it even have any – if it was a reconnaissance plane?' he queried, 'As I can't think what else this could be? If it had bombs and didn't get rid of them all previously then I would hazard a guess we have a very large bomb still on site, perhaps a 'Hermann'?'

Jonathan asked what a Hermann was? Whereupon several EMAG members informed him that, as a jest, the Luftwaffe, and indeed Allies, often referred to the larger German bombs as Hermann's. This was in reference to the girth of the wartime Luftwaffe leader, Hermann Goering, who was rather on the fat side.

'Well, what do we all do guys, any ideas?' asked Simon.

The decision was made to dig the signal, but to stop at the first sign of bomb tail-fin fragments, or any evidence indicating that a bomb, or bombs, were still present? They informed Jack, who with some trepidation, slowly began to dig the new area. The next deep scoop brought up a some fragments of orange-coloured tile fragments, which were of course ignored by EMAG, as they are obviously just infill from when the crater was backfilled and levelled off. Many farmers took advantage of bomb craters and aircraft crash sites, using the resultant craters to dump unwanted things into. In EMAG's experience, unwanted could range from old tires, bedsteads, piles of hardcore, dead livestock and so on. Even on one occasion, an almost complete old car chassis.

It was Franz who then rushed round the back; he had seen that tile and signalled to Jonathan to come over too. They both began to examine the muddy pieces of tile and Jonathan began to clean one with his hands.

'Franz. Look at this, it's that same scratchy spidery writing again.' observed Jonathan, gathering all the fragments together. They started to sort them out and to re-assemble what they could. After about an hour, fortunately they can then see that there is only one small piece missing. Judging by the precise shape, that piece was the very fragment they had just been looking at in the museum a short while before.

'Hey, you two. Its Junkers 88 today, OK? Not old bits of barn roof tile!' an EMAG member shouted jokingly. The smashed tile was assembled but Jonathan and Franz were not able to read Latin and neither,

Sketch of Tile 3 as seen upper right

Beneath this simple baked tile lies our noble Queen titled **BODVOCCA** and her two daughters CEARRA and BRETTA made of King PRASUTAGUS. I cannot foretell and do not know whether history will remember her as we do. In case she sleeps into the unknown then this inscription will serve to evoke her spirit once again into life by giving identity to the noble souls that rest beneath.

I am indeed her last dedicated servant **VELAS**

Tile 3 (placed above the burial chamber) inscription consisting of 15 fragments found in 2018 so far as they know, can anyone else on site. For the time being the tile is relocated to a safer place on some grass over by the hedge. Suddenly the JCB lurched backwards violently. An object of incredible weight had caught up in the teeth of the bucket.

Jack began to skilfully wrestle the controls and was obviously in trouble, as the engine screamed and thick black smoke belched from the exhaust stack. The bucket simply won't budge an inch. Then, with a mighty flint-crunching judder, followed by a hollow dull ripping sound, the bucket finally burst upwards with a huge sheet of white lead sheeting draped over it. Dragged up like a heavy damp carpet from a depth of four feet, the dry top soil tumbled and flowed down the thick sheeting in mini avalanches. A slight breeze picked up which created a series of flurries of white powder from the surface of the lead sheet.

'Crikey! That looks very old indeed!' announced Jonathan, 'That creamy white-coloured oxide takes a really long time to form on lead.'

EMAG members, and everyone else, were puzzled? What the heck were great sheets of lead doing on a World War Two aircraft crash site? Had a previous farmer, or someone else more recently perhaps, stolen a load of lead from a church or other rooftop and perhaps used the crater to hide their metallic contraband?

'If this lead came from an old church roof that would certainly explain its colour, I suppose.' Jonathan went on to say. 'Although thinking about it, perhaps not, as this lead is far too deeply patinated than anything from a church roof could be. In my opinion such colour is almost certainly indicative of Mediaeval, maybe even a Roman date? Or it could be much earlier? It's possible that it could be a Roman military deposit of lead perhaps? I know for a fact that the military had some presence around here in those times, and some huge stamped lead Roman ingots were found not that far from here some time ago.'

Most of the topsoil was then carefully removed. And very slowly the lead sheeting was pulled back by the JCB and removed to the side. Beneath this sheeting could be seen a very dark-coloured area and amongst this was evidence of the remains of what were once huge wooden beams or planks. Ed walked to the edge and examined the excavation so far. 'Reckon we might have an old well here, that's been capped? I've seen railway sleepers put across old well tops before. Might be an idea to be cautious, some of these old wells can be damn deep!' he said.

Some eighteen inches from the edge of one of the lead sheets a roughly hacked circular hole was found, approximately nine inches in diameter. This caused some passing interest; 'Oops.., looks like someone's been here before?' thought Jonathan. Initially it was suspected that some type of agricultural equipment may have somehow caused the puncture? However, repeated hack marks and scars looked more like the cut out had been deliberate, as opposed to an accidental impact. Someone even asked if it could be evidence from a soil core sampling borehole? Somewhat humorously, Ed added: 'Or what about an extremely determined badger?'

Unknown to anyone attending that day the roughly hacked hole had been made some seventy nine years before, by Waldemar Euker. Hours later all the lead had eventually been moved some distance away. Now the Forster metal detector was brought back into operation again and the large signal, or at least another signal discounting the lead, was still evident. 'Still something down further here, and also fairly deep!' said Ed.

What had been wooden planking had, in most areas, decayed away, remaining as just a rich peat-like darkness in the soil but adjacent to some of the lead sheeting small dry crumbling sections of wood were still to be seen. Excavating through this fine friable layer was very easy. Jonathan was looking over at Franz, who returned his look with a knowing smile. Both were thinking: what the hell is all this about? A layer of thick lead sheeting that had been placed over wooden planks at some period. Jonathan began to wonder if Ed was right. This could be an old water well that has been capped off at some stage.

Further down, at a depth of around five feet, they found a few iron nails and, rather unexpectedly, a small scatter of little silver Celtic coins, which Jonathan identified as the same type he had found from the period of King Tasciovanus.

'Can't be a well with all those coins, can it?' puzzled Franz. Jonathan was certain that the coins themselves were not sure date indicators. They could have been placed there at any time since they were minted. It's just one of those things, he thought, if my house in Charleston fell down and the builders later found all my Roman coins in the rubble, that wouldn't mean that the house dated to the Roman period would it?

'Perhaps this is a good time to take a short break and assess just what is going on here? This looks perhaps to be an area for your expertise, Jonathan.' suggested Simon. The others agreed, and immediately there was a rustling of wrapping papers as various petrol station-purchased pasties and pies were unwrapped, accompanied by the plumes of steam from several Thermos flasks.

The conversation then covered everything from the possibility of this being the foundations of an air raid shelter, to an old stable. Clearly such a copious quantity of lead was unknown, surely, in the construction of any such things? However it was always useful to discuss all the possibilities, as this could trigger recollections of previous encounters of similar findings.

'While we've got a moment, I don't suppose anyone knows anything about Latin, do they?'' asked Jonathan. This created a few puzzled glances that shot his way. 'Yeah. It's a dead lingo!' Ed piped up 'Only of use to the Romans, and those geeky scientist people.'

Looking a bit embarrassed, Vic, a relatively new EMAG member admitted, 'I know a bit about it, but my missus, I think, can read most stuff, including classical!'

Simon and Franz went over to the hedge and brought back all the tile fragments and placed them down, reforming them. 'What can you make of this lot then, Vic?' asked Franz, who was now obviously feeling secure, welcome, and rather at home in this environment of aviation archaeologists. Minutes later Vic stated: 'It's something to do with a Queen, or similar,' he began, 'with her two daughters. It doesn't make any sense to me? Tell you what, let me take a close up photo with my phone and send it by text to the wife. Sure she can help us with this?'

'Ok, shall we crack on then? Providing, of course, Jonathan and Franz haven't found any more tiles to delay things?' quipped Simon, sarcastically.

Jack jumped back once again in to the cabin of his JCB digger, definitely seeming a lot happier, as the chance of a large blast, courtesy of the Luftwaffe, had been drastically reduced. All of a sudden all was definitely not right with the excavation; a huge crack had appeared in the top soil that formed the ridge between the old excavation and this latest one. With a massive use of the throttle Jack reversed the digger quickly away, as it was slipping downwards with the sliding soil into the first excavation area. More throttle and the digger lurched backwards and onto the level. With a moist-sounding suction noise approximately ten tons of soil, chalk and clay slammed sideways and spread out into the original hole. At the bottom of the latest excavation something had just been revealed, something unexpected and very definitely not wanted.

Approaching the edge of the newly-formed cavity with great care, they all looked down to the side, now totally exposed, were the obvious remains of another World War Two airman. This time the body, amazingly, although severely damaged, wasn't smashed into fragments, as his fellow comrades had been. Incredibly, he had also been well preserved.

Closer observation revealed that the body only had one arm. The flying tunic, although torn and shredded, had held together. A throat microphone was clearly visible just under the lower jaw. No one said a word, until Ed piped up: 'Police, Coroners, MOD, here we go all over again. Is this site jinxed, or something?

No sooner than these exasperated words came out of Ed's mouth there was another small slide of soil, making everyone jump further back. This soil movement partially covered over the remains of the dead airman, but revealed a slight cavity to one side, approximately three feet in length. This latest cavity had the dark appearance of being only a small visible section of something that was much larger.

Ed was then elected to make all the necessary phone calls and Simon apologised to everyone: 'Sorry guys the digs off yet again, what with Human remains, and the fact there is some type of underground cavity opening up, we can't take any chances.'

As soon as he said that a mobile phone rang. It was Vic's. All everyone heard, as Vic moved away, was: 'Don't take the mickey! Are you sure about all this, love?' Several people assumed he had been called home, maybe for an urgent shopping trip to the supermarket, or perhaps another similar project that simply couldn't wait for a few more hours. Vic gestured to Jonathan and Franz to come over, 'OK you guys, this is all over my head but may mean something to you? But Sue, my wife, wants to talk to you, Jonathn, if that's OK?'

For the next few minutes Jonathan said very little, because his jaw kept dropping open as he was trying to balance the conversation he was hearing with known historical facts. The voice on the other end of the phone had said: 'I have translated the text, no problems at all, but I must admit to being puzzled as to what this is all about?'. She went on further to ask: 'I'm also puzzled further as to what this all had to do with my husband, Vic, who was supposed to be out digging up some old aeroplane.' The translation she gave to Jonathan was, in her opinion, about as accurate as she could provide. She spoke: 'Beneath this simple baked tile lies our noble Queen titled Bodvocca and her two daughters Cearra and Bretta made of King PRASUTAGUS.'

'Who's this 'Bodvocca', and this King 'Prasu..' what's it? Let me check again Prasutagus?' Vic's wife puzzled.

'Please, Sue, please! This is great stuff. Just carry on, this is really kind of you.' Jonathan hurriedly and diplomatically said, as he was trying to write all this down on a sheet of notepaper balanced on his knee.

Sue continued: 'I cannot foretell and do not know whether history will remember her as we do. In case she sleeps into the unknown then this inscription will serve to evoke her spirit once again into life and giving identity to the noble souls that rest beneath.

I am indeed her last dedicated servant VELAS

CHAPTER EIGHTEEN

JUST WHAT ARE THE CHANCES?

Jonathan clearly heard Vic's wife saying; 'Hello, hello is anyone still there? What are you all up to?' And then her conversation just seemed to fade away in Jonathan's ear. Of course he didn't mean to be rude at all, but almost like a robot, he then simply clicked the phone to off and passed it back to Vic.

Jonathan's mind was just all over the place. He knew all about King Prasutagus ,and how the Romans had allowed him to remain as a client king. He knew that when he died his wife had attempted to retain the kingdom of the Iceni tribe, and that the Romans had absolutely no intention of permitting this to happen. Her tribe and all its lands were eventually seized and absorbed into the Empire and would pay a tribute to Rome, like all such subjects. But her name, as far as history knew was Boadicea, or more recently it was claimed likely to have been Boudicca. Boadicea was after all most likely a suitable sounding name that the Victorians had given her. He was certain it was definitely the more recent publications that had named her Boudicca. But how did anyone know what she was really called?

As the excitement welled up it seemed clear to Jonathan that the references to this 'Bodvocca' were quite clearly one and the same person as Boadicea. How the hell was he going to deal with this? How would he tell those in his present company that the search for an old aeroplane wreck, German at that, had actually revealed something even more fantastic?

He was trembling and sweating to such a degree that those close to him thought he looked and felt decidedly unwell, or surely was about to have a heart attack? Franz stumbled over and looked at him 'What did she say it all means, Jonathan?' he asked. 'It is who we thought it was, isn't it? It's her it is, tell me it is! Tell me it is your long lost Queen Boadicea.'

Jonathan looked at Franz and quietly whispered: 'No, it isn't!' Franz looked devastated, Jonathan continued, 'She was actually. called Bodvocca. And to all intents and purposes, yes it appears that at last we have found her, and she is no longer lost!' They both then punched the air, shouting out: 'YES!'

Startled at this outburst everyone else glanced round. Normally on an aircraft dig, such an action heralds the discovery of a really superb and interesting find, an aircraft-related find. Everyone gathered around the tile and was told the meaning of the text, that had just been translated. Franz and Jonathan then took it in turns to relate the entire tale as they knew it from 1914 to the 1930's.

'What the hell do we do about this?' 'You are joking?' and other unrecordable expletives were soon heard in profusion. Franz filled in some more gaps, based on a flurry of questions and said emotionally 'It would seem that my great uncle had been correct all along? But there are great reservations I have in being joyful about his efforts. He seemed in my opinion to be involved in something that, potentially, would have used this discovery for political purposes. Although I can't be certain absolutely of my suspicions at this stage but, if what we suspect actually lies here, I'm glad he didn't succeed. If we are correct, then I can think of no better group of people who should have made this discovery possible than those I am with today, thank you everyone.'

'Well, no worries Franz. I guess it's not the first time someone in history has tried to make Boadicea, sorry.. who is it? Bodvocca, a puppet for their own purposes eh?' Said Vic.

'Very profound, Vic, but we are really in a dead serious situation here; none of us has the experience in any capacity to deal with such a major issue.' said Simon.

'Oh sod this for a laugh!' said Ed, 'Aren't we are all talking here about something that, as yet, none of us have even seen? We don't know it exists and here we are talking as if it does!' he continued. 'Ok you are the ancient history guy. What do you suggest we do then, Jon?' said Simon.

236

'I'm sorry. I know it's against all conventions and regulations, but I'm going down into the excavation to have a look.' Jonathan blurted out in response.

Everyone knew this wasn't safe. But so far, if the assumptions were right about all this, it was generally agreed someone should at least take the initiative, and the risks, of looking and confirming that something did actually exist down there? Since it was Jonathan who had helped out so much and got the permission to excavate then why not him?

'Ho! ho! That's what I like to see, go on boy get down there. Sod health and safety, and all that guff eh?' chortled Ed.

As if to half disagree with Ed's comments, Jonathan made an exaggerated gesture in putting on his bright yellow plastic safety helmet. Skilfully negotiating the freshly fallen soil, Jonathan made his way downwards, looking at the still visible sections of the dead airman. He was sure there was a musty smell emanating from them? Then finally, he clambered down to the opening. Looking inwards it seemed to be a large but very narrow space of air, partially filled with soil that had settled.

'Anyone got a small torch, so I can get a better look?' he shouted upwards.

Seconds later a small Maglite torch was lobbed down, and stuck upright in the soft clay. Grabbing it and twisting its top produced a thin beam, that then probed deep into the dark cavity. Not much could be seen at first. Jonathan, who was struggling to get into a more secure and comfortable position, then shone the torch downwards into the cavity more by accident than deliberately. There about six feet below he spotted something.

'Oh Jesus!' he gasped. Clearly, in the beam of light there were hundreds if not thousands of shining coins in the soil. Unable to contain himself, he shouted up: 'It's treasure! It's the treasure! There are thousands of coins – and they look gold to me? We had best get Craig and Candice down here, right now!' he said, somewhat surprised at just how authoritative he now sounded.

Inwardly he smiled and thought to himself: Blimey, if old Craig was annoyed at the cars that turned up when that rare bird appeared a few years back, just imagine what he will be like here? I reckon he's going to see a few more vehicles around here, and very shortly too. Still, somehow I don't think he will be all that annoyed this time?

He then shone the small torch back into the cavity, just to make sure it wasn't all a dream. It clearly wasn't. Feverishly, he carried on 'OK guys, there's no dispute. We've found the big one OK. I don't know if its Bodvocca, or Boadicea, or whatever she was called? But there are thousands and thousands of gold coins down here. Next second saw a stumbling Ed and Simon coming down, 'Come on, Jon, let us see mate. Give us that torch.'

Candice Melanby had been a frequent visitor to the aircraft excavation, popping down for a few minutes here and there. It was her that the team first met back up at the Manor. She was simply overawed. 'What a fantastic thing to happen on our estate! Thank you all so much.' she said, as she grabbed her wax coat and struggled to put on her Wellington boots. Her brother, Craig, she explained, was away on some agricultural conference in Kent. But when he returned a day later he, too, seemed very excited and decided to go immediately to the site. Beforehand, though, he went over to his office to get something, and came out looking rather happy.

At the excavation site, Craig was enthusiastic and listened with intent to every word. Then he called Jonathan over to one side, 'I trust we have not forgotten about this?' he said, holding up a crumpled piece of paper. It was their original land owner finder agreement.

'Not at all,' said Jonathan, smiling broadly, but finding his authoritative manner again said 'but perhaps there is a better time for us to discuss such matters eh, Craig?' Jonathan continued to smile outwardly perhaps for diplomacy, inwardly this was typical of Craig, he thought.

The discovery was reported immediately to all the correct authorities, from the Police to the Coroner, to PAS to the local FLO, and this information was then passed on very quickly to a select band of senior archaeologists and specialists. The question now was how to process this information, to get the best data in the early stages from such potential?

In fact this was never formulated into a rigid plan, as it was decided that within forty eight hours the site must be fully investigated, and excavated. It was simply far too huge a discovery to dither about with it, apparently. The Police were guarding the site under the general impression that they were protecting the human remains found there by some souvenir hunters? Actually the MOD had cleared the remains of the airman away from the site the very day they had been discovered. These were now placed along with the others, deposited at the Coroner's office for further investigation, and had caused no small level of embarrassment.

A few days afterwards, whilst the delicate layers of crumbling Luftwaffe combat tunic fabric were being removed, the skeleton began to dis-articulate. There was some embarrassment amongst the laboratory juniors when the skull, and remains of the flying head gear, detached themselves and rolled away down the stainless steel table. However, in doing so the mass of faded blue floral patterned material around the neck vertebrae had also come apart, revealing a small silver coloured metal chain. When this was examined it was found to have the airman's identity tag still attached to it. This had a series of numbers on it which would have to be verified, but just below them in die-punched lettering was the name W. EUKER.

Franz took a phone call a few days later from a very nice lady in the Ministry of Defence asking him to attend a Coroners hearing in relation to the remains. Jonathan attended with him, and when it was all over Franz stood outside and simply said: 'So, after all it seems my great Uncle really did come so very close to finding this treasure? But I bet he never ever could have imagined, even in his worst night mares, that one day he would physically die with it?'

Two days after the discovery had been made it was of course decided to officially excavate the site, which was not in accordance with the original hastily drawn up decisions. Consequently the rumour had time to spread around. In addition to the two hundred invited official persons, another hundred or so others were milling around trying to get a better view of things. Such numbers inevitably created further rumours and questions, many of which flew around in and out of the Waggoner's Inn bar area.

'What? Two hundred people here just for a load of old bombs? Don't be an arse Jock!' one villager was heard to say to his friend.

Whatever, though, it was obvious something serious was definitely going on down in Four Acres, and most villagers accepted that they would find out sooner or later and tried to resume their normal lives. Several small children tried to access the field to see what was happening. They were seen hiding in the hedge and ushered off the site by the Police, who were seen to be everywhere, protecting something, but doing little to reassure the villagers that all was well with their community. A huge marquee-style tent had been erected in the field, and so further obscured anything that was going on. Temporary accommodation came in the form of loads of those chip board-panelled, quick-build, office units, followed by lots of essential portable toilets.

CHAPTER NINETEEN

HAROLD'S RETURN

Just as the last toilet cubicle had hit the damp grass and was positioned at the site, a telephone began to ring in the office of Harold Foster. This 'office', as he always referred to it, was quite a large room in his house dedicated entirely to his dealings. Harold had had this room oak-panelled, not so much because he wanted it in that style, but more because he believed people who came there were slightly ill at ease by its officialdom and serenity. That was a good thing when one was dealing with some of the less intelligent clients that he encountered. 'It puts you at a definite advantage. You should see some of the unbeatable bargains that I have obtained in this room!' he would say.

The office wasn't exactly organised, or even tidy, but Harold had his systems amongst all this chaos, and he knew them well. Five years ago he had purchased some silver Celtic units from a group of night hawkers who came from north Oxfordshire. He had sold on all but two of them, making a tidy little profit; the two remaining coins were placed into a brown envelope labelled: 'Oxford Celts'. Harold had decided to retain these examples and he knew exactly where, amongst all the files and battered papers, those two little coins were. That was just the type of person he was.

Picking up the phone, he discovered it was Malcolm, 'Harry. I've just been told that there is something really big going on up at Melton? Can't say how I heard, but it's an ancient burial, or something? I just thought you would like to know? Bloody Police are crawling all over the show, though.' he added, 'But I reckon we should go up there and have a look around. You know, do the usual: take some binoculars and a bird identification book, so if anyone challenges us, we can simply say we are bird spotters.'

Melton Briarsville again! That damned village! thought Harold. I've had enough of that place. It seems to haunt me. But this does sound extremely worthy of investigation?

Minutes later, Malcolm's blue Ford Mondeo arrived. Suitably attired for their afternoons bird watching', they both departed. Arriving in the area, they eventually drove several times up and down the lane, looking over and trying to get a better view of what was going on. Malcolm swung the car into a very shallow passing point, which allowed them to get out. Hidden from view, they took a look over a tall grassy bank.

They were not alone, thankfully, there were several other people looking over the fields. Some had parked as they had, and others were innocently walking dogs down the narrow lane. Or had they simply taken the family pet out to use as cover. And, like Malcolm and Harold, they had their binoculars and a bird spotting guide.

It seemed there were rather too many dog walkers about? Obviously, everyone wanted to know just what was going on here? No doubt some of these people felt awkward, and perhaps a bit guilty, in doing this. Harold and Malcolm certainly felt slightly awkward, but as for guilt? No way! They wanted to see what was going on, and to see what opportunities the situation might have to offer?

Having checked the area, it was decided that, despite Harold not being a young man, the best way to examine its true potential was to gather up a team of their most trusted night hawkers, and hit it that very night. Hopefully, this would be before any really stringent security measures and organisation had been established. It may well be that there is nothing to be gained up there? But if there was? Well that could be a different story, and was not going to be a missed opportunity on their account.

It was planned that five of them would go, two would act as lookouts, Malcolm and another would detect, and Harold would personally check out any excavation areas. Well, at least that was the initial plan. Over on the site, many officials were aware that the whole area was being observed by villagers and others, but that's the way it was, they could take no further precautions. Simon glanced over to the far side of the field. Funny how many dog walkers are out today, he thought? He also saw the odd cars parked up, and noted that a blue Ford seemed to have been parked up in the area for a while now?

Jonathan and the EMAG team were of course involved in all the proceedings, from the boring meetings to the actual excavation plans. This was mainly, it must be said, due to Simon and Jonathan who, within hours of officialdom descending onto Four Acres, decidedly felt they were all being somewhat side-tracked? And they were having none of it. They both nipped this in the bud. It may not have been deliberate, but in their books, if they felt it, then it certainly existed. A talk with some of the most senior officials on site soon brought results. Helped by the insistence of Craig Melanby, who insisted that he wanted these guys to be fully included in all proceedings, seeing as they had made the discovery, plus he owned the land, etc.,

Back at Harold's house his guests for that evening's mission had started to arrive. One of them, named Paul, had arrived with a huge take away pizza, which did not exactly please Harold, but who tactfully remained quiet, he needed these guys for tonight. As they all sat around the large table it was business as usual. Pockets were unbuttoned and seal top bags opened, containing rare Norman pennies, Celtic quarter staters, Roman brooches and even a stunning Edward III Gold Noble. There was even a large bag filled with several hundred Roman "Grots" up for grabs. Harold bought the 'grots', as he now had a good outlet for these. Local schools were buying them for their history classes.

A few thousand pounds was dispersed over to the left hand side of the table, and almost all the bags with their contents, went over to Harold on the right. The owner of the Gold Noble was a little peeved that this superb coin wasn't part of the evening's deals. 'I've already got eight of those anyway, Mike.' said Harold, 'They're difficult sods to sell" he explained. 'I need some stock clearance to happen before I buy any more.' he reasoned. They still had several hours to wait until darkness and he was unsure quite how long he could go silently watching Paul drizzle hot pizza cheese down his unshaven chin and onto his newly-laid Axminster carpet!

Meanwhile, back at the site a small party of five archaeological students, closely supervised by some of the most eminent archaeologists in the UK, started their descent into the excavation. As well as being inside a large marquee the immediate surrounding area was also sealed with a boundary of tape, to prevent casual onlookers. Jonathan and the EMAG members were of course allowed through this, to get a first hand view of all the proceedings going on inside.

The students had started to remove some of the large clay lumps by hand, and these were being chain ganged to the surface. They wanted to open up the collapsed soil section and examine, if possible, a side view of this strange chamber. Experience told them that it was most likely some type of Celtic chieftains burial chamber, but even they have little to no idea whose remains could possibly lie within it?

At this stage it had been decided that the less people who suspect, or know, would definitely be a good thing. Progress was good and after an hour several tons of soil and clay had been removed. Every stage of the operation was photographed, and detailed drawings and measurements were being made. After about four hours, enough infill has been cleared and supports were now put in place. These allowed for, and gave the smallest of the students, a young lady named Erica, the opportunity to safely get inside the void and have the first close inspection.

The supports were double-checked and shortly afterwards all that can be seen is a yellow pair of waterproof trousers and two Wellington boots, and then these too disappeared from sight. After a short while they are all seen again, attached to a now very mud-caked female student. 'There are gold coins and things everywhere down there. And what appear to be large bronze objects too? But we are going to have to remove the upper layers and excavate downwards, carefully to examine the contents.' she said breathlessly.

It was planned to break the news of the discovery, and to what extent had so far been recovered, to the media. And it was not long before even more vehicles arrived, adorned with antennae and various sized dishes. Each one ejected excited groups of babbling journalists. This caused more concern in the village, and it was also decided that night to have an official meeting in the village hall to which anyone

244

was welcome to attend.

Complaints had been made by several eminent locals that the village was starting to feel excluded from whatever it was taking place right on their doorstep. At six o'clock the village hall doors were opened. Some people had been waiting outside for two hours, and a general air of excitement hung over the crowd. Just to hear what would be revealed to them?

Once everyone attending had been packed into the hall they were informed that there had been a major archaeological discovery made in the field, and as soon as the site had been fully excavated, there would be a series of official guided tours. There would also be allocated times for parties of schoolchildren from all the local schools to be allowed on site after the official tours had been completed. Cameras and mobile phones were clicking all over the place and outside, Jonathan and all the EMAG members, were filmed for both local and national TV. However, they did not reveal who, if indeed anyone historically famous, was connected with the incident. This had been agreed to be scheduled for a later date.

With the onset of early evening it had been decided to finish for the day, secure the excavation site and move everybody away into the living accommodation, to ensure that the site can be effectively patrolled and made secure at night by the police and other elected officials.

No one noticed anything untoward about the man who parked his blue Ford amongst the hundreds of other cars now present in the village. He was well dressed wearing a jacket and tie; also not noticed was the fact that he had a pair of Wellington boots on, with his trouser legs carefully rolled down over them. In the darkness, the strange shape of his trousers cannot be seen, and Malcolm looked around before mixing in with other people in the poorly lit gloom, but slowly he was edging away from everyone heading for the lane. He managed to melt away into the darkness, whilst just over a mile away two of his colleagues, who were sheltering on the edge of a wood, are looking over at the tented site using their infra red night-vision equipment.

In the yellowish light of the lenses they can see that the area of the large tent has hardly anyone around it, but a hundred or so metres away the site is still bustling with activity. Without doubt, this will be their cheekiest mission ever, and they all know it. The will be sneaking in under the very noses of the archaeologists, and be taking a look at whatever is there behind their backs, and even possibly looting some it. But this is the type of business these men are in and they are used to the thrill, as well as being aware of the risks involved. Creeping along the woodland edge they time it just right to avoid any passing cars and quickly cross over a small lane, up the steep bank and up onto a field. Here they make for another hedge and then suddenly have to fling themselves down. A car was turning into the site encampment area. Briefly, its powerful head lights shone right across the field. That was close.

Using the hedgerow as a shield, the five men slowly progressed down the edge having to get down several times, as more cars arrive and depart from the site. The temperature has dropped considerably, and they can see their breath in the cold damp evening air. At the same time these men were walking down the hedgerow, a phone call was received at Bourton Police Station. The caller, who wished to remain anonymous, simply informed them: 'I'd be keeping a very good eye on that site at Melton Briarsville if I were you.?'

'Excuse me, sir. Who are you and what do you mean by that? the desk sergeant had enquired. The caller responded: 'If what I believe has been found up, there then it is not safe, not safe at all. There are some very dedicated people out to steal it.' And then the line went dead.

Just another cranky call. There are enough people up at Melton anyway with that old dig, or whatever is going on, thought Sergeant Kilner. Probably just another crackpot trying to get involved? He didn't even bother to make a note of the incident; after all, it would be digitally logged and recorded anyway if there was a problem later? Feeling really strange, Peter Ellis put down the phone, his sweaty fingers leaving prints that evaporated quickly from the black plastic surface. 'Huh! That would teach Foster for trying to be the big man!' he said to himself, contentedly.

It was at nine fifteen pm, the first signs that perhaps all was not well at the site began to be experienced. Two police dogs had started barking uncontrollably and ,although not confirmed, a shadowy figure had definitely been seen down at the bottom end of the field. It could have been anyone, a nosey villager perhaps. Intense searching, however, and floodlighting the area had revealed nothing and even the dogs could pick up no trace of an intruder. Generally the response to this situation had been a bit disorganised and rather slow, hampered by the fact that the dogs simply couldn't just be released. There were far too many people in the area, and if it was just a student taking a pee, or someone returning a bit tipsy from the pub, there would be some very serious questions asked.

In some ways the environment, although secure, was just right for a clever opportunistic person, and just such a person was Harold Foster. He was observing the scene from some two hundred metres away, avidly watching all the activity resulting from him having sent that pizza-munching Paul to scout about just to check the security. Moving quite swiftly for a man with arthritis in one kneecap, Harold cautiously moved towards the middle of the field, shielded by dead thistles and other tall weeds. Earlier that evening a few of the others had noticed that he was having trouble with one leg which seemed to be unusually straight and unable to bend very well. 'Hope the old boy is up to this mission tonight?' several of them had thought.

Harold now moved from the middle of the field to a large pile of freshly excavated top soil. For the past few minutes the night hawkers had separated and, according to their modified plan, Mike, Paul and Keith are now to head to one side of the field, whilst Harold and Malcolm will try and head straight for the large tent as quickly as possible.

Out of breath, both Harold and Malcolm arrived at the damp canvas edge of the main tent. 'Phew! Made it Harry.' whispered Malcolm. 'Too right! Let's lift up the canvas and have a good old dekkers inside.' quietly responded Harold.

Over by the hedge from where they had all departed from just a few minutes ago, five out of the six carefully placed cigarettes finally began to burn out. As soon as they had got safely inside the main tent there was all of a sudden a tremendous series of whizzing rushing sounds. These were immediately followed by several people shouting and screaming, and all this commotion was then followed further by five huge aerial explosions. The giant shadows of people rushing about, hundreds of metres away, were played onto the sides of the main canvas tent as Malcolm and Harold watched from inside. The whole area was now briefly floodlit like a football stadium.

Malcolm had started violently at the first explosion, but Harold didn't seem to be concerned at all. Only six minutes previously, he had told Malcolm that he was just nipping off to relieve himself and had wandered off. Then, when some distance away from the others, he began taking a series of plastic tubes from inside his trouser leg and placed them along the hedgerow. Harold was glad to remove the bloody things as they had made it somewhat difficult to walk, and he had seen the ability-doubting looks of concern from the others. Protruding from each tube now was a medium sized firework rocket. Quickly taking some cigarettes from a pack, he carefully shielded the glare of the lighter flame by lighting each cigarette, whilst holding it near to the ground. Once alight he had a drag on each one and exhaled onto each glowing ash, and then Harold carefully broke off the filters. Sticking the smouldering cigarettes onto the lace-like fuse of each rocket would give Harold about six minutes before the rockets were ignited. He knew this as, some days beforehand, he had thought long and hard about how to create and cause such a distraction. Then the idea had just come to him 'Use a firework with a cigarette as a delay fuse. Simple enough!' he thought.

Therefore this basic method to delay the lighting of a firework was conceived and, in his typically methodical manner, Harold had completed a series of timed burning tests on quite a few filter-less cigarettes over the last few days. He had timed each burning and averaged the results, which had indicated a maximum delay time of six minutes, and no longer. So he had a pretty good idea of the time by which he knew he and Malcolm definitely had to reach the edge of the big tent and get inside it. If they could achieve this then it was plain sailing from then on.

The choice of firework to be used was obvious but the delay to lighting them had been the issue here. Once that was resolved he had walked down to the small shop at the end of his street. He remembered when you could only buy fireworks a few days before November 5th. Not nowadays, though, some shops held fireworks all year round now. Inside he was met with a veritable arsenal of stock, from so called aerial mines to huge display types. His purchase made, he hurriedly came out of the shop with six sizeable rockets, rather dramatically called 'Dark Destroyer Flare Blasters.' Harold was relieved, back in the shop he had felt slightly embarrassed when asking for these 'Dark Blasters', or whatever they were called, by name. It just sounded and felt rather stupid, and Harold hated such feelings. As he walked away the embarrassment faded, as he mused: 'Best tenner I've ever spent, though, if these little beauties do the trick later?'

The fact that three men, who he had been acquainted with for several years, would almost certainly get caught as a result had been of no concern whatsoever to him. There was only one driving force for Harold Foster. He knew when something was potentially big and profitable, and in this case he was definitely going to look inside that tent whatever the cost.

'What the bloody heck was that?' understated Malcolm, after the first bright aerial explosion.

'Let's just say, Malcolm,' said Harold, 'we should have at least ten minutes, or even longer, of peace to be left alone so we can see what it is we have here.'

Malcolm of course had no idea that Harold had set this up at all. He assumed some sort of firework celebrations had occurred, and Harold was taking advantage of the distraction. A few moments before, Mike, Paul, and Keith, had just been working their way to the cover of a large Ash tree, when all of a sudden, a rush of fierce noises made them turn round. 'What the....?' said Paul, as the skies overhead immediately turned to an intense magnesium-based whiteness. It didn't recede either, as each explosion then produced a small swaying parachute, a bright red, very intense, flare that floated slowly down the valley. The flares turned the darkness to daylight, and being a totally uninvited person in the middle of an occupied archaeological dig in this firework-created daylight was not a good situation to be in. Mike, Paul, and Keith had then found themselves in exactly that situation, and within a few minutes the three men, along with their metal detectors, had attracted much attention.

It was pointless running away, there was nowhere to go. Someone ran and fetched over a couple of the policemen, who had been having a crafty cigarette behind the portable toilets. An hour later the three intruders were all in separate cells at Bourton Police Station. As they were booked in, and their crimes outlined in detail, a rather nervous Sergeant, Stuart Kilner really hoped that no one would closely check the recorded calls for that evening.

Previously on the excavation site, as all the fuss and brightness seemed to slowly fade away, Harold and Malcolm found it strange how no one had even come over to check the main tent? They both knew by the shouting, etc., that the other three had definitely been located and caught. How could they possibly have got away?

Harold was pleased that his distraction and diversion seemed, so far, to be going to plan. Perhaps this whole thing would later prove to be a complete bloody waste of time? But Harold somehow knew it wasn't. It was the bright lights positioned outside the tented area that allowed for just enough light to percolate through the thick canvas of the main tent. Using this, the two intruders could clearly see a large area of very disturbed soil, using a tiny pencil torch Malcolm gave Harold a supporting hand as they unsteadily went down into the deepest part of the excavation. At the side there appeared to be a dark cavity like some sort of square-cut cave. It was still largely full of soil but an area just to one side revealed something, something of which Harold could not believe his eyes or luck. What the hell were the people in charge here playing at, he thought? The security here was abysmal to say the least; he just couldn't believe what he was experiencing. Just what had made Harold make these conclusions was the sight before him: thousands and thousands of gold and silver coins lying to one side. The soil above them was clearly infused with many more thousands of coins, as quantities of thick yellow coin edges could be seen, almost glowing, in the poor light.

Harold's first response was to grab handfuls of coins, but then he just carefully took a single coin and examined it. 'Just as I suspected?' he muttered, quietly, as his torch picked out the words 'CAMU - LON - VER' on the large gold coin.

That was enough, now it was time to grab as much as possible and get away. However, he had just got his first handful of coins when a strange thing happened. In the light of all his greed Harold just fell to his knees and savoured the sight. It was like he was transfixed, unable to deal with the sudden success. Seemingly the coins had hypnotised him into some type of archaeological-appreciative trance. Of course in reality, Harold Foster had no remaining real understanding and appreciation of archaeology and its methods at all. But here he was, Harold Foster, right here at last, after a life time of dealings - most of them illegal - he now faced having to remove and steal a large portion of what was definitely the largest 'hoard' of Celtic coins ever found.

Malcolm was speechless, and produced a scrunched up orange ball of supermarket carrier bags, bags that rustled alarmingly. 'Malcolm! No bloody way we can use those! Help me fill these and we will share what we get later.' ordered Harold.

Replacing the carrier bags were large double hand-stitched leather pouches, capable of holding huge quantities of coins. 'We have to be fast Malcolm, and I mean fast!' Harold said, as he wiped a filthy hand across his heavily perspiring brow. Minutes later both pouches were almost bulbous in shape, with so many coins having been crammed into them.

The problem was now one of weight, carrying them would be a problem; greed had overlooked the practicalities. But greed now drove them scuttling over to the edge of the canvas. Soon they were outside in the cool night air. Now the carrier bags would come in handy, four bags all inside each other, were slipped over the pouches. Providing you didn't rush, and walked calmly, the handles would be just about strong enough to support this weight, whilst hoping of course, that their bases would not split and burst open. They both tested the handles and that was it, off now as cheekily as they had arrived, but this time departing right through the middle of the camp site. They appeared just like two people involved with the archaeological operation that had been to get some supplies from the local town supermarket. Fine in theory in fact almost faultless. But some two hundred metres, or so, away a damp cigarette was still sparkling and making tiny saltpetre-based hissing and spluttering noises, until it finally started to go out. The long ash of the burned cigarette began to curl and fall apart in the damp air of the hedge, and then it was blown totally apart into a fine grey dust by a mad sudden rush of spark showered force. The last of the Dark Destroyer Flare Blasters had finally decided to rush off into the night sky.

'Oh bloody hell, no!' cursed Harold, as the sky was illuminated by an explosion. He did not notice the root from a nearby ash tree that had previously been exposed and snapped by the mechanical digger's linked tracks. This root had a feathered sharp edge and mostly stuck somewhat upright when not recently crushed by a passing vehicle. Unfortunately for Harold, nothing had passed over it for hours and it had sprung back upwards. When Harold struggled past, it snagged and stuck firmly into the base of his carrier bags and caused him to momentarily lose grip. With the carrier bags splitting the soft leather pouch inside fell open and released hundreds of the Celtic gold coins onto the ground. Malcolm looked around dropped his bags and looked resigned to his fate, they were totally illuminated and it now seemed so hopeless.

People in the vicinity had gathered quickly. 'Hey! What the hell are you two up to?' came a voice from across from the darkness, as the two men were slowly surrounded by more and more people. Malcolm watched Harold scrabble around in the dirt grabbing handfuls of clay, grass and coins, desperately stuffing it all back in the pouch. Harold was also muttering something that Malcolm couldn't quite hear. Then as the Police and site officials closed in on them both, Malcolm stepped forward touched, and then firmly tapped, Harold's shoulder and said: 'Harold......, Harold, it's been a great old journey my old friend, but we are stuffed mate! Look, it's all over. Come on, stand up.'

Malcolm looked up to see a Police helicopter, that now shone its bright white locater beam right down at them. If ever Malcolm had felt vulnerable and defenceless, it was then. Two hours later, both he and Harold were also down at Bourton Police Station. Whilst being taken to a cell, Malcolm saw Keith in the corridor who shouted:'What the hell was all that about, Malc? – Bleeding rockets and all that ruddy commotion going on! Malcolm looked at him and whispered quietly to himself; 'Just the results of one man's crazy dream that we all got caught up in mate...just a crazy old dream!'

Next day there was a rather determined knock on Peter Ellis's front door. He could clearly make out the distorted shapes of dark uniformed men through the frosted glass door panel, and as he opened it, his fears were confirmed. 'Mr Peter Ellis? We have a warrant for your arrest, on suspicion of the theft of antiquities and other associated heritage crimes!' said a thin very tall Policeman. Looking to the side of the Policeman, amidst the blue flashing lights that were reflected off all the fronts of neighbouring houses, embarrassingly, many curtains were moving sideways and people were watching with interest. Inside the large police vehicle Peter was not destined to feel too lonely, as sitting at the far end were two persons he knew very well, very well indeed. There, looking very nervous, were two of the 'idiots'.

CHAPTER TWENTY

SHE IS NO LONGER MISSING

J ust as Bourton Police station now seemed to be brimming with
night hawkers, the following morning the site of the excavation
was teeming with intense activity. The chilly morning air had been
accompanied by a mist, which still hung about in streaks across the
valley, and had soaked everything. Not put off, there was soon a hive
of activity around the main tent and the now further-increased police
presence was also rather obvious, no doubt resulting from the previous
night's occurrences?

With reference to the night hawkers involved, and consequently
caught, here one senior archaeologist when interviewed by BBC had
stated that; 'It was like a suicide mission here, what with all this security? It was doomed before they even started. Just shows how guided
by greed and how foolish some people can be!'

Later that evening, many watched this account being broadcast on
television and thought along the lines of: 'Good! Glad they got caught,
trying to steal our heritage indeed!' However, only a few of the people
who saw it were only too well aware and realised just how close to
actual success the night hawkers had been.

ITV broadcast an interview with Neil Fisher, the senior archaeologist from Bristol University, who found it hard to conceal his passion
and excitement. 'I think it fair to say we have the UK's greatest archaeological discovery to date here. A major and magnificent discovery, and
it is directly linked to one of our most important periods of history....
Oh, and yes..., I should, and most certainly must add and take great
delight in doing so, that it was made by metal detectorists!'

Neil Fisher was one of the original archaeologists who, in the nineteen nineties, aqcuired the foresight to see metal detecting for what it

could really achieve. He wasn't interested in pandering to officialdom, or the 'Dinosaur Archaeologists', as he called them. Those back then still thought of metal detecting as an 'amateur and very destructive pursuit'.

Neil gathered detectorists together for all his excavations, listened to their expertise, as they did to his, and consequently both parties contributed phenomenal results to the archaeological community, both here and as far away as the Middle East. Many of which soon found their way into the contents of many enlightened publications.

In the main tent were jammed bustling film crews from every major TV Channel, the media had been invited some time back, but now it was in a frenzy, and required far more control. Someone, somehow, had leaked out the name 'Bodvocca' and 'Boadicea', and linked it to Melton Briarsville, and that had been that. But nothing could be allowed to get in the way of today's proceedings. After the events of the previous night it was desired to uncover and to lift the contents of the burial chamber today – even if that means working well into the night. But in reality, it was soon accepted that in doing so, the greatest ever British archaeological discovery would then forever have its critics stating it had been rushed, and that important information had as a consequence been lost. So, amidst the fervour, excitement, decisions, the remaking of decisions, and sometimes total confusion, it was decided that the excavation would proceed in an orderly manner for exactly as long as was required.

On site, people seemed to be giving TV interviews everywhere one looked. True to the historical nature of some of the residents from Melton Briarsville, that seemed to have existed for some time now, it was quickly found that embellishment could quickly turn into multiple beers in the Waggoner's Inn. Well, at least if the brewery could keep up its deliveries to match the recent surge in demand?

It was all reported and recorded no matter how farcical it was, one day all this farce would of course become part of the actual history of the event itself. The rumour that it was an important ancient burial spread fast and most of the village seemed to acknowledge it.

Consequently, the pub was drunk dry on two occasions in one day! The village museum made as much in entrance fees on the first day of the event as it had the entire preceding two years. There were squabbles about parking, that sometimes got quite heated, whilst some villagers were offering apples and trays of sandwiches to just about anyone who walked by. The more opportunistic ones actually cut holes in their hedges allowing cars to park in their meadows, or on their lawns, all for a fee of course. It was for certain that this village would really never be the same again, as everyone just waited for confirmation as to the identity of the historical figure responsible for all the fuss.

At the site all was well and truly under way. Initial panic about last night's activities had been calmed and in general there was now an air of 'this excavation will be done in the time needed and perhaps not so rushed as anticipated just a few hours ago'.

Once again, it was Erica who was back down in the excavation, this time accompanied by Jonathan. For ages they seem to be just sifting through disturbed soil, whilst a team above were carefully cutting away and sieving, where possible, the layers down wards. In fact it took another nine dedicated days to reach the actual chamber, and start removing the tons of infill. Each bucketful was carefully sieved and more detailed drawings were completed, showing the layers and deposits that were painstakingly excavated through. By this stage it was well reported that a tile had been found previously on this site, indicating certain details that the human remains, purported to lie here, were those of Boadicea, or more accurately now, Bodvocca along with her two daughters, Bretta and Cearra.

Of these young girls, it must be said, history had no record of their names, until this tile had been found, assembled and translated. Much work remained to see if any human remains were actually contained in the chamber at all? Or whether it could be established scientifically that, in all likelihood, there had been a burial of any bodies there at all? This could be determined by measuring the decomposition phosphates in the soil, but hopefully there would be something far more substantial to confirm human burials than a piece of paper with a print-out on it?

Days later, a series of incredible finds were revealed, a massive set of five silver plates, each was one and half times the size of the 'Great Plate', found at Sutton Hoo in 1939. Beneath these had slid thousands of Roman gold and silver coins, also mixed with Celtic issues. And, to one side, were two magnificent bronze hanging bowls, richly decorated in blue red and yellow enamels. One was in near perfect condition but the other had a huge split and jagged crack across its base. Slightly to the left hand side of this was huge lump of corroded iron which, when later X-rayed, was revealed to be hundreds of iron arrow heads, whose corrosion deposits had preserved a considerable amount of textile imprints. Ten feet away from this, inside a bronze bowl, were found the skeletons of two adult hares. When the bowl contents were completely removed later, on a stunning solid silver model of a running hare was discovered.

Notes on the Silver Hare

This had been modelled from a thick 10mm sheet of pure beaten silver and bore a similar design to some of the 'Dragonesque-style' brooches found mostly in Northern Britain. In all, its total weight was 1.2kg of silver. Once cast, it had been finished to a very high standard and then huge cells of enamelling had been applied. Mostly it was red enamel that had been used; however blue and yellow were also featured in the circular design representing the oversized eye. No similar animal model had ever before been recovered from a Celtic / Iron Age burial deposit.

Further down, Erica carefully brushed soft soil and coins away to reveal a large thick twisted band of gold. This was then cleaned further and revealed itself to be an immense golden torc with two huge bulbous decorated terminals. Further excavation around this magnificent artefact revealed the first evidence of Human remains: these being the top of a skull and some badly deteriorated neck vertebrae

Notes on the Golden Torque

Apart from its colossal size and weight, which was just short of 4.5kg, in all other aspects the torc was quite similar in shape to the so

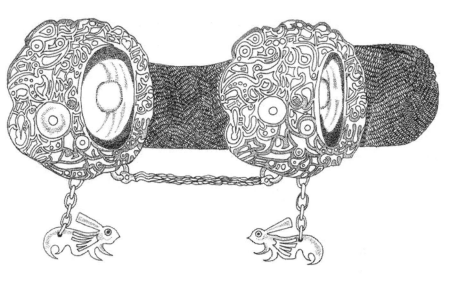

Sketch of the stunning gold torque found in burial deposits
(Via author)

called 'Marriage Torc', found at Snettisham in 1948. This example, too, had an umbilical-like, twisted gold wire loop that joined the two huge terminals together. However, it was the sheer size, and incredibly detailed terminal decoration, that distinguished this new torc once again from anything that had previously been found in Britain, Ireland, or anywhere else for that matter. As if these features were not enough to distinguish this magnificent object from all other known types of torc, there was indeed something else. Beneath each terminal was a loop that supported a few links that were attached to a miniature golden Hare. Later research suggested that the simple, stylised decorations evident on these little animals were loosely based on the 'Bird Hare' gold coin design of well known Braughing fame.

Finally, amidst great excitement on the far side of the chamber, where the torque had been uncovered, the soil was cleared to reveal a near complete adult skeleton lying on the floor of the chamber. The only incompleteness were the bones from several fingers of one hand which could not be located, even in the final sieving results. There was also evidence for a serious fracture of the associated wrist. As each individual bone was carefully lifted, photographed and then catalogued it became clear that there was another mass of iron corrosion underneath the bones of the upper body, including the skull. Brushing aside the fine soil revealed a cluster of magnificent corroded Celtic swords that had been laid beneath the head of the body at the time of burial. The iron corrosion deposits had deeply stained the back section of the skull also several molar teeth to a deep orangey brown colour. A large unidentified thin sheet copper disc had also corroded against the left side of the skull, causing the bones to become a rich blue green colour. Another small section of copper sheet had rested upon the forehead of the skull. This had also left a light green and blue stain on the associated areas of bone.

As the skull was carefully lifted it could be seen that it was somehow attached to the lump of iron corrosion created by the sword blades. Careful assessment and later X rays revealed that a long and thick plait of preserved hair had become infused with these corrosion deposits. The skull, despite the stains, was in otherwise good condition. The excellent condition of the teeth was also noteworthy, although a small hole in the lower jaw and a single decayed tooth above it showed that there had been one occasion of a serious mouth abscess.

When re-assembled in the main tent it could be seen that further iron corrosion was evident in the spinal column. Two vertebrae had been violently split open by an iron object, a five-inch section of which remained firmly stuck into the lower example of the two. Brief assessment of the skull and pelvic region led the osteoarchaeologist involved, Dr Miriam Pilch, to make the following statement: 'This excellently preserved skeleton conforms to the details of the previously discovered tile, in that it is an adult woman, most likely aged between twenty eight and forty.'

Further evidence as to sex of this skeleton was established by the discovery of fine golden threads in the soil around the remains. These were attributed to having originated from a garment of luxurious silken fabric, most likely having derived from India. Similar threads had been found, on rare occasions, in other high status burials, mostly Roman of course. But their presence here was taken as indication of extensive, well-developed trade connections.

Great care had been taken in lifting the bones, as it was soon apparent that there was definitely more than just the one body involved here. On each side of the main adult skeleton the domed upper sections of two slightly smaller skulls could now be clearly defined. After being fully revealed, and later examined, it appeared that these belonged to persons of about thirteen to fifteen years of age. More examinations were required but it was stated that 'due to certain skull features, it is likely that these remains were possibly of two teenage females? Given the indications from the associated tile then we are now quite happy to state that these two additional sets of remains are indeed female.'

Associated grave goods, amongst which were two small silver hand mirrors, also had a strong female orientation. Despite the tile having been authenticated, and many people now being aware of the other tiles that had previously existed, it was still an archaeological prerequisite before definite confirmation that the skeletal remains be confirmed to the highest possible level. After all, this was no ordinary burial and the announcements that would be associated with it had the potential to be earth-shattering in the modern archaeological world.

Representatives from the British Museum had of course been in attendance here for some while now, and they had been organising a series of meetings and discussions on how best to deal with the situation from now on. It was eventually determined that when fully excavated and conservation had been completed, the three skeletons, coins and associated artefacts would form the basis for a huge exhibition.

Piecing together all the available evidence another meeting of senior academics, and a wide variety of other contributors, including Jonathan and his EMAG colleagues, was then held. It didn't take long to reach its positive verdict, by now it was widely suspected whose remains had actually been found here. But as with many things, it had yet to be officially confirmed.

Professor Norman Roundsby took the chair and stated formally:

'Amongst so many esteemed colleagues, observers, and those who are directly responsible, I am humbled in the great capacity of recent events. Never did I ever imagine that I would be saying such things as I am just about to. So let us begin. Ladies and gentlemen it has been confirmed above and beyond all reasonable doubt that the tile, the skeletal remains and the vast amount of grave goods, can only relate to one thing here, and that is this:- that here in this Oxfordshire field, we can now formally announce and reveal that the mortal remains of Queen Boadicea, apologies.., Bodvocca and her two daughters named..', a rustle of papers was heard, 'ahem.., Cearra and Bretta have been unearthed. It must be made clear that although finally we have the two names of this queen's daughters we do not know from history which was born first, or second? Or which of them bore which name? So consequently, the two additional skeletal remains cannot be precisely identified by name. At this stage I don't believe I am capable of saying anything further, it's so overwhelming. Neil if I may possibly have a word? I think it is your field of expertise that qualifies you to initially face the world's press and make an announcement, I would of course do it, but as you know that is not really my sort of thing, so would you please draft a press release?'

With all the evidence having been assessed , Neil Fisher quickly prepared a release, and two hours after the meeting formally attended a gathering of the world's media. He began: 'After an initial discovery by EMAG, and Mr Jonathan Pearson, of the remains of a crashed Second World War aircraft, a German Junkers 88, it was discovered that something and indeed someone else had also been buried in the village of Melton Briarsville. Something that history had recorded but of course, as is prone to happen, had got several facts wrong.... The something else that was unearthed here in Oxfordshire is the greatest Celtic hoard of artefacts and coins ever discovered on mainland Britain.'

He went on, 'The someone else who was buried here for nearly twenty centuries was a British Queen, whom we have known as Boadicea, or Boudicca, but who we now know was actually named Bodvocca. So until that new correct name sinks into acceptance, for simplicity's sake, I had better state that the body of the great British

Queen Boadicea and her two daughters, we now know to have been named Bretta and Cearra, have been found and carefully excavated.'

Neil paused for a breath, then continued: 'History had never recorded exactly what happened to this, our most enigmatic of Queens after the battle? For so long she had quite simply disappeared. Scholars had long believed it unlikely that she could not have been afforded the usual burial ceremony with, perhaps, a large tumulus or some other type of marker, as it is most certain that the Romans would have desecrated this. It was assumed that she would quite possibly have been cremated or either quite correctly, as recent events prove, that she would have been placed in a very hastily prepared chamber.....perhaps quite near to the scene of battle. For an equal length of time, as she has been missing so to speak, historians have wondered where this battle had also taken place, if indeed it ever actually did? Well I can now also announce that due to the dedicated work of the metal detectorist, Simon Pearson, in this district. He has been able to unearth a selection of objects from a site in the locality that clearly suggest there has been some type of large-scale military confrontation between soldiers of the Roman Empire and warriors of the Celtic tribes.' again, he paused for breath.

'This finding has in turn provided answers as to why the battle ground had never been found? Well firstly, no one had recorded where it took place, and most importantly, it was located under mature woodland and rich pasture meadows that were never ploughed until quite recently, and then once again reverted mainly to grassland. This grassland being on a private estate with limited public access, combined with the fact that it had never been night hawked - as presumably pasture had put them off - and of course, that Jonathan was the only detectorist ever to be given permission, and have the time, to methodically work the area. Had Craig Melanby and his sister, Candice, never given Jonathan permission to search this estate then the outcome, as we know, would have been very different and all this national treasure would most likely have been dispersed all over the world and sold to the highest bidders. Therefore we see yet another positive benefit of allowing people to metal detect on your land.'

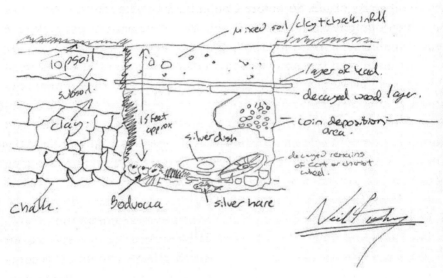

Photograph of an original rough sketch from Neil Fisher's excavation
notebook showing the layout of Bodvocca's royal burial chamber.
(Courtesy Neil Fisher)

'This battle ground, in due course, will become the subject of
in-depth research and later excavation and obviously is at a location
only known to a few people at present - for rather obvious reasons,
of which we have recently had some very serious experience of.' he
added, regretfully.

'I would just like to finally add that metal detecting and archaeology
have not always been positive bedfellows in the past. However, I have
always believed in the immense positive findings that metal detection
has achieved in this country. No matter what the critics may have said
before, after this phenomenal discovery there are absolutely no grounds
for such unjustified criticism to continue? When one states metal detecting, this is of course in reference to those who positively and actively
metal detect and record all that they find. There are of course negative

elements to this, and all other, past times and hobbies, but that's life! We should focus far more on the positive issues here and perhaps should do so in all walks of life. So before I potentially digress into the realms of personal opinion in all matters I will, with your permission, now take my leave, Ladies and Gentlemen, I thank you all for listening.'

Minutes later the news was worldwide and news channels from as far away as Mexico and Australia were starting to have newsflashes cutting into their normal daily routine programme broadcasts. It certainly seemed that Boadicea, as she was still being called, to maintain understanding and familiarity of just who was involved was very big news. Most announcements however did inform viewers of the name change that would now be required, as well as the establishing of her two daughters' names.

Four weeks after Neil Fisher made the above statement the excavation site was totally devoid of any activity at all, the grassed sections were still flattened in extensive areas and all the temporary accommodation had now been removed. It was quite clear to anyone who

Some of the double staters recovered from the site of Bodvocca's burial
(Courtesy of Neil Fisher)

Just a few of the thousands of double staters recovered from the site
having undergone provisional cleaning in the "site office"
(Courtesy of Neil Fisher)

looked that a large excavation had taken place here, even if they had
not been reading the world's newspapers.

The grass had been re-laid but looked a little bumpy in some areas
and, if one really looked carefully, some shreds of red and white security
tape could be seen having been blown into the hedge. I suppose not
that much was evident, when one considers that one of the greatest of
British mysteries had been resolved in this grass field.

Life had also returned to some normality for the villagers who
resided here, they could now park their cars for example. The local pub
saw its profits slump back slightly towards normality too, after the media and everyone else had departed. However, almost immediately, an
increase in tourism soon had these profits soaring again.

Now began the long process of recording, assessing, cataloguing and
conserving the thousands of coins and artefacts that had been revealed
and unearthed from this field. It would be some while before the first
in-depth publication was produced, outlining the discovery from start to

The bullet holed cockerel weather vane as seen and drawn
in 2010 by the author

finish. Realising this and, of course not wishing to tread on anyone's feet, Jonathan (who is now also a member of EMAG) worked with Simon in producing a short thirty-page booklet with some illustrations, that seemed to satisfy the intense demand for something to be made available.

Of course Jonathan had no idea that over a century before, his relative, Frederick Pearson, has once considered doing exactly the same sort of thing. The booklet is for sale, priced £7.50, in the museum, pub and also the village shop, with all proceeds going to repair the church roof. Some might say the cockerel-shaped weathervane also needed repairing, but to fill in that bullet hole would be like removing a piece of village history.

Leaving the village to recover further it's probably a good idea to have a glimpse into just how it was the remains of Queen Bodvocca and her two daughters, Cearra and Bretta, came to be deposited here deep in the Oxfordshire countryside.

CHAPTER TWENTY-ONE

AN EXPLANATION OFFERED

It is early October AD 61. The main section of the majority Icenian and Trinovantian Celtic tribal army were in a position along a very prominent chalk ridge, halfway down a sparsely wooded chalk land slope roughly facing northwards. Several large detachments of Celtic warriors had assembled further down the slope, but not totally, so as not to lose their advantage of high ground positioning. Looking further northwards, approximately a mile away over some flat wet marshland, and also on slightly raised ground, stood a section of the Imperial Roman army. Some ten thousand men, mainly consisting of soldiers belonging to Legio X1V Gemina under the command of the Governor, Gaius Suetonius Paulinus.

Paulinus himself had arrived at the scene just some two hours before and looked over at the swirling mass of Celtic warriors before them. True enough, daunting numbers, but clearly no cohesion or order amongst them, he thought. Despite this some of Paulinus' less experienced soldiers, and even some of their junior commanders were clearly nervous. The only point of consideration Paulinus was not entirely happy with was that his army was facing a rather bright autumn sun. Other than that, he felt confident, very confident indeed.

He had of course been in battle many times and experienced trepidation, fear, success and yes, confidence to some degree, but never before had he felt so supremely confident than he did on this particular day. It was he who had led an expedition south of the Atlas Mountains, thus becoming one of the first Europeans to encounter Saharan Africa. Perhaps it was the influence and will of the Gods, to whom he had earlier made votive offerings at a temple, and again at a smaller rural shrine. Even Paulinus was not quite sure where these feelings of supreme confidence came from? Were they derived purely from in-grained experience or was it his tactical learning from years ago? When history had proven time and time again that a bigger army most certainly did not guarantee success, and what was facing him this day, was indeed a massive opposing army. Whatever, he was no inexperienced leader either and would of course treat this confident feeling with caution, it needed controlling. Over -confidence, as he also knew, could have serious consequences.

Paulinus back-tracked his thoughts for a second and decided to re-phrase the word 'army' in this case, as that, in his opinion, was a collection of men defined by order, training and precision. Such definitions could hardly be applied to the mass of men, and chariots, scrambling around in front of him. Nevertheless, although he faced these masses of Celts across a valley he was vastly outnumbered. Therefore he had issued orders almost as soon as he had arrived at the scene to ensure that the rear and flanks of his own army were organised and secured for the initial phases. He was also aware that amongst his men were a few infantry vexillationes and cavalry detachments, who originated from Legio 1X Hispana. These would be of great use. This very Legion just a few months before had attempted to relieve the City of Londinium, whilst under the command of Quintus Petillius Cerialis, and had consequently been almost annihilated by this British Queen, Bodvocca, and her followers.

These survivors were all experienced soldiers, each one fuelled with revenge for slaughtered colleagues, each one also wondering what this day would bring? Triumph? Or the final destruction of Rome's influence on this forsaken isle? Paulinus knew that he could rely on such men to fight and, above all, fight hard.

Rumours and information supplied by scouting parties had brought news that the British so-called Queen was here herself this day. Paulinus had of course suspected this Bodvocca would be, she would surely not be absent from her own tribes. But it was useful to acknowledge her presence, as he was very keen to finally be a part of her personal destruction. He wanted her to experience fully the reprisals for daring to challenge the might of Rome, and Paulinus was determined those reprisals would know no limits.

Something else without limits would surely be the accolades poured on him by Rome for success, and he considered, might even find him 'taking the purple', as a future Emperor. But before this he knew he had to deal efficiently with the problem of that day alone, and not just this immediate aspect either. It would be all too easy for the Queen of the British to become some type of rebel myth if indeed she was killed here. Paulinus knew that he had not only have to annihilate an important social figurehead, he had to annihilate her followers, and her legend, before it could spring back up again. He was going to crush these insurgent Britons, and teach them a lesson they would never forget.

Also present here were several hundred men from Legio XX Valeria Victrix. On the field of battle Paulinus knew these men to be good and efficient under pressure of close-combat battle. Despite sending frantic communications to other military commanders, Paulinus was only able to muster just over ten thousand men. How many of his messengers had got through was unknown, he had allowed for some elements of ambush and failure but had in fact received no return notifications of assistance whatsoever, and that was of some concern. If he was to undertake the day's victory alone then so be it, it would naturally condense his own personal glory to unparalleled heights.

Being shortfall of as many men as he would have liked, and it was now obvious that he was not getting many more. Paulinus had, just seven days previously, fortunately drafted a tactical plan like no other ever before conducted by the Roman army. He had allowed for the possibility of only having a smaller army and so would in effect, if successful, utilise his men to the maximum, and trap Bodvocca's army.

Advanced Roman scouts had for weeks been following the masses of Celtic warriors, and had at last reported the position where they had seemed to congregate. Facing a massed Celtic tribal army of over eighty thousand individuals, the size of the opposing Roman forces had already caused both excitement and some curiosity amongst the somewhat disorganised masses of the Celt warriors and their chieftains.

Behind these warriors, some one hundred and fifty metres away, were the hundreds of heavy wooden carts pulled by oxen. These were laden with women, children, and all manner of requirements, small horses and even dogs were also tethered to many of them. The barking of these thin-bodied and coarse haired, whippet-like, dogs added to the multitude of noises here. Some of the heavy carts were also serving as a treasure train, positioned some way back from the main encampment. Bodvocca had wanted a considerable part of their plunder to be present at the battlefield, to act as an insult to her Roman opposition.

Above all this commotion could be heard the laughter of small groups of children playing, chasing around the huge carts, this alone seemed to justify the very reason for this tribal defiance. The vast majority of these huge lumbering wooden carts had been positioned slightly downwards of the high ground, so as to be out of the rather chilling October winds. This campaign had been one of a very mobile nature. So far, most of these carts had at some stage been used as a train for transporting the bulk of looted coins and valuables from major cities such as Verulamium, Colchester and many other smaller settlements. However these specific loot-loaded carts were now positioned along an ancient track some three hundred metres back from the main Celtic forces. As a precaution, surrounding them were numerous horses. In the case of an emergency it was possible to quickly harness additional horses to and therefore to dramatically increase the speed of these carts, despite their size.

It was difficult to precisely determine just when the main confrontation had started, for several hours now, small parties of Celts had crept up and shot arrows into the Roman sections, small antagonistic actions that, so far, had achieved very little response back. Then all of a sudden a large unwieldy mass of Celtic warriors had rushed downhill and began running across the flat wetlands. Still their Roman enemies did not respond, but simply watched. This was true military discipline indeed.

History informs us that the Celtic Tribal army was defeated by the time-honoured, traditionally used, 'Wedge Formation' being adopted by their Roman counterparts. However, that was normal procedure, and might just have been anticipated by the British? But today was not normal, and called for tactical variations.

The Roman soldiers that day assumed they where not facing an organised disciplined tactically-aware opposition, but their commanders knew well to never underestimate. As it was also known that even a rabble with a good cause could quickly become a dedicated fighting unit. This collection of British tribes was indeed a rather disorganised mass in the opinion of its Roman onlookers, but it was fuelled with loathing and fear, and it confronted them from all angles. Despite appearing to be everywhere, being so disorganised was never really a good thing. But on very rare, or unusual, occasions, it was just such a lack of discipline that could, and did, sometimes render precision tactics rather redundant, resulting in a totally unexpected outcome.

As the Celts got nearer some of the younger Roman auxiliaries started praying quietly to their gods. Fear of what lay out in front, combined with that of being seen to be fearful by their commanders, was a terrifying mixture. The attack order must come soon, surely?

They didn't have to wait long, a new sound now met the running Celtic warriors, one of twanging and whistling from the first hails of ballista bolts and lead slingshot that had finally been unleashed. Witnessing the impacts of these into their fellow warriors suddenly caused great swathes of the Celtic army to condense into large and confused groups, as the bolts continued to cut swathes through them. These groups of warriors were then subjected to concentrated slingshot fire. Some of the less perfectly moulded oval slingshot actually whistle and hum as they streaked through the damp air, adding to the suspense. This was followed by a brief respite from the Roman ballista's. Archers and slings men, forming into neatly organised sections of soldiers, then began running forward and throwing thousands of the long iron-tipped spears, called pilae, which now stuck firmly into flesh and bone. When these impacted the Celtic shields they could not be removed, as the long iron tips bent, thus rendering the items useless for retaliation.

This attack was then followed by three sky-blackening salvoes of arrows from the Roman archers who would wound and kill hundreds of their adversaries within less than fifteen minutes. Forced backwards over the flat wetlands, the vast majority of the Celtic warriors were now negotiating the steep slope upwards towards the carts. When they reached the level top of the scarp they noticed smoke and flames spreading from one of the lines of carts, these had been left virtually undefended in the mass surge forwards, everyone had wanted to be involved. Now these horse-powered vehicles were under attack by a section of over two thousand Roman soldiers from Legio X1V Gemina, who had appeared from the South. With absolute uncontrolled ferocity these soldiers killed and maimed all they could. Due to the fluidity and physical exercise of battle these had been mostly pregnant women, small children, the much older men and those of an invalided disposition.

Rushing from the scene of slaughter, approximately five hundred soldiers now advanced northwards, retaining the freshly-captured high ground and moving off to the left. Although imbalanced in numbers, the situation now showed that the Celts were in an extremely poor strategic position, and were facing attack mainly from the front, but now also from the rear.

The flow of battle for the Celts had been poor tactically, and so far mostly disorganised, and this appeared to be their continuing style of approach. The entire Celtic warrior masses surged forward and then backwards amidst hailstorms of arrows, pilae, ballista bolts and thousands of humming slingshot rounds. Then they appeared to polarise into one large group, which suddenly divided into two huge sections. The Roman commanders observe that this could be the early stages of some implementation of a crude battle plan? To the inexperienced, it appeared that Rome had already won the day, as one section had started to move eastwards and the other westwards. This left a huge vacuum right in the centre of the divided Celtic forces and this was immediately taken advantage of. The Romans now used this opportunity to fill the void with their own soldiers. Once achieved, this would totally divide the Celtic forces, also hopefully denying them forever the ability to regroup again as one unit.

A small group of Roman commanders had stayed in position on the high ground, monitoring and controlling the flow of the battle. Their Celtic counterparts, on the other hand, had no idea of the flow of battle, how it looked, or where to tactically go next to take advantage of any situations. Instead they were all in the thick of the fighting, and as they were gradually slain the chances for any future possibility of any cohesion, or command structure, for the Celts slowly ebbed away.

The Roman commanders, in contrast, had pre-planned actions based on a wide variety of responses from their enemy on this day. But even they did not believe the ease with which things were then happening - and happening in their favour, too. Assessing the pressured fluidity that was visibly occurring the remainder of the Roman army positioned itself to the north, consisting of some three thousand individuals, and then spread out, forming the shape of two horns from the main body of soldiers. In effect the escape movements, if that is indeed what they were, to the east and west were now effectively blocked. This brought about a move back into the central area of the battlefield and condensed thousands of men, both Celt and Roman, into extremely close hand to hand fighting.

There didn't seem a spare inch in which to move. The Roman archers, and Ballista commanders, ceased fire. It was impossible to distinguish friend from foe, and this was also aggravated by the drifting smoke from the furiously burning carts.

At this time, the two thousand soldiers to the south had regrouped as best as they could. The battle had now regained some order on the Roman side, finding it difficult to maintain any tactical advantage in a mass of men ,each soldier had then heard a trumpet and headed for special coloured pennants that were held aloft. To some degree this had separated large sections of the two battling armies. It was then that the regrouped southern unit had captured and emptied several more carts of their loot and had then rolled them to the start of the gentle slope. Here they set fire to them and pushed them downwards into the main pitched battle. This act was slightly premature as the burning wagons resulted in the deaths of several of their own soldiers in the confusion.

Whichever way the Celtic warriors looked there appeared to be

Roman soldiers, and now the arrows and other aerial missiles recommenced. Amidst the smoke and ever-increasing confusion to variable degrees, the clever placement of soldiers had now given the Roman army an appearance of being a lot larger than it actually was. So deceptive that in many areas of the battleground the Celts had even thought more reinforcements must have joined them at some stage? The surrounded Celts now tried to force their way north, but Roman cavalry units, and yet more arrows, began to wither their numbers.

The main mass of Roman soldiers, supported by three flanking cavalry units, now hurled themselves forward again, driving a huge wedge into the Celts with the result that over ten thousand of them tried to surge backwards uphill. By now almost every wooden cart in the area was ablaze, and the drifting smoke disorientated them. Despite still having vastly superior numbers, the Celts were running this way, and then that, with no direction or planning. Some had managed to break through the burning lines of carts, where a group of several hundred Roman archers awaited them, driving them back into the thirty foot high flames. Flanking movements of archers and slings men, as well as the ballista's, now hurled projectiles down onto the Celts, and in the next two hours over twenty thousand warriors and others would die.

The battle now degenerated into large areas of hand to hand fighting once again. During yet another sky-blotting dense hail of arrows a solitary grey heron was disturbed from the marshes, it arose and arduously flapped its way slowly towards the Roman archers. Moments later it fell spiralling downwards, and lay flapping on the damp grass having been struck by two arrows.

The general lie of the land had made it difficult for the Romans to inflict a decisive manoeuvre right here, as of course had the smoke and general confusion of their opponents. There were still forty five thousand Celtic warriors massed in the valley. Like wildfire, the rumour of a massive Roman army bearing down on them from the south had started to spread amongst them. True enough, they had already observed what they now believed had been an advanced section of this army setting fire to the carts earlier. This army was claimed to have been seen by someone, exactly who was of no importance. Then as if like a scythe through ripe crops, the entire nature and honour of the battle being fought collapsed. Celtic warriors were seen throwing away their treasured swords to the ground and just running off.

In little more than twenty minutes, the entire Celtic tribal army has broken down. Fighting is still furious, but absolute panic had finally broken out and within a short time the entire vacuous mass of men, women and many children simply blunder towards the east. Such a large group of people on the move was impossible to stop or control, and even the well-trained Roman soldiers could do little but stand and swipe at the thousands of fleeting shapes in the smoke as they ran or walked past. Some soldiers start to move with the flow of these people hacking at and killing all around them. Although the Roman army could not impede such a rush of people it could most certainly harry them. It did this by loosing off just about every variety of projectile available into this huge group of people, resulting in over fifteen thousand further casualties over a very short distance.

After heading for about a mile to the east, this mass of defeated warriors and people then began to separate into smaller groups, but all basically moving northwards. Some organisation had returned as they were seemingly being led by an unidentified tribal chieftain, mounted on a larger than normal grey-coloured horse. Another mile or so northwards and this huge mass or people divide into hundreds of smaller groups, all heading off in different directions, dictated by family demands and tribal locations.

After just five hours the battle is truly over and the ravaged Celts were now trudging back in all directions over eastern Britain. Unknown to most of them, their Queen was dead, and some estimated thirty thousand of their warriors, women and children had been slain. The once-proud army was now scattering itself northwards and many would eventually head east again, trying to put as much distance as possible between them and the battlefield.

Gaius Suetonius Paulinus looked on in both awe and pride at the scene but was experienced enough to order a detachment of soldiers to immediately scour this battleground, to kill all the remaining wounded and look for the any evidence of the bodies of the Queen, her daughters, and any other royals who may have been here. Very few people at that stage were even certain she had been killed? The Roman army finally stopped and took assessment of their victory, but like any superbly trained military machine they awaited details of how they were to proceed from that point onwards?

For days they rested, having simply ground to a halt revelling in victory, but aware that large sections of the defeated Celtic army could still be in very close proximity? The celebrations were large but had an uncommon air of caution about them; to be caught unawares by any small avenging Celtic force would be an unforgivable situation for any Roman commander to find himself in.

The days eventually turned to weeks and huge groups of weary, and dispirited, soldiers had also gone east and lay encamped just outside the patched, and now fully repaired, outer walls of Verulamium. The city, which in itself, was then undergoing large scale internal repairs and redevelopment after Bodvoccas earlier visit. At first, local Villa owners, small settlements and of course the struggling civic amenities in the town were delighted with this increase of well-paid military personnel just outside their City walls. Every encouragement was given to demonstrate they were welcome to use all the facilities of the City It was not unnoticed by the City officials that such men would also be extremely useful in assisting to strengthen the city's defences.

Despite being somewhat suspicious of this welcome, and also of the over-enthusiastic officials, the Roman army commanders also realised the importance of keeping their men occupied, once boredom and frustration set in it would take ages to re-condition these men for further military activities. For certain, no one quite knew if serious military activities would be required again, possibly at very short notice? Incredibly it took five weeks for confirmation of orders to investigate and pursue the disintegrated, and now widely-dispersed, sections of the Celtic tribal army to be received from the Emperor.

A further four weeks were then taken up by counteracting the civic officials' rebuilding requirements and readying the men, once again, for pursuing and running these now widely scattered groups to ground. Although towards the end of this period things had begun to get rather strained in Verulamium, as the increasing demands on food, clothing and general amenities were now totally out-stripping supply and the citizens began to get irritable that, after all their hard work recently, there were fewer and fewer supplies left to buy. Then as swiftly as they had arrived there, the military personnel and soldiers were mostly gone, just a few administrative personnel had remained to settle debts and other obligations on behalf of the recently-departed army.

Someone in authority must have realised very shortly afterwards that the City was still in some potential danger and two days after the main departure, several hundred soldiers reappeared again. It was confirmed very hastily that this was only a temporary measure to counter-act the threat of any wandering bands of defeated Celts, who may make opportunistic small attacks on the still-weakened city.

Heading north, and then east, the Roman army was now on a campaign of revenge with no diplomatic opposition likely to be imminent from Rome - and certainly none able to be organised by the recently crushed Celts. Although one might consider here Rome's inadequacy to provide more detailed plans at an earlier stage for following up their victory. The major problem was in pursuing people now long -departed from the battlefield. It was problematic for the Romans to identify just who these people were that they, once again, found themselves looking for?

The Celtic warriors had soon been reabsorbed back into their communities; they were now farmers, bronze smiths, blacksmiths and builders. Reprisals were instigated, offers of reward for information, but very few had any real measurable results. So another tactic was implemented, simply abandoning the aims of pursuing those responsible, indeed why should they bother? It was considered a waste of time trying to find responsible individuals when one could simply order the entire communities to be executed, efficient in result, and in the saving of such things as time.

The task in hand now had been developed into one of a much simpler and easier nature, involving persecution, rape, murder and wholesale destruction of Celtic settlements. There was deemed to be a lesson to be learned, and it would be taught by the most aggressive and vicious of methods available.

Minor individual skirmishes, involving small groups of Celts and Roman soldiers, would rage over Hertfordshire and Essex for nearly a year afterwards. Until all was finally quelled by a mix of Roman military might, starvation, and in some exceptionally special cases, the diplomatic offering of peace and promotion by Rome. What was never really appreciated in these matters was that the Roman army was also now rather tired of continually killing innocent women, farmers and children, and rather unusually, it was starting to be said that 'such continuous efforts in these matters are not really befitting soldiers of the mighty Roman army'.

The principal action of offering peace and bribes had often worked far more quickly in solving disputes after battle than a policy of continued aggression. But opposed to any practicalities of correct politics, just after the battle, Rome had wanted revenge, and not resolution. To support this later philosophy a new Governor, a certain Publius Petronius Turpilianus, was appointed by the Emperor Nero to administer the healing process. Even after interviewing, torturing and killing hundreds of individuals, which unknown to the Romans had actually included a considerable number of the battle veterans they had sought, they still had no real evidence of Bodvocca's death, or current whereabouts at all?

Some people now started to question as to whether she had even been present at the battle? This was hotly disputed amongst Celtic tribal inner circles, who knew the truth of the matter anyway. But for a short period Rome had started to imply that perhaps she had deserted the scene very early on in the battle, once she had tasted the flavour of Roman superiority? However, behind the scenes this did not salve the knowledge that of course as everyone was aware she was present. Of course she simply had to have been there. But the remaining questions concerning what exactly had happened to her, and most importantly, where she was now, would just not disappear.

In such situations there was no shortage of claimants who proffered stories of being in the actual group that had killed her, but which if any of these were genuine? One soldier had even produced a congealed bloody mass of red plaited hair, claiming he jumped up onto her very chariot with some others and had hacked at her with his sword, quickly cutting off this souvenir. The problematic thing here was that the vast majority of the Roman soldiers in the immediate vicinity of the killing of these British Royals stayed at the location, and were themselves slain, too, about half an hour afterwards.

The entire battlefield had also been periodically obscured by drifting smoke from the hundreds of burning carts, making eye witnesses further away even fewer. The Romans had no body to parade, and thus denied any facts relating to her 'disappearance', it was hard to control the situation and indeed basically this just added momentum to her rapidly-developing mythical reputation. A factor which was just what Paulinus had earlier anticipated could happen. Without a corpse to display and defile, her spirit and defiance could not be broken that easily. Physically, she and her forces were defeated, but not even Rome could defeat rumour and myth. Without a body there would always be the possibility that she could one day end up wandering the counties again, rousing another British rebellion?

For months, and then years, afterwards, behind the political scenes every persuasive method was used to find out what had happened? Infiltrators moved into local settlements, living, looking and listening for the slightest clue. Tales around camp fires were analysed for the slightest hint and reported back to officials in Verulamium and Londinium, and from there outwards across the Empire to Rome itself.

But nothing was heard. Shortly after the battle, surveyors were sent into the countryside and were asked to report any obvious soil disturbances that might possibly indicate a burial, but there were none ever located, or reported. Some four months after the battle the badly decomposed bodies of what appeared to be three Roman soldiers were found covered by an oak branch, not a great distance from the main battleground. Whilst the location of their demise was considered unusual, nothing further could be gleaned from their discovery. By AD 70, almost nine years afterwards, there were still many organised insurgent actions by the Celts, but nothing on the scale of something indicating a major uprising was about to occur. Inter-tribal conflict saw to that.

However, villas were still burned down in the night, potteries attacked and Roman economic business was hassled and upset on numerous occasions. It was now accepted by most in Rome, and Britain, that Bodvocca had either been killed in battle, or would in all probability have died by now from wounds received? Conveniently, Tacitus, and Cassius Dio, later produced accounts ,whereby they claimed she had either killed herself to avoid capture, or as stated, had died of an illness shortly after the rebellion.

That was all well and good, but her absence still haunted the minds of many people. After years of consideration there was some minor consolation for Rome, and that was the fact that, either way, the culture of British Royalty and tribal culture had by now largely been suppressed and brought into line. Consequently, this woman who had defied the Roman Empire, would herself be denied any large monument, such as a large barrow, or any type of mausoleum, as befitting the burial of a tribal dynastic Queen.

At the battle ground the Celts' bodies were just left to rot, but over a decade locals managed to dig a series of huge pits in the soft damp soil and placed the remains of over thirty thousand individuals into them. It was alleged by some that finally even the local Roman commanders tolerated this after about ten months, as eventually, and skilfully, even they concluded that not to allow this action could be inflammatory and could perhaps re-ignite dangerous tensions?

CHAPTER TWENTY-TWO

THE DEATH OF A QUEEN

So, what actually had happened to Queen Bodvocca, and her two daughters, amidst all this carnage of the battle? Driving her two-horsed chariot furiously, she had led a section of some three thousand warriors down the slope, accompanied by several of her most trusted warrior chieftains. Her two daughters, Cearra and Bretta, however, were both, for some unknown reason, in one of the cumbersome carts slowly following their mother, but safely at this stage surrounded by thousands of warriors.

Soon the initial three thousand warriors had become almost fifty thousand, as many other men had joined the advance. Boudicca had so far managed to avoid being hit by the hundreds of arrows zipping through the air. This was witnessed, and interpreted as clear evidence of her invincibility. As the battle progressed she had swung her heavy sword around wildly hacking at the occasional Roman auxiliary, and other soldiers, many of whom seemed to stand transfixed as she crashed past them with arrows flitting past her everywhere. This tall red-haired woman was a mysterious figure in a man's world, with two freshly killed hares tied to the sides of her chariot and huge sword in her hand, she was truly an incredible and awesome sight. The two hares had been trapped by surrounding them, and then making them run downhill, just five hours or so before. It was well known amongst Celtic huntsmen and farmers, etc., that this noble, and mysterious, creature was unable to run down a slope. Afterwards, to the flanks of each Hare had been sewn the wings from a pair of Carrion Crows. Therefore the resultant assembled beast would bear the spiritual qualities of not only speed and agility, but also craftiness and cunning.

As she sped towards an area of particularly dense hand to hand fighting, Bodvocca had crouched down to remove two spent arrows that kept rolling around the floor of the chariot. Throwing them out as she rose upwards again, a Ballista bolt then created a spray of water ten feet to the side of the chariot, as it bounced off the sodden ground at high speed. It cracked through the thin wooden side of the chariot, and straight into the abdomen of the Queen. Fragments of grass, soil and wooden splinters were deposited deeply inside her body for the entire length of the impact. The thin iron-tipped section had also smashed through the side of her spinal column. Her chariot almost immediately slewed sideways as the reins sudden slackness was felt by the two horses. In agony, trying to unfasten the tangled reins and leather support belts, Bodvocca found she could not get free, The ballista bolt head that had passed through her was now jammed into a chunk of thick ash wood which was part of the axle mechanism. She watched for a split second as blood, her blood, poured down the wooden and steel shaft of the embedded Ballista bolt, and then a stinging blow to her arm was felt, as a young Roman soldier hacked at it with his Gladius sword. Another swipe of this thick, short-bladed, sword crashed down on her hand severing two fingers, but stopping short of the others. The blades impact had been brought to an abrupt halt by a huge gold ring.

The ring, a huge golden circle, caste with swirling tear-drop shapes, had the name Bodvocca deeply engraved into the bezel, a gift from her chieftain father. As the gladius blade had hit and slid across the soft gold, it disfigured the lettering on the ring, before finally skidding off and removing one of her finger tips just beneath the nail. Lubricated with warm blood, the large gold ring flew off the shattered hand of the Queen as she brought her arm up. Over and over it tumbled through the air landing in the grass. Unnoticed by anyone, the pale sun briefly reflected off the ring in the muddy wheel-rutted and crushed grass. Seconds later the huge wooden wheels of a cart had ground the gold ring deep into the sloppy grassy soil. Later on, other passing chariots, carts and feet, churned the soil over and over until the ring eventually lay partially visible once again.

Just as the soldier manoeuvred to take a third swipe, his own arm was then totally severed at the elbow. Frowning, and then looking bewildered, as he stared sideways at the bloody stump, and then down at his severed limb. The fingers of his detached limb were still flexing as they gripped the handle of his sword. A teenage Celtic warrior looked at his blood-streaked sword, and then at his Queen. She looked back at him briefly, only perhaps for just for a second, but it was a look of extreme gratitude. Suddenly, an arrow seemed to sprout from the young warrior's mouth, and then another from his throat, and he too was dead.

Looking around, she could see there were now considerably more Roman soldiers in this particular area than fellow Celts. In her enthusiasm she had penetrated quite some distance into the frontal sections of the Roman defences. Now it was imperative to about turn and fight her way out of there, she looked around desperately as several brave efforts were made to assist her exit. The control she could now exert over the chariot was severely restricted by the fact she was jammed to the side of it by the ballista bolt. Groups of warriors rushed towards her to assist, but being hacked with swords, impaled with spears or hit with arrows and sling shot, were not able to do so. She saw three of her warriors all screaming in an untidy heap, they had been pinned together by a single ballista bolt. Her chariot spun round and round, the two horses wild with fear.

Adjacent Roman soldiers could see that here was a very special prize and swarmed around Bodvocca, themselves all fighting fiercely. Then it happened - about five soldiers managed to clamber up onto the toppling chariot and began wildly stabbing and hacking at her. Briefly, a blood spattered arm rose up and that was all that could be seen. Then the blood-drenched Queen rose up again as best she could. With her sword she severed the head clean off one soldier, and stuck her short bladed dagger sideways deep into the ear of another. Again she fell down under the rain of blows, amongst the smoke and turmoil. That was the last sighting of her in action.

Several Roman soldiers hastily grabbed souvenirs from the dead woman's body. Strips of fabric, a small gold chain, some of her hair, one soldier struggled to remove the huge golden torque from her neck. It wouldn't come away and was sliding about with blood, just as he was contemplating cutting off the head to obtain the prize, he was killed.

Simultaneously, a slingshot round had hit him in the eye and an arrow shot deeply into his nose. Bodvocca's two daughters, who were about a hundred and twenty metres behind their mother, were still in the cumbersome cart when a shower of arrows fell in the vicinity; one of these embedded itself in the left thigh of her eldest daughter, Cearra, ripping through a femoral artery - killing her within several minutes.

Panicking, the youngest daughter, Bretta, slid over in her sister's blood and then jumped off the side and ran, tripping up over bodies and mutilated shrieking horses. She was being pursued by just a single unarmed soldier, who finally caught her. Grabbing her by the hair he swung her round ripping the top off her tunic, he then executed her immediately. As she was screaming he simply grabbed a nearby Celtic spear that was stuck in the mud and thrust it deep into the young girl's chest twisting it back and forth. He then picked up a sword, punched her very hard in the face and ran the edge of this sword blade deftly across her pale thin neck. Briefly, he looked down at what he had done and then ran off to help a fellow soldier, leaving her young thin blood-soaked body entwined in the still-thrashing legs of a dying horse.

A large and ferocious counter-attack by thousands of Celtic warriors managed to sweep back through the area and for a time, hundreds of individual skirmishes flared up, Romans running, Celts running this way, then that, for a short while the Celts had seemed to obtain some level of superiority here. Combined with the shouting, the dull thumping clattering sounds of sword against shield and blade against blade were deafening.

Quickly, several of the Celtic tribal chieftains, and even a future short-term client King, had seen the terrible situation, and thought it best to remove the royal bodies as quickly as possible, to reduce the numbers of those who knew their fate, and hopefully maintain some morale.

Removing the slaughtered royals immediately from the battlefield was a decision that had to be both hastily made, and implemented. Some initially suggested it would be better to quickly strip them of their gold and then disfigure them, hoping the Romans would not recognise the bodies and leave them here. That way it may be possible to collect and bury them later? But this simply could not be done, these were royals, they couldn't be disfigured by their own, and no way could even the slightest chance be taken that would allow their bodies to fall into the hands of the Romans.

The battle was raging around them, but dedicated groups managed to weave in and out of the hundreds of conflicts. Many of these gathering groups were themselves killed but eventually, in the height of battle, the three mangled bloodied royal bodies were located and brought back to a group of awaiting chariots. Despite being surrounded, the encirclement was thin at the eastern and western areas of the battle ground. The eastern section of the wide valley was chosen, as it looked the most promising, it also terminated in a thick section of mainly dense oak woodland and beyond this lay the boundaries of a relatively friendly tribal territory.

Fifteen chariots and a large cart had been hastily gathered and the bloody remains stuffed onto several of them, all being covered in coarse cloth blankets. The Queens body presented a problem, as the lengthy ballista bolt was lodged firmly through it, but this could be dealt with later. For the plan to be successful it was now or never, and the chariots raced off towards the east, smashing into friend and foe alike. Several chariots upturned, their wheels spinning off and frames disintegrating as they tried to ride over a dead horse, or the scattered clumps of dead and dying men. One warrior chariot-driver was just correcting his careering chariot when his head suddenly opened up like a rotten birds egg - split apart by a passing ballista bolt. This bolt carried on and punched into the side, and split open, the abdomen of one of the horses attached to a nearby chariot. The wound was huge, and a mass of blue-pink steaming entrails immediately fell from beneath the frightened animal. It reared up in pain, un-harnessing itself, and the other horse, from their chariot, which was then catapulted upwards, smashing to earth, instantly killing its driver in a splintered, tangled mass of wood flesh and bone.

The remaining chariots were getting nearer to the woodland and although the fighting was thinning out, they were aware of Roman soldiers running from the left and right sides towards them. The reins cracked across the steaming horses' backs, salty tasting white sweat foam, manure and mud splatters flew back into the faces of their drivers as they still crashed on forwards. There ahead of them lay an overgrown track into the woodland, just wide enough for them to all smash through. If only they can make it to the woodland cover they will be much safer.

Incredibly none of the Royal body-bearing chariots had so far been damaged, until just before the wood an unarmed Roman auxiliary simply threw himself at one of the chariots as it flashed past. Trapped in the wheel mechanism he was instantly mangled, his leather belt, and other accoutrements, flailing around, clattering against the chariot sides. With the stretched, bloody, sinuous mass now completely jammed in it, the wheel could rotate no more. Tightening even further what had only seconds before had been a living man, then forced the entire wheel to detach, spinning and bouncing away. Sixty feet away this wheel was finally stopped, as it thumped into the chest of a middle aged Celtic man smashing his ribs like dry sticks. Tilting at high speed the chariot's axle began to score the weed-ridden soil, and then it got completely stuck fast. The chariot flicked sideways and tumbled over and over, hurling its driver into the rear hooves of the horses. Viciously kicked about by the flailing hooves, the body of the driver was then hit by what was left of his hurtling chariot. Impaled by three huge splintered pieces of wood from its shattered structure he was then dragged along the ground face down. A second body, wrapped in a blanket, had also been catapulted out from the strewn wreckage of this chariot and tumbled over the ground. When it stopped rolling the blanket opened slightly in the breeze and a pale blood-splashed arm, of what was clearly a woman, fell limply to one side. Quickly this body was gathered up by a huge warrior with tousles of black and grey hair who, spotting the massive gold torc around the neck, then simply threw the body up and onto the nearest passing chariot that had slowed down a little. This man knew something very important was going on here, but only later on would he find out that he had previously touched the body of his lifeless Queen.

Reaching the woodland, the chariots smashed through the undergrowth, snagging overlying briars, snapping fallen branches, and bursting onto the rough track way. Not until they had gone some distance did they spot some of the heavy wagons laden with looted valuables. On one of these was a travelling mint. This had been incorporated to follow the campaign. With the fast mode of attack, and logistics, Bodvocca had known that swift payment secured continued loyalty. It was not always possible to rely on loot being acquired, and used as payment.

Being away from their home settlements had meant she would need large sums of money to be speedily available and was determined to make provision for this. Undoubtedly their cause was just and perhaps many would have fought loyally without payment, but that was another assumption that couldn't be assumed. Hence from the start of her campaign the cart, with its five associated moneyers, accompanied by their die sets and several die cutters, and metal smelters ha,d under heavy guard, always followed her.

Originally, just over three hundred pounds in weight of raw gold had accompanied the cart, and this was continually being added to. Huge quantities of coin, and more raw precious metals, for minting had fortunately been secured from Colchester, as well as Londinium. Bodvocca had acknowledged that after the attack on Verulamium, her rebellion now seemed to be unstoppable, achieving a previously only dreamed-of levels of success. As a result she had confidentially discussed with several chieftains that the campaign should have a specially struck commemorative type of gold coin produced to mark these victories; a coin that would emphasize their total victory over Rome. Consequently, it should be twice the size of anything previously struck. As Queen, she wanted this new coin to make a real political statement, she knew others had used coinage in this manner before. Some chieftains had suggested to her that there would be time enough later for such extravagances, and might it not be too premature, even unlucky, to take such a defiant stance at that stage?

The suggested design of the coin would certainly be very thought-provoking, that was for certain. Bodvocca was of the opinion, and made it clear, that had she and her people always bowed to caution, then perhaps the present successful rebellion may never have arisen. She also made it clear that the coin would most certainly be struck, and struck as soon as possible, as the die cutters were already nearly finished! It was also decided primarily by Bodvocca again, that this coin should incorporate mixed designs, featuring the styles of most of the rebellion participating tribes, 'a symbol of our unity' she had said. In all senses the style, and sheer size, of this new coin was very different from the many different tribal varieties already in circulation. The new design incorporated not one, as usual, but two running horses, and to the sides of these were the images of two mythical winged animals, known to the Celts as 'Bird Hares'.

As a very young girl her father had taken her on a trading tour and they had stopped for a while at a large settlement near a place known today as Braughing. Whilst there she had seen several coins that bore the design of the 'Bird Hare' and for some reason this image, and its associated mysticism, had always remained with her.

The other side of this new coin bore the Queens full name 'BOD-VOCCA' for the very first time. Previously she had issued gold staters and small silver coins that did not bear any reference at all to her name. Then as she grew in confidence and began to be accepted as a true leader in the Celtic world she had minted several issues with the abbreviated name of 'BODVOC' on them. This had been themed so because her father had always referred to her by the names BODO, or BODVOC, as a child, and she was now paying tribute to him.

As she grew in influence she had suggested that coins bearing her abbreviated name of BODVOC should, wherever possible, be used for inter tribal or distant trade dealings. She considered this was a subtle way of almost increasing Iceni influence, people far away would know of the Iceni and their Queen. Now however, she wanted no such abbreviations, she wanted her name clearly featured on the coins so everyone knew her full name.

Situated below her name would be an enclosed tablet design bearing the abbreviated names of the three Roman towns they had recently destroyed, CAMU, LON and VER. The choice to abbreviate the names of the towns was twofold. Firstly, it saved the die-cutters time, and secondly, she had hoped it would show disrespect once again to Rome. As if she would mention the names to antagonise but in reality hardly gave them any recognition whatsoever. Above this she had insisted the die-cutters incorporate stylistic flames, so that the message to Rome, and its oppressors, would be once again unmistakeably clear.

It would always be known from this point that these coins represented the struggle and, at that stage, total success in taking on their Roman opponents. Days before the battle Bodvocca had given her final consent to begin striking these most unusual coins, and progress so far had been good. Even then some of the more hesitant had wondered if these coins would ever see circulation, this factor would of course be definitely confirmed in the next few days to come.

Those who had been driving the large wooden vehicles were now speedily told of the battle and how it was going, and then the chariot riders, due to their rank and position, then took charge of the carts. The majority of cart drivers, moneyers and chariot drivers would now leave the scene at this point, hoping to avoid capture, but three chariots and one lumbering cart kept onwards.

Behind them they had set fire to all the remaining unrequired carts and a few chariots, partly to block the track but also to prevent the capture of anything useful to the Romans. Following on foot behind the cart and chariots were thirty or so carefully selected Celtic warriors and chieftains. Now there was a final mission to be completed. Just two miles east of the battle area the track widened and ran below some chalk downland, capped with thick clusters of beech trees along with dense mature oak woodland down in the valleys, it was quiet and above all peaceful.

CHAPTER TWENTY-THREE

FINALLY AT PEACE

In this quietness and tranquillity, the small party of Celtic warriors and chieftains reverently laid the blanketed Royal bodies onto the damp grass. Boudicca's body was covered in blood that had matted her hair, and a splinter of wrist bone protruded from the palm of one hand, caused by the earlier chariot crash. Her upper lip had a huge gash across it, was swollen and bore bruised colouration, likened to that of partially ripe sloe berries. Despite this, her bruised and cut features were still handsome, even in such violent death. Even when two flies alighted on her face and started to scurry over and into one of her bloodied nostrils.

Vastimarus, one of the chariot drivers, like the rest of them was now exhausted; his legs were scratched by brambles and lumpy from nettle stings. He now had the opportunity to look at the body of his Queen, who, or what, he wondered, had cut a section from one of her long braided plaits?

Several of the warriors dispersed some distance away choosing large trees to stand against, constantly looking for any Roman soldiers, or others who may be in the vicinity. It looked like the vast majority of combatants had swung westwards, or at least most of the Romans had. There was no sign of any pursuers and it would be dark in a few hours. A few minutes before, whilst looking for a quick, but permanent, burial site a badger set had been found, this would be ideal.

In the late afternoon shouts and cries could be heard, keeping hidden in the woods they witnessed a huge mass of people in their thousands, about a mile away, led by a chieftain on a large grey horse. So that was it, the Celtic tribal army was on the run, routed from battle by a Roman army a fraction of the size. The invincibility of Rome was once again no mere myth to these conquered peoples.

Using swords, daggers and parts of chariots, working through the night, forty nine dedicated followers, and even other Royals, had dug out the badger set into a square-shaped pit over fifteen feet deep. Into this clay and chalk hewn cavity were placed the Queen and her two daughters.

Five chieftains lifted up the battered head of Bodvocca and placed their personal swords underneath in a radiate cross pattern. The bodies were followed by piles of other carefully-placed grave goods, donated from her previous victories, and now accompanying her in death. Three chariots were then taken apart and then placed over the remains The soft chalky soil was poured back into the chamber, when the space remaining was only about four feet deep one of the heavy wagons was dismantled and its rough blood-stained floor slats were placed over the back-filled chamber, leaving a small two foot uncovered section on one edge.

Suddenly there was a crunching sound and the soil inside the chamber had seemed to sink down, something had obviously broken deep below, crushed by the weight of soil above it. Into this new void was thrown, and poured, literally thousands of silver and gold coins, issues from both the Roman Empire and those of allied Celtic tribes. All the special double sized coins that had been struck from the travelling mint were also poured into the remaining space. Although not quite all, Mantoteros and Celoditos, two chieftains, had afterwards selected five of these special issue coins, these being passed around to each person in opposite directions. Each recipient looked at the coins and kissed them before passing them solemnly to the next person. When this had been completed, Mantoteros took each coin and placed them into the palm of one hand and then flung them far out into the woodland.

Afterwards, a thin rather undernourished looking, warrior named Velas helped organise the filling of the remaining section with soil, treading it down as best as possible. This was not easy due to the wooden covered layer below and necessitated some warriors rolling up large balls of clay in their hands, leaning down into the pit and trying to throw them over the far side. After some hours a burning torch was thrust into the remaining space and showed that the far side was as evenly filled as possible. Over this was laid a series of huge lead sheets that had been unrolled previously on site, this same lead having been looted from a storehouse in Colchester. This was trampled down and the remaining depression backfilled to ground level.

They had all done very well, only about three hundred pounds of surplus soil remained. Cleverly it was decided as dawn was breaking to remove this several hundred feet away and then deposit it outside another badger set so as to not arouse any curiosity. Returning to the burial site damp leaf mould and twigs were finally scattered over the disturbed surface. Just as they were about to take a brief rest a thin wild bird-like series of whistles echoed through the trees, it was from one of the look outs.

Everyone froze at first, then some started to pat the horses to calm them, but they all just watched. Soon, the reason for the alarm was evident: a group of three Roman soldiers, one with a rather battered eagle-topped standard came walking down the valley track. They stopped beneath a large oak tree, sat down and removed their helmets warily looking around, as one then relieved himself against the large tree.

Such disrespect for the noble oak was carefully noted. Velas, ensuring they had no other company, broke cover a short distance away and slowly walked towards them. They seemed to be very tired as not one of them noticed him until he was about forty feet away. Then when they did, they clumsily tried to stand quickly on their tired and aching legs, stumbling around clumsily placing their helmets on whilst unsheathing their swords. Just as the last of their swords was brought into readiness a flurry of arrows cracked and clattered through the thin beech tree canopy towards the edge of the wood. Two of the soldiers were hit simultaneously, several times, and were killed almost immediately. However, one arrow hit the thigh of the third soldier and seemed to just spring away into the decaying undergrowth.

Unknown to Velas and his associates, this particular iron-tipped arrow had impacted a silver denarius coin in the leather purse of this third man, and this had protected him. With the soldier then starting to shout loudly, and seeing that the unarmed Velas was now in a very dangerous predicament, a young Celtic noble named Curnos took aim. A single arrow shot from his bow, it passed cleanly through a solitary dying oak leaf on a branch in front and then sped on straight towards the soldiers face. The Roman had heard the slight sound and turned around, glanced into the trees, and then back at Velas. With remarkable accuracy the arrow hit the side of the man's head with a tinny crack as it smacked in hard. The iron arrowhead took with it several small fragments of the thin sheet bronze from the man's helmet deep into his brain tissue, killing him.

Curnos walked over and admired his handiwork, and then ripped the damaged purse from the belt of the now very dead soldier. Pouring the contents into his palm, he moved the coins about with a single finger as if carefully selecting them. Whilst sneering at the Emperors portrayed, he noticed one coin was badly damaged, as it had a large near circular shaped dent in it, rejecting it, Curnos simply threw it away. There was no time, and no wish anyway, to accord these fallen soldiers a burial, so their bodies were stripped and simply dragged into a deep patch of nettles, and then a large freshly fallen branch from the oak was positioned over them. They had disrespected the mighty oak and now in turn it would assist in the concealing of their fate.

Velas picked up one the helmets but quickly reconsidered keeping such a fine trophy; to be caught later in possession of this could be difficult to explain. He would either be accused of having been a participant in the battle against Rome, or had looted the body of one of her fallen, and neither would be a good situation to be in. Velas had some difficulty removing the helmet from the last soldier as it was pinned to his pierced skull by an arrow, but finally he collected up all the headware. Jamming them into a large crevice at the base of the tree trunk, the sacred oak had helped them once again.

Unknown to anyone else here, and not long before, one of these same soldiers had been fortunate enough to find a huge gold ring amongst the churned up soil as he departed from the battle scene. Unknown to him at the time, it had later fallen out of his leather purse due to some frayed stitching. For the second time that day the ring had been lost and was now on the ground several hundred metres away from where his dead body now lay.

The immediate problem now dealt with, the burial party gathered once again at the site. A few brief words were spoken it, it was truly time to depart. Every man attending knew the denial that each had participated in here. It was with great relief that they had had managed to safely bury the Royals but nothing marked the spot, no regally dimensioned burial mound, as would have been the normal custom of the time, not even a simple stone. But they all knew this was the way it must be. Each participant then looked at one another, nodded, grasped shoulders, and finally went their separate ways. Within twenty or so years all but one of them here that day would be dead. True to their sworn word, not one of them had ever revealed the happenings of that day and consequently, the bodies of their Queen and her two children remained safe and secure.

Where the battle had taken place, thousands of warriors, women and childrens' bodies lay on the damp soil. The Romans however, had removed all their dead and injured within a day or so. A few days later local settlement farmers and craftsmen arrived at the scene to make preparations for a mass burial. However a section of the Roman military arrived soon after and it was made abundantly clear that the bodies of the defeated must be left to rot, serving as a warning.

Such actions could well have given rise to another tribal uprising, but they didn't; there was simply no cohesion between any of the fleeing Celtic tribes that would have been able to organise such an event. It would take another decade for decent things to slowly take place here. Over the next fifteen years , the residents of local farmsteads and the settlements manually dug out a series of large and deep pits. Into this were cast as many human remains as could be located. Wild animals, souvenir hunters and the weather had all played their part in concealing, removing, and hiding many of their bones and artefacts over quite a wide area. The local Roman officials had been well aware of this gradually-gathering activity and had decided it was better to tolerate it. Having a change of mind from earlier times, they now skilfully concluded that, in such uncertain times, to continue to refuse this action could be inflammatory and could once again re-ignite tribal tensions. The defeated corpses, and later skeletons, had served their purpose for a long while now, even Rome thought that was sufficient a length of time for the lesson to be appreciated and hopefully fully learnt.

CHAPTER TWENTY-FOUR

A MAN CALLED VELAS

For Velas, like many thousands after the battle, it was time to firstly consider avoiding any association with the recent uprising, to evade capture and then settle down and try to fit back into the shattered community once again. Having been originally born into a family of potters, this occupation now seemed the most logical thing to him to become involved with. Within a year he had started up a small pottery in the form of a series of sizeable kilns producing mostly coarse-ware domestic items for mainly local demand. So successful was he in this venture that after time he found himself slowly becoming accustomed to the life of a successful Romano-British merchant. Rome, and its life style, have crept up on him to such a degree, that sometimes he sat down in wonder at how life, especially his life, could have changed so drastically. In fact very often he was referred to, not as Velas, but as 'Velatianus The Potter'. His life, and now even his name, appeared to have changed, but his dedication to his previous values and concerns would never be forgotten, he could always be certain of that. However, he considered this 'Romanisation' was also a good thing, a thing that he could successfully hide behind. Who would consider a successful business man and merchant would ever have been an angry uprising Celtic warrior?

Over the years since, many of the original burial party had kept in reasonable contact after the event, and Velas heard occasional bits of information about the others. Who had died, been successful and who not so successful, the inter-tribal grapevine could, when required, still be very reliable. It was someone who had saved his life many years before, who would now suddenly return into it.

For a man of nearly forty five years of age, Curnos still looked good. He joked that he still had hair, and only last year had produced his eighth child, 'from seven different mothers', he proudly announced.

Velas appreciated his wit, but wondered at the reason for the visit, it was quite simple really. Curnos knew that every eye-witness to the Royal burial, apart from himself and Velas, were now dead. 'That makes us sort of like special brothers!' Curnos had said. It was perhaps purely reminiscing on his behalf, with such a secret to bear he had simply wanted to locate Velas, something to do with kinship and suppressed tribal honour. Or was it something else, Curnos considered? Something deep and meaningful, a calling, not understood but controlled by gods, and spiritual things. Just a year later and Curnos himself was also dead, eight children, wine and women had probably all played their part in this finality. The news of his death brought sadness to Velas, as well as a feeling of total individuality, for he was now the last survivor from the Royal burial party, a keeper of the faith. His individuality and own mortality now began to make him, too, consider some other issues.

Velas' hard work had recently started to bring him luxuries, often from strange and distant lands, and now he had managed to purchase the final part of his 'total deception', and this was to be in the form of a moderately-sized villa. Not a large building initially, but given time, and of course finances, Velas would expand this into quite a considerable property. This was after all not just a random location he had chosen, the site was in quite close proximity to the burial site of his beloved Queen, and from here he could observe and maintain her protection.

When business permitted, he would occasionally walk over to the ridge in the beech trees and look down at the ground, at the very soil, containing Bodvocca, and her two daughters. Sometimes his youngest children accompanied him, none aware that just fifteen feet below them were the remains of a British Queen alongside her two daughters. However, they are well aware of their heritage, and the fame of this Queen is something Velas had frequently informed them of; these children will definitely not lose their British ancestry ,or knowledge of it.

Improvements to the villa continued, and could all be paid for rapidly now. Combined with long -standing military supply contracts, Velas had diversified even further and his kilns now produced several high quality decorative and domestic wares. Velas now managed over sixteen major kilns, and numerous smaller ones in the district. Seasonally, some of these could also be rented out for the drying and malting of barley and other cereals. Now having the capacity to produce floor, roof and hypocaust tiles, for which a steady demand from Verulamium and its outlying villas and settlements, has now also made for further success and increased wealth.

Sometime around 100AD, Velas had a stunningly-detailed mosaic commissioned and, at around the same time, for some unknown reason, he had started considering his own mortality once again. But unusually, he began to consider a number of related issues. One of these occurred to him as he was seated one day, 'When I am gone I don't suppose after a few years many people will know who, or what it was that I achieved in my life? Strange to think that, after all you do, it finally just shrivels up into to death and dust!' he had considered. However, for his family's continued safety, that was probably a good thing. Velas then had a truly strange thought indeed. He had imagined someone finding his own buried remains in the future and, not knowing who they were, or indeed anything about him. It was this line of thinking that made him conclude: 'Well that's fine for someone like myself; I have played no real part for years in significant history, so why indeed should anyone remember me? But when you consider a Queen, and her children, for that to happen is without doubt beyond contemplation.'

Velas also wondered why he had started to consider death and decay once again, and pushed a frightening, nagging thought far to the back of his mind. He felt well and healthy, but perhaps this was the Gods' way of gently letting him know that his own mortality was of course was limited. Perhaps the time of his own death was now nearing? Spending a few weeks considering what his actions were to be, he finally decided upon a plan.

One day he had requested the foremen of one of his kiln works to bring him two moist, unfired clay tile blanks; he used the excuse that his children wished to make some grave markers for one of their dogs, which had died in the last week. Carefully and discreetly, Velas re-moistened the tile blanks, and with the stiff quill of a goose feather he began to write in Latin on one side of each tile. Each tile was then laid side by side and the writing continued over both surfaces, as did a crudely detailed map that Velas also added. As he drew the simple map onto the surface he noticed how similar to a creature the contours of the land appeared. So with inherited abstract Celtic skill he absorbed those very features of the land, including some Bronze Age barrows and a henge into some type of four legged animals, which he later decided were to be two hares, yet another tribute to his Queen.

Immediately he noticed he had given one of the hares a horse-like tail, he hesitated, should he change it? He decided against this as his design could be now be part hare and part horse instead, much easier than making a mess of the design. Standing back he admired his creations. Later that evening when the tile works were firing the last batch of products, his own ones were discreetly included in the final firing. Next morning Velas oversaw the batch being extracted from the kiln and removed his two examples. This was nothing unusual in itself, Velas frequently took samples to examine quality and for samples to show potential clients. However he felt for some reason he just had to say to the foreman 'Children eh? Making markers for a dead dog, of all things, whatever next?'

Having got the tiles back into the main room of his villa he now examined them, they would do perfectly. Months later, when Velas was increasing the size of the villa, as well as including some additional outbuildings, the tiles would be put in place. During the construction Velas had carefully lain each tile in the separate buildings himself and this, very conveniently, went totally unnoticed. Each tile has been placed upside down so it appeared as a normal everyday floor tile. However, Velas intended that one day someone should find these tiles and perhaps, just perhaps, would also locate the second one, and by placing them together, would understand what happened - and where the Queen and her children were buried.

What he had done was of course surrounded by a level of great risk, and therefore he had to complete this purely on his own and in total secrecy. After much consideration Velas decided that the mechanism for potential discovery of his inscribed tiles could be enhanced by curiosity. He would he knew somehow have to stimulate someone to examine the tile, or area, and hopefully make them turn it over and also maybe look for the second inscribed example as well. Quite how this could be achieved he could not guarantee, but decided the best thing would be to force two gold coins down the side of the each special tile and then cover these coins with a very thin capping of white mortar.

With two gold aureii coins down their sides, just under the mortar, this might just hopefully encourage someone in the future to move the tile itself. Perhaps in the hope that more such coins may lie beneath and then they might notice the inscriptions on the reverses. Although he knew he had made some degree of preparations for the revelation of his Queen and where she was buried, he was also well aware that they are without any guarantee of success at all. With the tiles in place, Velas considered he had at least done something to ensure that it was possible that one day his Queen would be discovered.

It seemed the effects of being the last survivor, and therefore custodian of knowledge, would never leave him, as about a year later another complexity made itself present in Velas' mind. That being: it was of course quite possible that one day someone might discover the Royal burial purely by accident, without ever seeing his tiles, and then what?

He knew that inside the chamber were significant quantities of clues and indicators, but there was nothing to positively confirm that this was the actual burial of Bodvocca, the woman who for such a short time had been his main source of admiration and guidance. To Velas, the fact that his Queen, and ruler, might be found by accident and still never be recognised was something that he also had to attempt to prevent. He knew this was going to involve yet another very dangerous plan on his behalf. Should he be caught, or even worse, if the royal burial was discovered in the next few years by the occupying Romans, then they would know the identities of those buried. Should they also find any of the related tiles it wouldn't be too hard for them to deduce who had been responsible for their manufacture?

The actions he now planned to undertake could possibly have horrendous premature results and could enable his revered royals to be identified and their bodily remains defiled by these, still very much hated, occupiers. However he was so sure of the security, there was no real strength of Roman military presence, nor had there been in this area for a very long time.

All the questioning about Bodvocca, and the whereabouts of her remains, had to all intents and purposes, apparently long ceased. So was then that this last living eye-witness completed the manufacture of yet another earthenware tile, the third, and hopefully final one, he would have to produce. But this third tile was of even more importance because inscribed upon this example would be the key to understanding the burial chamber, and the identities of those it contained.

Briefly, whilst inscribing this tile, he had thought about somehow dating it, but he had no knowledge of the Christian calendar. This left only one consideration: a reference to Roman times and something like: 'In the third year of the Emperor Trajan', was simply not going to defile this tile, so he left it as it was. Although he did smile to himself on how he had allowed all the tiles to be defiled by using the Latin language of the Roman invaders. This had happened with a view based on practicality, Velas knew full well that Latin was a very established and prolifically-used language. Therefore there was a greater chance that persons in the future would have records of it, or at least be able to translate its meaning. So fraught with risk was the production of this additional third tile that Velas decided it would have to be put in place on a very dark night, and of course by himself.

Despite his advancing age, and still reasonable health, this important issue simply cannot be entrusted to anyone else. This was not that Velas didn't trust members of even his own immediate family; it was more that what they had no knowledge of, could not be talked about, or worse, extracted from them in whatever manner.

Velas could not risk anyone seeing him acting strangely. Should he be stopped in possession of this new tile by a stranger the whole game could well be given away, with perhaps awful consequences for him, his family and their somewhat opulent, but very hard worked-for lifestyle. Velas placed the tile in a large leather bag and succeeded in finding the burial area late one night. It had not been an easy task, although he knew precisely where to go, negotiating small streams, woodland and the numerous rabbit holes in the dark would be tiring and strenuous even for a much younger individual.

As he carefully made his way through a dark section of mature woodland, the sudden call from a tawny owl made him tense. Finally through the woodland, with only a pale cloud bathed crescent moon to shed any light, he came to the area of his concerns. Looking around him to ensure he was precise, he saw a familiar large beech tree, and beyond this stood the oak where the three Roman soldiers had been slain. Looking down he knew that he was standing directly above the sleeping Queen and her two daughters.

Despite the moonlight being pale, it still managed to reflect and glisten from a stream of moisture that ran below both the elderly man's eyes. This is no time for such emotions, I am really so very tired and only the Gods could definitely know just who else may be prowling around this land at night, he thought?

Carefully using a knife, he knelt down, with some discomfort, and began to cut away at the soil. Quite soon he had excavated a hole slightly larger than the dimensions of the tile he carried. Removing the tile from its leather bag he looked at it for one last time, then gently eased it down with care into the hole so that it would lie level. Releasing a corner, the tile made a satisfying thump as it impacted the soil. Backfilling the hole very carefully, it was finally level and Velas then grabbed a handful of leaves and spread them over the freshly dug area. Wiping the dirt from his hands onto a patch of grass, his job was now done; he had at last reached a stage in his life where he considered he could truly rest now. Looking around, he nodded several times, arose slowly and carefully walked the difficult route to the villa. At the burial site he had nodded several times in acknowledgement for the spirits of those dead friends and associates that he knew were hidden in the surrounding dark trees watching him.

Apart from his continued success in business, there was really nothing from this point onwards very remarkable about Velas's life. The life he had led appeared to be one of an exemplary model Romano-British citizen, and he had overseen that his family were educated and attained the skills then available to the wealthy. However in April 104 A.D, one of the smaller kilns caught fire and the flames quickly spread to some minor outbuildings. Velas never did adopt the practical suggestion from fellow colleagues of isolating your industry some distance away from your villa; he enjoyed the smoke, the dust and the earthiness of contact with the potters and kiln workers that he employed. Consequently when the outbuildings had been consumed by the fire there was little that could be done to halt its spread towards the main living complex of his villa.

It was a sheer good fortune that no one was injured, or even killed, and for that, Velas was most thankful. He witnessed the tiles on the villa roof top as they began to crack and explode in the intense heat. Seven days afterwards Velas was to pass away peacefully, his family noticing that from the period of the fire his will to eat, or do anything much at all, seemed to quickly ebb away. Fortunately, due to the wise business nature of Velas, his family were financially secure; made possible from the many other investments he had made and entered into, so he had died all the more peacefully with no concerns on that account. They could now afford to do pretty much as they so wished, and consequently they had decided to move into the city of Verulamium - no more the rural wealthy, but isolated, life for them.

However, when it came to the burial of Velas, he had previously wished to be cremated, and this was duly honoured. It was decided to place his remains in the small cemetery that already existed here when Velas had first purchased the land. Every family member had suspected that he had far more of a connection to this area than he ever spoke of and so they felt it was fitting that he should remain here. After all, he had always insisted that the little cemetery never be disturbed, or destroyed by building, out of respect for the occupants who were almost certainly as British as he was.

Through his family's numerous pottery business-based contacts, an extremely fine decorated burial urn was commissioned from the Nene valley-situated potteries. This duly arrived, a cream coloured vessel with deep red colour slip decoration showing a man feeding a deer, above this, also in red slip capital letters, was the name 'VELAS'. This unusual example of a named urn, with the ashes it now contained, was then taken from Verulamium, and across country, back to the remains of the villa. It was then placed in a small hole, very similar in dimensions to the one that Velas had himself made to place that third tile in a few years back. He was now spiritually with his Queen, and most appropriately had been placed in the ground only half a mile or so from where she herself had been buried.

CHAPTER TWENTY-FIVE

A RETURN TO MODERN TIMES

I t would take just a fraction over three and half years before the cleaning, cataloguing and conserving of the entire contents, removed from the burial chamber, had been completed to any satisfactory degree. Scores of conservators had been employed to clean the corrosion deposits from the bronze artefacts, and many people found secure employment drawing and photographing the stunning finds. Finally on the 23rd April 2022, the British Museum was finally to open its doors on the first day of what was titled: 'The Lost Queen Exhibition'.

Of the many millions of people who attended, not a few of whom had been stimulated by the continuing mass media coverage of the year-long exhibition, none were to be disappointed. In a huge gallery hall there laid all the separate finds with full explanations and photographs of their discovery, as well as schematic diagrams of each precise location in the burial deposit. Curators and experts were on hand in significant numbers to field the inevitable questions from adults and children alike. Centrally positioned was a huge temperature-controlled glass structure, in which could be seen the skeletal remains of Bodvocca and her two children. Also in this display was the shattered, and now fully reassembled and restored, floor tile found during the excavation of the Junkers 88 bomber.

Of course Jonathan, Simon, Craig and Candice Melanby, as well as many others involved, had all been invited to the opening ceremony. Which also involved over fifteen thousand guests who had been invited, including the Royal Family, and many other titled persons, notable civic dignitaries and Mayors from various boroughs, Ministers of Parliament and of course the Prime Minister himself.

Jonathan and Ed had managed to briefly smile as the Prime Minister announced that it was during his period of enlightened Government that had made it possible to conserve such findings through education and, of course, increased funding. Actually this was something to which Jonathan and the Melanby's had largely contributed towards themselves in this case. There's always someone trying to jump on the band wagon and claim influence, expertise or that it was their efforts made something or other possible. When in all truth they had little if anything to do with such things. Still, let them carry on, Jonathan thought to himself.

Discussing this with Ed, and some other EMAG colleagues shortly afterwards, Jonathan said: 'Well I reckon, when I have time we should all get together and write our own detailed account of all of this in a book, so that everyone will know exactly what the facts were behind our discovery!'

'Yep.., I reckon so, too.' agreed Ed, 'but I'm not sure I like that title you came up with for it earlier? What was it again, 'The Three Tiles'? Sounds a bit dull to me, Jon, for such a great discovery.'

Jonathan looked at him, thoughtfully, 'Perhaps your right, Ed,' he said, 'but its early days, mate, early days, so who knows, eh?'

Considered most impressive indeed, in the exhibition, was a large glass table display, upon which were placed the fifteen thousand silver coins, next to the thirty eight thousand four hundred and seventy nine gold Celtic staters, and the three thousand and seventeen gold Roman coin issues, found in the chamber. Many onlookers, however, were initially surprised at the stained and slightly corroded oval -shaped aluminium object, that lay adjacent to the reconstructed Roman tile? Even after examination and reading the description of it, some people who didn't know the exact story behind the discovery still looked a bit puzzled?

The museum authorities had considered it most befitting that Waldemar Euker's identity tag should also be shown in the same display case, and so having secured Franz Stihlmann's permission, it was. It took almost took as long as it did to create the exhibition for the Treasure

Valuation Committee to arrive at a precise figure for valuation of the entire findings. A few hundred staters, or hammered gold coins, were the very occasional norm. But a complete royal burial was something else......? It was said by some; 'Finally, they have a good excuse for taking so long to arrive at a figure commensurate with the find! Eventually, it was estimated, and reported in the press, that the reward to all parties involved would amount to at least £68,000,000. However ,the reality, although still a phenomenal reward, proved to be substantially less, and was finally fixed at £43,000,000.

Whilst outside the Museum, Jonathan and Simon were interviewed by the National News team, along with various other Worldwide newspapers and magazine-based journalists. 'So, what are you going to do now, Mr Pearson?' shouted out one elderly grey-haired, and very distinguished reporter.

'Well,' said Jonathan, 'after this, it's about time we think that someone went on and did some research about this so-called King Arthur person? Finding the legendary sword, history knows as 'Excalibur' now that really would be something, don't you think? Wouldn't that just be something indeed?'

Ed looked at Simon, lit up a cigarette, inhaled, and then exhaling a large jet of grey smoke whilst staring upwards, said: 'If he bloody well does find King Arthur's grave, what's the betting there will be a crashed Spitfire on top of it, eh?'

Two days before the exhibition was about to close, an elderly disabled gentleman came into the British Museum. His behaviour seemed rather erratic, and for that reason two security guards linked up via their digital communications system and began to follow him. No one was taking any chances whatsoever with the multi million pound exhibits. Although they were following as closely as possible, neither of them were able to prevent the elderly man from raising his walking stick and smashing it repeatedly against a glass display cabinet that contained a small silver chalice full of gold coins. The two guards managed to restrain the man, who then without warning, liberally applied his walking stick to them, much to the amusement of several onlookers.

Drawing of Velas' cremation urn by the author
(Courtesy of staff at Melton Briarsville Museum)

The man then started to repeatedly shout: 'This should all have been mine! All mine!'

Shortly afterwards the security guards had the man arrested, and he was taken away under police escort. It certainly seemed that Harold Foster's dreams had not lessened to any degree during the rather lenient two and half year prison sentence he had just served.

Today Melton Briarsville's now-famous museum has a display of its own that you can also go and see, consisting of several silver and gold coins, sections of the lead sheeting and one of the two small silver mirrors. It is also possible to sit down and, with thanks to EMAG, view a short film of the entire excavation. It was rightly assumed that the 'Velas' named on the cremation urn was indeed the Velas who had created the tiles, and consequently the urn now has pride of place in the museum's display.

At the right time of year, for £8.50, the museum tour guide will take you down to Four Acres field – when it's not cropped, or too muddy, and show you where Bodvocca was found. Of course there are always no end of villagers who have their own story to tell any listeners, over a pint in the Waggoner's Inn. As agreed originally, over twenty six years previously, the reward was shared out accordingly between the Melanby's, and Jonathan, and also their chosen charities. However, that wasn't it, Jonathan also gave an undisclosed sum to all the EMAG members who had also helped make the discovery possible. Furthermore, another undisclosed sum was provided by the Melanby family, and Jonathan, that has paid for, and allowed, the archaeological work to continue up at the site of the battlefield – and will do so for many years to come.

Now it was about a decade after this incredible discovery, Dave Meacher was metal detecting near the Hertfordshire village of Ardeley, when he literally stumbled across another related discovery.

Searching a meadow, he had walked slowly over to an area of molehills, each one a mini dark mountain, capped with frost. A wood pigeon made a very noisy exit from the centre of a nearby hedge, causing Dave to look round. As he did so, he stumbled over one of the frozen molehills, knocking its frosty topping off. There, amidst the frozen soil, clear as day, lay a large gold coin.

Stunned Dave picked it up and brushed of the ice and soil particles. It was a coin he did not recognise immediately, but then considered he had indeed seen something like it about ten years before, in a metal detecting magazine, when he had just started the hobby. Detecting in circles around the find spot, he recovered several more coins, and then he had a larger signal.

Digging into the hard clay, he came across the remains of a greyware pot, and mixed in with these fragments were around sixty more gold coins. Excited and trembling, Dave decided to celebrate by having a few lunchtime pints in the pub, with the damp earthy coins still in his

Photo of the Ardeley Hoard (Courtesy of Dave Meacher and family)

coat pocket. The pub was called 'The Jolly Waggoner', the irony being unknown to Dave. He later declared his discovery and was informed that, despite being a wonderful find, they were also indeed truly remarkable coins.

They were struck, it must be said, very badly on extremely irregular flans, and with weights varying from 15 to 50 grams. The dies used to strike the coins were not worn, but appeared to be quite badly corroded. Each coin was remarkably similar to the double-staters found in Bodvocca's burial pit. Differing only in that they appeared cruder, and the design was also in reverse. It was surmised that these coins were struck much later than the Bodvocca examples, as amongst them were also four Anglo-Saxon sceats. It was considered that perhaps one of the test-die cutters had retained, as a keepsake, an early trial set of dies? Perhaps these were then handed down for generations as treasured heirlooms, which would at least allow for the evidence of corrosion? Then, some time after the Romans had departed these shores, the family decided to create some rough-sized blanks and re-strike some coins, coins that acted almost as commemorative medallions, attempting to evoke a past culture. Struck in a time when it was safe from Roman persecution, they would almost act as a signal of Britain's freedom to be circulated amongst the tribes. But how did they really come to be buried in a Hertfordshire field? Well like most things I suppose that's anyone's guess.

CONCLUSION

After some two thousand years, fate decided that it was not the carefully manufactured and deposited tiles of Velas' after all, that gave the direct reason for Bodvocca's burial site to be located. Ironically, it was a stray Luftwaffe bomber, that had crashed virtually on top of it some one thousand eight hundred and seventy nine years later, that finally led to the discovery. The sheer determination of aviation archaeologists, and a metal detectorist, were the main factors that led to its eventual unearthing, despite Velas's efforts in attempting to leave markers, so that hopefully one day in much safer times, his great Queen would be found.

It is with some certainty, that I feel sure that he would have been contented to know that his aims and ideals, as regards her location, would be eventually fulfilled, albeit with sophisticated equipment, far beyond his comprehension and ability to recognise. I'm certain, too, that as regards the positive identification, definitely determined by his kiln-based efforts, as was the revelation of the names of Bodvocca's two daughters, that he would be content. Something that he would have been familiar with himself would undoubtedly have been the level of dedication and commitment of all those involved.

However, one must say that, despite the luck and dedication, it had been his tiles that created the initial interest in the area, and the third one placed over the burial chamber that gave final positive confirmation as to the identity of that chamber's occupants. Reflecting on young Tommy Warner's comments to Millicent Klake, back in the nineteen thirties, when he had concluded that, if a sleeping chieftain was to arise in Britain's hour of need, then the version supposed to be interred at Melton Briarsville was rather inert.

With the delightful accuracy of hind sight, when examining Bodvocca's case, one may wonder now if indeed Tommy had been a little harsh all those years ago? The Germans certainly came very close to discovering Bodvocca's remains - and the associated treasure. But after expending great effort, they didn't manage to find it. Would this 'German Discovery' have made any difference in pre-war Britain's outlook, as regards the German Reich's ambitions in Europe? Could it therefore, have affected, or at least potentially delayed, the course of the war? It is perhaps doubtful, but one never quite knows?

It could be said that no matter how small the obsession with Bodvocca, from a then very strong potential enemy, it did tie up some of their time and resources, which in all honesty may well have been utilised to more positive effect elsewhere. I'm not sure whether this is giving Bodvocca too much credit, as it was, the war came and went. However, I like to think that the resources of Germany, that she caused to be diverted to the matter, had some effect, and therefore Melton Briarsville's own slumbering British leader did actually live up to the associated legend.

Factually, it is of course left with the reader to determine to what extent the effect the whole issue back then really could have had, or did have, on World events? Some might also add that in the hard financial times the UK was experiencing from 2010 onwards, the finding of Bodvocca in 2018 did indeed come to the rescue when Britain was in financial peril. Her discovery went on to deliver millions of pounds of tourism-based money into Britain's economy, provided secure careers and made it a boom time for the village of Melton Briarsville. So, all in all, yes one might say that was another aspect of her living up to the legend of rising up to assist.

All this debating aside, of course the reader is, I know, fully aware, or at least I imagine so, that factually the remains of this missing British Queen have not as yet been unearthed? But they do stand every possibility of being so. Amongst the combination of fiction, and non-fiction, that I have written here, there may well indeed be far more fact than even the author is aware of? A stunningly fortunate metal detectorist might well make just such a phenomenal discovery? It would certainly be the 'crowning glory' for the hobby of metal detecting if they did.

Somewhere in this green and pleasant island, our resting Queen certainly lies, just awaiting for the discovery of the century, or indeed, the Millennium. She certainly conjures up the element of mystery, but not really myth, for it was always certain she had existed. She is not an 'Arthur' of legend and fable, possibly based on someone, but she is factual and, it must be said, was a true leader of people, a unifier of her society's differing factions under a time of great pressure.

I'm sure every metal detectorist and archaeologist in England dreams of making, or being involved in, such a find, and that's just where the elements of luck, fate and chance appear. Those who conduct academic research, and field study, stand as much chance as the lucky first timer, or seasoned metal detectorist, in making such discoveries. It matters not your political opinion, your nationality, beliefs, practices etc., the hobby of metal detecting is a fantastic melting pot, and so one could fairly claim that the quest for such discoveries is indeed a unifier of to-day's society. The search for the past, and to discover our heritage, is after all a creditworthy and honourable pursuit. Now it's obvious, due to the dates and years mentioned within the latter stages of this book, that I have extended into the realms of fiction, albeit being based greatly on hopes and aspirations. However, sometimes, though, having such hopes and aspirations in life can occasionally put a few people at a potential advantage in the quest for just such a success.

This is provided, of course, that such people have the ability to acknowledge the advantageous situation that they are in. Sometimes that can be rather difficult and in most cases, unfortunately, does not happen. Well I have nearly completed this account now, and very much hope that you, the reader, have not only enjoyed, but also given some thought to what you have just read. There is however, one last section of this account that I would like to include, if only for the element of completeness.....so far : - I have just leant back in my chair thinking: Well, that's it! This novel, story ,or account, call it what you will, is very nearly finished now. Whether anyone will ever read it, or even if it's published, are of course the main thoughts going through my mind. But if the format in which you have just read it consists of pages bound in a cover, then I guess that's marvellous - as it will have been published!

So far, one text proof-reader has said: 'This account is a myriad of complexities, all related to historical time lines.' and admittedly, I quite like that. Anyway, it's time to put this manuscript away for a while now. When I open up the somewhat dusty, antique oak book cabinet, I can see all my research books and hundreds of Treasure Hunting magazines, and files of notes. Some of these notes contain information on sites that have led to me, and my colleagues, finding hundreds of ancient coins, antiquities and other small historical treasures. There is also one brown, waxed paper-covered file that smells of age, you know - just like an old book shop does, that strong musty odour. In fact, I actually say that this old file 'just seems to have the aroma of the nineteen thirties about it?'

On the sunlight -bleached cover, one can just make out a faded purple-inked eagle above a swastika. Inside are just three sheets of yellowish-coloured notepaper with roughly torn edges where, at some stage, they have been carelessly, or perhaps violently, removed from a note book. One still retains a steel staple that is covered in fine crusty rust, which has created an orange stain on the paper around it. The ink of the hand written notes is now rather a light bluish-brown in colour, and there is a rough pencil sketch of a tile that has that typical scratchy Roman-style writing on it. Below this writing on the diagram is quite clearly what is part of a crude map, or some type of plan? All of these note paper sheets are dated 1914. They have been folded many times in their history, and are now very brittle, one is badly burned at the top edge and has an almost black patch with lots of little splatters of the same around, and they seem to consist of a tacky treacle-like substance that has stained right through the paper. Now this is in fact Human blood, and although I can't say how, but I also know that it is the very blood that once flowed through the veins of a young man called Frederick Pearson.

How did I get these brittle fragments of history? Well that in itself is rather complicated issue, indeed very much connected, though, to the same events that enabled me to also acquire a rusted section of

315

American 500lb GP bomb. This is part of the very same bomb, which back in 1945 killed SS Obersturmfuhrer Bruno Prussmann. So what happens now? Well it's a bit of a mixture really, luck and fate, of course, all have their parts to play as always, as does the assistance of my metal detecting friends, and all our research. One thing that is certain, though, as my good friend, Dave Stuckey, said the other day: 'Jules, you ain't half got your work cut out for you over the next few years, with this project!'

But perhaps, having read this book, winkled out some of the clues, and hopefully having your own determination fired up as well, one statement remains from me, directed to you, the reader, personally, and that is: – 'Should you decode all the facts herein contained, and those connected that are not, consequently establishing the precise location of Bodvocca's burial chamber, before we do. Then please do consider doing the decent thing and invite me and my colleagues to attend your excavation!

Actual "Clod Shot" of the double stater found in January 2012
(Courtesy of the finder)

316

Authors Note:- Finally, there is just one other thing that must be added here, something which fortunately happened before this was book sent to press. Regarding the five double-staters that Celtic chieftains, Mantoteros and Celoditos, had handled nearly twenty centuries before, during the burial ceremony, only four have so far been recovered. However, in the last few weeks at the time of writing this text, the fifth example has just been located in Oxfordshire, and it is from this very coin that I was able to draw the diagrams seen in this book................ After much persuasion, the finder finally allowed me use one of his actual photographs taken at the time of making this incredibly rare find.

The coin is currently under intense academic study, and the finder, to whom I am indebted for allowing me to originally examine his find, as is so often the case in such matters, wishes to remain anonymous.